T. 28.10
P9-CRO-612

S. Haykin

NUMERICAL METHODS FOR CONSTRAINED OPTIMIZATION

Edited by
P. E. GILL and W. MURRAY
National Physical Laboratory
Teddington, Middlesex

1974

ACADEMIC PRESS
LONDON · NEW YORK · SAN FRANCISCO

ACADEMIC PRESS INC. (LONDON) LTD.
24/28 Oval Road,
London NW1

United States Edition published by
ACADEMIC PRESS INC.
111 Fifth Avenue,
New York, New York 10003

Copyright © 1974 by
ACADEMIC PRESS INC. (LONDON) LTD.

All Rights Reserved
No part of this book may be reproduced in any form by photostat, microfilm, or any other means, without written permission from the publishers

Library of Congress Catalog Card Number: 74–18502
ISBN: 0–12–283550–6

PRINTED IN GREAT BRITAIN BY
ROYSTAN PRINTERS LIMITED
Spencer Court, 7 Chalcot Road,
London NW1

Contributors

R. FLETCHER *Department of Mathematics, The University, Dundee*

P. E. GILL *Division of Numerical Analysis and Computing, National Physical Laboratory, Teddington, Middlesex*

W. MURRAY *Division of Numerical Analysis and Computing, National Physical Laboratory, Teddington, Middlesex*

M. J. D. POWELL *Computer Sciences Division, Atomic Energy Research Establishment, Harwell, Oxfordshire*

D. M. RYAN *Operations Research Group, Atomic Energy Research Establishment, Harwell, Oxfordshire*

R. W. H. SARGENT *Department of Chemical Engineering and Chemical Technology, Imperial College of Science and Technology, London, S.W.7*

W. H. SWANN *Imperial Chemical Industries, Mond Division, PO Box 13, The Heath, Runcorn, Cheshire*

Preface

This book is based on the proceedings of a symposium on numerical methods for constrained optimization held at the National Physical Laboratory on the 10th and 11th of January 1974. Sponsored jointly by the Institute of Mathematics and its Applications and by the National Physical Laboratory, the symposium was a sequel to one on unconstrained optimization held three years earlier. Like the proceedings of the earlier symposium, also published by Academic Press, this volume has two objectives: the first is to give a comprehensive and detailed survey of the numerical methods currently available and the second is to provide the reader with a framework to help him follow future developments.

The programme was formulated by a committee consisting of J. G. Hayes (Chairman) of the NPL, M. J. D. Powell of the AERE Harwell and ourselves. It was agreed that a uniform notation should be used throughout and the number of contributors should be kept small, with a considerable amount of consultation taking place before the symposium. It is hoped that this policy has enabled the authors to give a well co-ordinated and balanced account of constrained optimization and thus prevented the proceedings from resembling, like those of many conferences, a loosely collected set of research papers from a learned journal. The contributions are basically of an expository nature but, because all the authors are actively engaged in research in optimization, some previously unpublished material is included.

It was decided when planning the first symposium that constrained optimization would not be included since at that time the subject was in a largely undeveloped state. With the passing of three years some broad trends have become identifiable; this is particularly true for linearly constrained optimization. As a consequence of this and because linearly constrained algorithms are the basis for many of the methods for dealing with nonlinear constraints, a considerable proportion of the book has been devoted to describing them.

In all the chapters there has been an emphasis on methods which can be used as practical tools. Occasionally the underlying structure of a group of methods has been discussed but generalization has never been sought for its own sake. It is hoped that this book will be read and understood by the non-specialist; inevitably, the description of complex algorithms to solve what are essentially difficult problems requires the inclusion of some non-trivial mathematics, but we hope that a reader who is acquainted with the rudiments of numerical linear algebra will be able to follow most of the material enclosed. Familiarity with the text on unconstrained optimization will be an added advantage.

We would like to take this opportunity of thanking J. G. Hayes of the NPL and Barbara Mayne of the IMA for their excellent work in organizing the conference. We are grateful to the authors for their co-operation in the preparation of their various chapters for publication and to Irene Good and Margaret Thomson for their speedy and diligent proof reading. Considerable personal thanks are due to D. W. Martin and Margaret Wright for the help they gave us in the preparation of our own contributions.

National Physical Laboratory P. E. GILL
September, 1974 W. MURRAY

A Glossary of Symbols

A common notation will be used by the authors of each chapter and this is set out below. In devising the notation consideration has been given to those symbols in common use which result in the least ambiguity or confusion. Unless the historical use of symbols is discarded, it is impossible to devise a notation which is completely free of inconsistances.

The problem of concern in this book can be stated as follows

P1

$$\underset{\mathbf{x}}{\text{minimize}}\ \{F(\mathbf{x})\}$$

subject to the constraints $c_i(\mathbf{x}) \geqslant 0, \quad i = 1, 2, \ldots, m, \quad \mathbf{x} \in E^n$, where $F(\mathbf{x})$ and $c_i(\mathbf{x})$ are functions of the variables

$$\mathbf{x} = \begin{bmatrix} x_1 \\ x_2 \\ \vdots \\ x_n \end{bmatrix},$$

and E^n denotes n dimensional Euclidean space.

c(**x**) is the $m \times 1$ vector of constraint functions.

g(**x**) is the $n \times 1$ gradient vector of $F(\mathbf{x})$, that is

$$g_i(\mathbf{x}) = \frac{\partial F(\mathbf{x})}{\partial x_i}, \quad i = 1, 2, \ldots, n.$$

A is the $n \times m$ matrix whose ith column is denoted by $\mathbf{a}_i(\mathbf{x})$, where

$\mathbf{a}_i(\mathbf{x})$ is the gradient vector of $c_i(\mathbf{x})$.

In the special case when the $c_i(\mathbf{x})$ are all linear functions of **x** the constraints

$$\mathbf{c}(\mathbf{x}) \geqslant \mathbf{0},$$

are denoted by

$$\mathbf{A}^T\mathbf{x} - \mathbf{b} \geqslant \mathbf{0},$$

where **b** is an $m \times 1$ vector of given scalars.

$\mathbf{G}(\mathbf{x})$ is the $n \times n$ Hessian matrix of $F(\mathbf{x})$, that is the (i,j)th element of $\mathbf{G}$ is given by

$$\frac{\partial^2 F(\mathbf{x})}{\partial x_i \partial x_j}.$$

$\mathbf{G}_r(\mathbf{x})$ is the $n \times n$ Hessian matrix of $c_r(\mathbf{x})$.

$\mathbf{x}^{(k)}$ is the kth approximation to $\overset{*}{\mathbf{x}}$, a solution of *P1*.

$F^{(k)} = F(\mathbf{x}^{(k)})$.

$\mathbf{c}^{(k)} = \mathbf{c}(\mathbf{x}^{(k)})$.

$\mathbf{g}^{(k)} = \mathbf{g}(\mathbf{x}^{(k)})$.

$\mathbf{a}_i^{(k)} = \mathbf{a}_i(\mathbf{x}^{(k)})$.

$\mathbf{y}^{(k)} = \mathbf{g}^{(k+1)} - \mathbf{g}^{(k)}$.

$\mathbf{y}_i^{(k)} = \mathbf{a}_i^{(k+1)} - \mathbf{a}_i^{(k)}$.

$\mathbf{s}^{(k)} = \mathbf{x}^{(k+1)} - \mathbf{x}^{(k)} = \alpha^{(k)}\mathbf{p}^{(k)}$, where $\alpha^{(k)}$ is a scalar and $\mathbf{p}^{(k)}$ is a search direction.

$\mathbf{B}^{(k)}$ is an $n \times n$ matrix that is a kth approximation to some Hessian matrix.

$\mathbf{H}^{(k)}$ is an $n \times n$ matrix that is a kth approximation to some inverse Hessian matrix.

J is the index set of active constraints.

t is the number of elements in J.

$\boldsymbol{\lambda}$ is the vector of Lagrange multipliers.

$L(\mathbf{x}, \boldsymbol{\lambda}) = F(\mathbf{x}) - \boldsymbol{\lambda}^T\mathbf{c}(\mathbf{x})$ is the Lagrangian function.

$\mathbf{w}(\mathbf{x}, \boldsymbol{\lambda})$ is the $n \times 1$ vector whose ith element is given by $\dfrac{\partial L(\mathbf{x}, \boldsymbol{\lambda})}{\partial x_i}$

$\mathbf{W}(\mathbf{x}, \boldsymbol{\lambda})$ is the $n \times n$ Hessian matrix of $L(\mathbf{x}, \boldsymbol{\lambda})$ with respect to $\mathbf{x}$.

$P(\mathbf{x}, r)$ is a penalty function with parameter r.

$B(\mathbf{x}, r)$ is a barrier function with parameter r.

C^r denotes the class of functions whose rth derivative is continuous.

$\|\mathbf{y}\|$ denotes an arbitrary norm of $\mathbf{y}$.

If it does not lead to ambiguity the argument or superfix may be omitted. For instance $\mathbf{g}(\mathbf{x})$ may simply be written as $\mathbf{g}$.

Contents

CHAPTER IV

Methods for Large-scale Linearly Constrained Problems

P. E. GILL AND W. MURRAY

CHAPTER V

Reduced-gradient and Projection Methods for Nonlinear Programming

R. W. H. SARGENT

CHAPTER VI

Penalty and Barrier Functions

D. M. RYAN

CHAPTER VII

Constrained Optimization by Direct Search

W. H. SWANN

CHAPTER VIII
Methods Related to Lagrangian Functions
R. FLETCHER

CHAPTER IX
Algorithms and Future Developments
P. E. GILL AND W. MURRAY

Chapter I

Introduction to Constrained Optimization

M. J. D. POWELL
Computer Sciences Division,
Atomic Energy Research Establishment

1.1. Descent Methods for Minimization

This book describes and studies iterative algorithms for calculating the least value of a given function of n variables, $F(\mathbf{x})$ say, subject to inequality constraints $c_i(\mathbf{x}) \geqslant 0$ $(i = 1, 2, \ldots, m)$ and possibly some equality constraints too. Because the algorithms are iterative they require an initial estimate of the solution, $\mathbf{x}^{(0)}$ say, and then for $k = 0, 1, 2, \ldots$ the kth iteration replaces $\mathbf{x}^{(k)}$ by $\mathbf{x}^{(k+1)}$, which should be a better estimate of the solution. In some of the algorithms all the calculated points $\mathbf{x}^{(k)}$ are forced to satisfy the constraints, but other algorithms allow the constraints to be violated some or all of the time. For example, constraint violations are often unavoidable when a nonlinear equality constraint is given.

To introduce the subject we consider descent methods for minimization when the constraints on the variables are the linear inequalities

$$\mathbf{A}^T\mathbf{x} \geqslant \mathbf{b}, \tag{1.1.1}$$

$\mathbf{A}$ being an $n \times m$ matrix and $\mathbf{b}$ being a column vector with m components. When all the constraints are linear it is usual to choose an algorithm with the property that the calculated points $\mathbf{x}^{(k)}$ all satisfy the constraints (1.1.1). Further, in a descent method the inequality

$$F(\mathbf{x}^{(k+1)}) < F(\mathbf{x}^{(k)}) \tag{1.1.2}$$

is obtained for every value of k, except that occasionally we may let $\mathbf{x}^{(k+1)} = \mathbf{x}^{(k)}$.

Each iteration of a descent method consists of the following two or three basic parts. The first part calculates a downhill direction, $\mathbf{p}^{(k)}$ say, at $\mathbf{x}^{(k)}$, which means that for sufficiently small $\alpha > 0$ the inequality

$$F(\mathbf{x}^{(k)} + \alpha\mathbf{p}^{(k)}) < F(\mathbf{x}^{(k)}) \tag{1.1.3}$$

should hold. Also we require the point $\{\mathbf{x}^{(k)} + \alpha\mathbf{p}^{(k)}\}$ to satisfy the constraints. The second part calculates a steplength, $\alpha^{(k)}$ say, and we let $\mathbf{x}^{(k+1)}$ be the vector

$$\mathbf{x}^{(k+1)} = \mathbf{x}^{(k)} + \alpha^{(k)}\,\mathbf{p}^{(k)}. \tag{1.1.4}$$

The third part, which may be absent, uses the information gained by parts one and two to revise any auxiliary information, for example derivative approximations. This general approach is described by Zoutendijk (1970) under the heading "feasible directions". Note that when $F(\mathbf{x})$ is differentiable we may satisfy inequality (1.1.3) by meeting the condition

$$\mathbf{g}^{(k)T}\mathbf{p}^{(k)} < 0, \tag{1.1.5}$$

where $\mathbf{g}^{(k)}$ is the gradient of $F(\mathbf{x})$ at $\mathbf{x}^{(k)}$ and where the superscript T denotes a row vector, so the left-hand side of expression (1.1.5) is a scalar product.

Given a feasible point $\mathbf{x}^{(k)}$, the gradient $\mathbf{g}^{(k)}$ and the constraints (1.1.1), it is reasonable to enquire whether there exists a direction $\mathbf{p}^{(k)}$ satisfying inequality (1.1.5), and such that the vector

$$\mathbf{x} = \mathbf{x}^{(k)} + \alpha\mathbf{p}^{(k)} \tag{1.1.6}$$

satisfies the constraints for all sufficiently small positive values of α. If we find such a vector $\mathbf{p}^{(k)}$, then we may use it as a search direction for a descent method. Otherwise, if there is no direction satisfying these conditions, then often $\mathbf{x}^{(k)}$ is the required solution to the main problem of minimizing $F(\mathbf{x})$ subject to the constraints. Thus we obtain conditions necessary for $\mathbf{x}^{(k)}$ to be the required solution, which are called "first-order conditions", because they depend on first derivatives. They are derived and discussed in Section 1.2. This analysis has many applications. For example in Section 1.4 we find when it is advantageous to let $\mathbf{x}^{(k+1)}$ be away from the boundary of a constraint that is satisfied as an equality at $\mathbf{x}^{(k)}$.

However, it happens occasionally that the first-order conditions are satisfied at $\mathbf{x}^{(k)}$, but it is not a constrained minimum of $F(\mathbf{x})$, because the conditions are necessary rather than sufficient. Indeed sometimes there are descent directions at $\mathbf{x}^{(k)}$ that satisfy the equation

$$\mathbf{g}^{(k)T}\mathbf{p}^{(k)} = 0 \tag{1.1.7}$$

instead of inequality (1.1.5). For example, when the problem is to minimize the function

$$F(x_1, x_2) = x_1 + \cos x_2 \tag{1.1.8}$$

subject to the condition $x_1 \geqslant 0$, then at $\mathbf{x} = \mathbf{0}$ the directions $\mathbf{p} = (0, \pm 1)^T$ are both downhill directions, although they satisfy equation (1.1.7).

Theoreticians have worked hard at filling the gap caused because the first-order conditions are necessary but not sufficient. Some of this work is reported in Section 1.3, including the important case when not only first derivatives are known, but also second derivatives of $F(\mathbf{x})$. However the design of algorithms is usually governed by only the first-order conditions, because, if a calculated point satisfies the first-order conditions then one expects it to be the required solution, and if it is not the required solution then the extra fineness of the second-order conditions may not help in practice. In particular when no constraints are satisfied as equalities at the final point, we are taking the risk that we have calculated a saddle point instead of a local minimum. This is not a bad point of view because the search directions of descent algorithms tend to veer away from saddle points.

In Section 1.4 we consider applying the first- and second-order conditions to obtain descent algorithms. The main point of interest is that if descent directions exist at $\mathbf{x}^{(k)}$, then usually there is a whole cone of descent directions, so in order to specify an algorithm one requires a technique that selects a particular descent direction from the cone. In the algorithm proposed by Rosen (1960) the descent direction $\mathbf{p}^{(k)}$ is calculated to minimize the negative quantity

$$\mathbf{g}^{(k)T}\mathbf{p}^{(k)}/\|\mathbf{p}^{(k)}\|, \tag{1.1.9}$$

where the vector norm is the Euclidean norm

$$\|\mathbf{x}\| = \left\{\sum_{i=1}^{n} x_i^2\right\}^{\frac{1}{2}}, \tag{1.1.10}$$

while Zoutendijk (1970) imposes some conjugacy conditions on $\mathbf{p}^{(k)}$, and Goldfarb (1969) takes account of an approximation to the second-derivative matrix of $F(\mathbf{x})$ in his choice of $\mathbf{p}^{(k)}$. We study a variant of Rosen's method in Section 1.4, and we note that it exposes the interesting zigzagging problem. The other methods that take account of second-derivative terms are considered in Chapters II and V by Gill, Murray and Sargent.

In fact Sargent will describe the use of descent methods when there are some nonlinear constraints, which is more difficult than the case when all the constraints are linear, because a correction procedure is needed in a numerical method that tries to follow a curved constraint boundary. Therefore techniques that are quite different from descent methods have been developed, and in my opinion some of them are more promising than descent methods for problems that involve nonlinear constraints. They are described in Chapters VIII and VI by Fletcher and Ryan. However the results reported by Abadie and Guigou (1970) indicate that, among the methods for nonlinear constraints for which general purpose computer programs are written and working, descent algorithms compare very favourably with the other techniques.

Many of these other techniques are penalty-function methods. In a penalty-function method the objective function $F(\mathbf{x})$ is replaced by the function

$$P(\mathbf{x}, r) = F(\mathbf{x}) + \phi(\mathbf{x}, r), \tag{1.1.11}$$

where r is a single parameter or a vector of parameters, and where $\phi(\mathbf{x}, r)$ is a penalty term that tends to be very large or infinite when the constraints are violated, and that tends to be small when $\mathbf{x}$ satisfies the constraints, depending on the value of r. An algorithm for unconstrained minimization is applied to minimize $P(\mathbf{x}, r)$, and we let the calculated value of $\mathbf{x}$ be $\mathbf{x}(r)$. It is usual to calculate $\mathbf{x}(r)$ for a sequence of values of r, and by choosing $\phi(\mathbf{x}, r)$ and this sequence carefully one can obtain many penalty-function algorithms such that $\mathbf{x}(r)$ tends to the solution of the original problem.

In these penalty-function methods $\phi(\mathbf{x}, r)$ usually has some or all of the following three properties: (i) unboundedness, (ii) discontinuousness and (iii) discontinuousness in the gradient vector at the solution. Any of these properties makes the unconstrained minimizations difficult. Therefore recently a number of methods have been proposed whose general technique is that of the penalty-function methods, but where the functions $\phi(\mathbf{x}, r)$ have nice smoothness and boundedness properties. Often these new methods are also called penalty-function methods, but I prefer the name *augmented Lagrangian methods*, because we no longer have the characteristic that $\phi(\mathbf{x}, r)$ tends to be very large when a constraint is not satisfied. Some of these methods are considered by Fletcher in Chapter VIII, and also the review by Rockafellar (1973) is recommended.

They are called augmented Lagrangian methods because they may all be derived from the theory of Lagrangian functions. This theory is intimately related to the first- and second-order conditions of Sections 1.2 and 1.3. Therefore the final section of this chapter gives an introduction to Lagrangian functions that is biased towards the construction of augmented Lagrangian methods, in order to provide a background to some of the techniques that are described later in this book.

1.2. First-order Conditions for a Solution

In this section we consider conditions that are necessary for a point $\mathbf{x}$ to give the least value of $F(\mathbf{x})$ subject to the constraints

$$c_i(\mathbf{x}) \geqslant 0, \qquad i = 1, 2, \ldots, m. \tag{1.2.1}$$

They depend on first derivatives, so throughout this section we suppose that all functions are differentiable, and we use the standard notation $\mathbf{g}(\mathbf{x})$ and $\mathbf{a}_i(\mathbf{x})$ for the derivatives of $F(\mathbf{x})$ and $c_i(\mathbf{x})$ $(i = 1, 2, \ldots, m)$ respectively. The conditions come directly from the discussion of descent directions in Section 1.1, for they are all special cases of the following very general theorem.

THEOREM 1.1. *Let* $\mathbf{x}$ *be feasible (i.e. it satisfies the constraints). A necessary condition for* $\mathbf{x}$ *to solve the constrained minimization problem is that there is no vector* $\mathbf{p}$ *satisfying the inequality*

$$\mathbf{g}(\mathbf{x})^T\mathbf{p} < 0 \tag{1.2.2}$$

and such that $(\mathbf{x} + \alpha\mathbf{p})$ *is feasible for all values of* α *in an interval* $0 \leqslant \alpha \leqslant \bar{\alpha}$, $\bar{\alpha} > 0$.

Proof. Suppose that a vector $\mathbf{p}$ does satisfy these conditions. Then inequality (1.2.2) implies that there exists a constant $\hat{\alpha}$ such that $F(\mathbf{x} + \alpha\mathbf{p}) < F(\mathbf{x})$ for all α in the range $0 < \alpha < \hat{\alpha}$. It follows that, if α is in the interval

$$0 < \alpha < \min\,[\bar{\alpha}, \hat{\alpha}], \tag{1.2.3}$$

then $F(\mathbf{x} + \alpha\mathbf{p}) < F(\mathbf{x})$ and $(\mathbf{x} + \alpha\mathbf{p})$ is feasible, in which case $\mathbf{x}$ is not the solution to the constrained minimization problem. The theorem is proved. ▮

It is convenient to order the constraints so that just the first t of them are satisfied as equalities at the point $\mathbf{x}$. In this case the continuity of the constraint functions implies that there is a neighbourhood of $\mathbf{x}$ such that the last $(m - t)$ constraints are satisfied at all points of the neighbourhood. Therefore in the statement of Theorem 1.1 the existence of $\mathbf{p}$ does not depend on the last $(m - t)$ constraints, but the actual value of $\bar{\alpha}$ probably does depend on these constraints.

Theorem 1.1 can be expressed in a very elegant and useful way by making use of the following lemma due to Farkas, which is fundamental to the subject of constrained optimization. For a good discussion of this lemma and of related theorems the book by Mangasarian (1969) is recommended.

FARKAS LEMMA. *Given the vectors* $\mathbf{a}_i$ $(i = 1, 2, \ldots, t)$ *and* $\mathbf{g}$, *there is no vector* $\mathbf{p}$ *satisfying the conditions*

$$\mathbf{g}^T\mathbf{p} < 0 \tag{1.2.4}$$

and

$$\mathbf{a}_i{}^T\mathbf{p} \geqslant 0, \qquad i = 1, 2, \ldots, t, \tag{1.2.5}$$

if and only if $\mathbf{g}$ *is in the convex cone spanned by the vectors* $\mathbf{a}_i (i = 1, 2, \ldots, t)$.

Proof. If $\mathbf{g}$ is in the convex cone it can be written in the form

$$\mathbf{g} = \sum_{i=1}^{t} \lambda_i \mathbf{a}_i, \quad \lambda_i \geqslant 0. \tag{1.2.6}$$

Then condition (1.2.5) implies that $\mathbf{g}^T\mathbf{p}$ is non-negative, so it is not possible to satisfy conditions (1.2.4) and (1.2.5) when $\mathbf{g}$ is in the cone.

Conversely, when $\mathbf{g}$ is not in the cone, we let $\mathbf{h}$ be the point of the cone that is closest to $\mathbf{g}$ in the sense of the Euclidean norm (1.1.10), and we note that the equation

$$\mathbf{h}^T(\mathbf{h} - \mathbf{g}) = 0 \tag{1.2.7}$$

is satisfied. We let $\mathbf{p}$ be the vector

$$\mathbf{p} = \mathbf{h} - \mathbf{g}. \tag{1.2.8}$$

Then equations (1.2.7) and (1.2.8) give the inequality

$$\mathbf{g}^T\mathbf{p} = -\|\mathbf{h} - \mathbf{g}\|^2 < 0. \tag{1.2.9}$$

Moreover the definition of $\mathbf{h}$ implies that for every vector $\mathbf{v}$ in the cone, the inequality

$$\|\mathbf{h} - \mathbf{g}\|^2 \leqslant \|\mathbf{h} - \mathbf{g} + \theta(\mathbf{v} - \mathbf{h})\|^2 \tag{1.2.10}$$

is satisfied for all θ in [0, 1]. Thus we obtain the bound

$$(\mathbf{h} - \mathbf{g})^T(\mathbf{v} - \mathbf{h}) \geqslant 0, \tag{1.2.11}$$

so equations (1.2.7) and (1.2.8) imply the relation

$$\mathbf{p}^T\mathbf{v} \geqslant 0. \tag{1.2.12}$$

In particular we may let $\mathbf{v}$ be any of the vectors $\mathbf{a}_i (i = 1, 2, \ldots, t)$. Therefore expressions (1.2.9) and (1.2.12) show that the vector $\mathbf{p}$ satisfies inequalities (1.2.4) and (1.2.5). The lemma is proved. ▌

By using this lemma we deduce the following result from Theorem 1.1.

THEOREM 1.2. *Let* $\mathbf{x}$ *be a point that satisfies the linear constraints*

$$\mathbf{a}_i{}^T\mathbf{x} \geqslant b_i, \qquad i = 1, 2, \ldots, m, \tag{1.2.13}$$

where just the first t of these constraints are satisfied as equalities. Then $\mathbf{x}$ *minimizes* $F(\mathbf{x})$ *subject to the constraints only if* $\mathbf{g}(\mathbf{x})$ *can be expressed in the form*

$$\mathbf{g}(\mathbf{x}) = \sum_{i=1}^{t} \lambda_i \mathbf{a}_i, \qquad \lambda_i \geqslant 0. \tag{1.2.14}$$

Proof. We prove that if equation (1.2.14) is not satisfied, then $\mathbf{x}$ is not the solution of the constrained minimization problem. In this case the Farkas Lemma shows that there is a vector $\mathbf{p}$ that satisfies inequalities (1.2.2) and (1.2.5). Expression (1.2.5) and the linearity of the constraints imply that the first t constraints are satisfied at $(\mathbf{x}+\alpha\mathbf{p})$ for all $\alpha \geqslant 0$. Moreover the remarks following immediately after the proof of Theorem 1.1 show that there exists $\bar{\alpha} > 0$ such that the last $(m-t)$ constraints are satisfied at $(\mathbf{x}+\alpha\mathbf{p})$ for all $0 \leqslant \alpha \leqslant \bar{\alpha}$. Therefore $(\mathbf{x}+\alpha\mathbf{p})$ is feasible for all values of α in the interval $[0, \bar{\alpha}]$. Thus the vector $\mathbf{p}$ satisfies the conditions of Theorem 1.1, showing that $\mathbf{x}$ is not the solution to the constrained minimization problem, which proves Theorem 1.2. ▮

It is less easy to obtain from Theorem 1.1 and the Farkas Lemma a theorem that applies when the constraints are nonlinear, because we use the linearity of the constraints in the proof of Theorem 1.2 to deduce that, when inequality (1.2.5) is satisfied, the constraint functions $c_i(\mathbf{x}+\alpha\mathbf{p})$ $(i = 1, 2, \ldots, t)$ are non-negative for all $\alpha \geqslant 0$. Indeed the following pathological example shows that Theorem 1.2 does not generalize directly to nonlinear constraints.

Minimize the function $x_1 + x_2$ subject to the constraints

$$\left.\begin{array}{r} -x_1^2 + x_2 \geqslant 0 \\ -x_1^2 - x_2 \geqslant 0. \end{array}\right\} \qquad (1.2.15)$$

The only feasible point is $\mathbf{x} = \mathbf{0}$, so this must be the solution to the problem. However $\mathbf{g}(\mathbf{0})$ cannot be expressed in the form (1.2.14), because $\mathbf{a}_1(\mathbf{0})$, $\mathbf{a}_2(\mathbf{0})$ and $\mathbf{g}(\mathbf{0})$ are the vectors $(0, 1)^T$, $(0, -1)^T$ and $(1, 1)^T$. The following theorem shows that this kind of behaviour occurs only when the vectors $\mathbf{a}_i(\mathbf{x})$ $(i = 1, 2, \ldots, t)$ are linearly dependent.

THEOREM 1.3. *Let* $\mathbf{x}$ *be a point that satisfies the constraints* (1.2.1), *where just the first* t *of these constraints are satisfied as equalities. Then, if the constraint gradient vectors* $\mathbf{a}_i(\mathbf{x})$ $(i = 1, 2, \ldots, t)$ *are linearly independent,* $\mathbf{x}$ *minimizes* $F(\mathbf{x})$ *subject to the constraints only if* $\mathbf{g}(\mathbf{x})$ *can be expressed in the form*

$$\mathbf{g}(\mathbf{x}) = \sum_{i=1}^{t} \lambda_i \mathbf{a}_i(\mathbf{x}), \qquad \lambda_i \geqslant 0. \qquad (1.2.16)$$

Proof. Suppose equation (1.2.16) is not satisfied. Then by the Farkas Lemma we may let $\mathbf{p}$ be a vector that satisfies inequality (1.2.2) and the condition

$$\mathbf{a}_i(\mathbf{x})^T\mathbf{p} \geqslant 0, \qquad i = 1, 2, \ldots, t. \qquad (1.2.17)$$

Because the vectors $\mathbf{a}_i(\mathbf{x})$ $(i = 1, 2, \ldots, t)$ are linearly independent, there exists a vector $\mathbf{q}$ such that the inequalities

$$\mathbf{a}_i(\mathbf{x})^T\mathbf{q} > 0, \qquad i = 1, 2, \ldots, t, \tag{1.2.18}$$

hold. We replace $\mathbf{p}$ by $\mathbf{p} + \varepsilon\mathbf{q}$, where ε is any positive number that is so small that $\mathbf{g}(\mathbf{x})^T\mathbf{p}$ remains less than zero. Thus all the inequalities (1.2.17) become strict. It follows that the constraint functions $c_i(\mathbf{x} + \alpha\mathbf{p})$ $(i = 1, 2, \ldots, t)$ are positive for all values of α in a certain interval $0 < \alpha < \alpha^*$. Let $\bar{\alpha}$ be defined as in the proof of Theorem 1.2. We replace $\bar{\alpha}$ by α^* if $\alpha^* < \bar{\alpha}$. Then again $\mathbf{p}$ satisfies the conditions of Theorem 1.1, showing that $\mathbf{x}$ is not the solution to the constrained minimization problem. Theorem 1.3 is proved. ∎

Note that Theorem 1.3 may be proved under weaker conditions, for instead of the requirement that the vectors $\mathbf{a}_i(\mathbf{x})$ $(i = 1, 2, \ldots, t)$ are linearly independent, we may employ any condition that provides a vector $\mathbf{q}$ satisfying inequality (1.2.18). For theorems that are stronger than the ones proved in this section see Fiacco and McCormick (1968) for instance.

Fiacco and McCormick refer to the Kuhn–Tucker conditions, which differ mainly in notation from the conditions that we have derived. Their notation is due to developments of linear programming techniques, where it is usual to have a parameter λ_i for every constraint, instead of following the style of equation (1.2.16), where there is a parameter λ_i only for the constraints that are satisfied as equalities. Therefore, in the more usual notation, equation (1.2.16) would be expressed in the form

$$\mathbf{g}(\mathbf{x}) = \sum_{i=1}^{m} \lambda_i\mathbf{a}_i(\mathbf{x}), \qquad \lambda_i \geqslant 0, \tag{1.2.19}$$

where the conditions $\lambda_i = 0$ $(i = t+1, t+2, \ldots, m)$ are obtained by imposing the auxiliary restrictions

$$\lambda_i c_i(\mathbf{x}) = 0, \qquad i = 1, 2, \ldots, m. \tag{1.2.20}$$

However, I prefer to make a definite distinction between constraints that are satisfied as equalities and constraints that are not binding at the current point $\mathbf{x}$.

1.3. Second-order Conditions for a Solution

The theorems of the last section give various ways of saying that, if at a point $\mathbf{x}$ we can find a direction $\mathbf{p}$ pointing into the feasible region such that $\mathbf{p}^T\mathbf{g}(\mathbf{x}) < 0$, then $\mathbf{x}$ does not solve the constrained minimization problem, because $\mathbf{p}$ is a feasible descent direction. Therefore, if $\mathbf{x}$ is a point of convergence of a descent algorithm, we expect that for all feasible directions $\mathbf{p}$ the inequality $\mathbf{p}^T\mathbf{g}(\mathbf{x}) \geqslant 0$ is satisfied. When $\mathbf{p}^T\mathbf{g}(\mathbf{x})$ is positive the objective function increases initially if a move is made from $\mathbf{x}$ along the direction $\mathbf{p}$, but the example (1.1.8) shows that when $\mathbf{p}^T\mathbf{g}(\mathbf{x})$ is zero then it can happen that $\mathbf{p}$ is a descent direction. Therefore the main purpose of the second-order conditions is to identify when feasible directions that are orthogonal to $\mathbf{g}(\mathbf{x})$ are descent directions. These conditions depend on the second-derivative matrix

$$\mathbf{G}(\mathbf{x}) = [\partial^2 F(\mathbf{x})/\partial x_i \partial x_j]. \tag{1.3.1}$$

Also they require a definition of a local minimum, and we use the following one.

The point $\mathbf{x}$ is a local minimum of $F(\mathbf{x})$ subject to the constraints, if $\mathbf{x}$ is feasible, and if there is a neighbourhood of $\mathbf{x}$, such that at all feasible points of this neighbourhood the value of the objective function is greater than or equal to $F(\mathbf{x})$. Further, we call $\mathbf{x}$ a strong local minimum, if the objective function is greater than $F(\mathbf{x})$ at every feasible point of the neighbourhood except $\mathbf{x}$.

When the matrix $\mathbf{G}(\mathbf{x})$ is positive definite and the constraints are linear, then conditions for a local minimum are easy to obtain.

THEOREM 1.4. *Let* $\mathbf{x}$ *be a point that satisfies the linear constraints* (1.2.13), *where just the first* t *of these constraints are satisfied as equalities. If* $\mathbf{G}$ *is positive definite then* $\mathbf{x}$ *is a strong local minimum of* $F(\mathbf{x})$ *if and only if* $\mathbf{g}(\mathbf{x})$ *can be expressed in the form* (1.2.14).

Proof. The truth of the "only if" part of the theorem is shown by Theorem 1.2. Conversely, if $\mathbf{g}(\mathbf{x})$ has the form (1.2.14), then by the Farkas Lemma there is no direction $\mathbf{p}$ satisfying conditions (1.2.2) and (1.2.5). However, condition (1.2.5) must be satisfied if $(\mathbf{x} + \alpha\mathbf{p})$, $\alpha > 0$, is a feasible point. Therefore if $(\mathbf{x} + \mathbf{d})$ is a feasible point the inequality

$$\mathbf{g}(\mathbf{x})^T\mathbf{d} \geqslant 0 \tag{1.3.2}$$

holds.

We now prove a contradiction if $\mathbf{x}$ is not a strong local minimum. In this case there is a sequence of vectors $\mathbf{d}$, converging to the zero vector, such that for all vectors in the sequence the point $(\mathbf{x} + \mathbf{d})$ is feasible and the condition

$$F(\mathbf{x} + \mathbf{d}) \leqslant F(\mathbf{x}) \tag{1.3.3}$$

is satisfied. Now a property of Frechet derivatives (see Ortega and Rheinboldt, 1970, Section 3.3.12) is the condition

$$\lim_{\|\mathbf{d}\| \to 0} \frac{F(\mathbf{x} + \mathbf{d}) - F(\mathbf{x}) - \mathbf{g}(\mathbf{x})^T\mathbf{d} - \frac{1}{2}\mathbf{d}^T\mathbf{G}(\mathbf{x})\mathbf{d}}{\|\mathbf{d}\|^2} = 0. \tag{1.3.4}$$

Therefore inequalities (1.3.2) and (1.3.3) imply the bound

$$\lim_{\|\mathbf{d}\|\to 0} \mathbf{d}^T\mathbf{G}(\mathbf{x})\mathbf{d}/\|\mathbf{d}\|^2 \leqslant 0, \tag{1.3.5}$$

which contradicts the positive definiteness of $\mathbf{G}(\mathbf{x})$. Therefore Theorem 1.4 is true. ∎

In practice it often happens that the objective function $F(\mathbf{x})$ has negative curvature along some directions, and then Theorem 1.4 is not relevant, because the matrix $\mathbf{G}(\mathbf{x})$ is not positive definite. If a good algorithm for constrained minimization is applied to such a function, then directions of negative curvature are followed to decrease $F(\mathbf{x})$ until a constraint is encountered. Thus, at the point of convergence of a descent algorithm, one should find that constraints prohibit further moves along directions of negative curvature. The following generalization of the sufficiency conditions of Theorem 1.4 usually applies to this important case.

THEOREM 1.5. *Let* $\mathbf{x}$ *be a point that satisfies the linear constraints* (1.2.13), *where just the first* t *constraints are satisfied as equalities. Further let* $\mathbf{x}$ *be such that the gradient* $\mathbf{g}(\mathbf{x})$ *can be expressed in the form*

$$\mathbf{g}(\mathbf{x}) = \sum_{i=1}^{t'} \lambda_i \mathbf{a}_i, \qquad \lambda_i > 0, \tag{1.3.6}$$

where $t' \leqslant t$. *If there is a positive constant* ε *such that for every vector* $\hat{\mathbf{d}}$ *satisfying the conditions*

$$\hat{\mathbf{d}}^T\mathbf{a}_i = 0, \qquad i = 1, 2, \ldots, t', \tag{1.3.7}$$

the inequality

$$\hat{\mathbf{d}}^T\mathbf{G}(\mathbf{x})\hat{\mathbf{d}} \geqslant \varepsilon\,\|\hat{\mathbf{d}}\|^2 \tag{1.3.8}$$

holds, then $\mathbf{x}$ *is a strong local minimum of* $F(\mathbf{x})$.

Proof. Let $\bar{S}$ be the linear space spanned by the vectors $\mathbf{a}_i$ ($i = 1, 2, \ldots, t'$), and let $\hat{S}$ be the orthogonal complement of this space. There exists a positive constant, $\bar{\eta}$ say, such that for every vector $\bar{\mathbf{d}}$ in $\bar{S}$ the inequality

$$\max_{1\leqslant i\leqslant t'} |\mathbf{a}_i{}^T\bar{\mathbf{d}}| \geqslant \bar{\eta}\,\|\bar{\mathbf{d}}\| \tag{1.3.9}$$

is satisfied. We define η to be the positive number

$$\eta = \bar{\eta} \min_{1\leqslant i\leqslant t'} \lambda_i, \tag{1.3.10}$$

in order that the bound

$$\sum_{i=1}^{t'} \lambda_i |\mathbf{a}_i^T \bar{\mathbf{d}}| \geqslant \eta \|\bar{\mathbf{d}}\| \tag{1.3.11}$$

holds.

We suppose that **x** is not a strong local minimum, and construct a sequence of vectors **d** converging to zero as in the proof of Theorem 1.4. Thus the points $(\mathbf{x} + \mathbf{d})$ are feasible and conditions (1.3.3) and (1.3.4) are valid. For each **d** we define $\bar{\mathbf{d}}$ and $\hat{\mathbf{d}}$ by the equation

$$\mathbf{d} = \bar{\mathbf{d}} + \hat{\mathbf{d}}, \tag{1.3.12}$$

where $\bar{\mathbf{d}}$ is in $\bar{S}$ and $\hat{\mathbf{d}}$ is in $\hat{S}$. Therefore the use of Euclidean norms gives the identity

$$\|\mathbf{d}\|^2 = \|\bar{\mathbf{d}}\|^2 + \|\hat{\mathbf{d}}\|^2. \tag{1.3.13}$$

The feasibility of $(\mathbf{x} + \mathbf{d})$ gives the inequalities

$$\mathbf{a}_i^T \mathbf{d} \geqslant 0, \quad i = 1, 2, \ldots, t'. \tag{1.3.14}$$

Therefore from expressions (1.3.6), (1.3.12), (1.3.11) and (1.3.7) we obtain the bound

$$\begin{aligned} \mathbf{g}(\mathbf{x})^T \mathbf{d} &= \sum_{i=1}^{t'} \lambda_i |\mathbf{a}_i^T (\bar{\mathbf{d}} + \hat{\mathbf{d}})| \\ &\geqslant \eta \|\bar{\mathbf{d}}\|. \end{aligned} \tag{1.3.15}$$

It follows from expressions (1.3.3) and (1.3.4) that the inequality

$$\lim_{\|\mathbf{d}\| \to 0} \frac{-\eta \|\bar{\mathbf{d}}\| - \frac{1}{2}(\bar{\mathbf{d}} + \hat{\mathbf{d}})^T \mathbf{G}(\mathbf{x})(\bar{\mathbf{d}} + \hat{\mathbf{d}})}{\|\mathbf{d}\|^2} \geqslant 0 \tag{1.3.16}$$

is true. Now, since the sequence of vectors **d** tends to zero, we may assume that we have reached the stage where the conditions

$$\left.\begin{aligned} \|\tfrac{1}{2}\mathbf{G}(\mathbf{x})\,\bar{\mathbf{d}} + \mathbf{G}(\mathbf{x})\,\hat{\mathbf{d}}\| &\leqslant \tfrac{1}{2}\eta \\ \|\bar{\mathbf{d}}\| &\leqslant 1 \end{aligned}\right\} \tag{1.3.17}$$

are satisfied. In this case we have the bound

$$\begin{aligned} &-\eta \|\bar{\mathbf{d}}\| - \tfrac{1}{2}(\bar{\mathbf{d}} + \hat{\mathbf{d}})^T \mathbf{G}(\mathbf{x})(\bar{\mathbf{d}} + \hat{\mathbf{d}}) \\ &\quad \leqslant -\eta \|\bar{\mathbf{d}}\| + \|\bar{\mathbf{d}}\| \, \|\tfrac{1}{2}\mathbf{G}(\mathbf{x})\,\bar{\mathbf{d}} + \mathbf{G}(\mathbf{x})\,\hat{\mathbf{d}}\| - \tfrac{1}{2}\hat{\mathbf{d}}^T \mathbf{G}(\mathbf{x})\,\hat{\mathbf{d}} \\ &\quad \leqslant -\tfrac{1}{2}\eta \|\bar{\mathbf{d}}\| - \tfrac{1}{2}\hat{\mathbf{d}}^T \mathbf{G}(\mathbf{x})\,\hat{\mathbf{d}} \\ &\quad \leqslant -\tfrac{1}{2}\eta \|\bar{\mathbf{d}}\|^2 - \tfrac{1}{2}\varepsilon \|\hat{\mathbf{d}}\|^2 \\ &\quad \leqslant -\tfrac{1}{2}\min(\varepsilon, \eta) \|\mathbf{d}\|^2, \end{aligned} \tag{1.3.18}$$

where the last two lines depend on expressions (1.3.8) and (1.3.13). Since both ε and η are positive numbers, inequality (1.3.16) is contradicted. Therefore Theorem 1.5 is true. ▮

The following converse of Theorem 1.5 is easy to prove.

THEOREM 1.6. *Let* $\mathbf{x}$ *be a point that satisfies the linear constraints* (1.2.13), *where just the first* t *constraints are satisfied as equalities. Let* $\hat{\mathbf{d}}$ *be any direction satisfying the conditions*

$$\hat{\mathbf{d}}^T \mathbf{a}_i = 0, \qquad i = 1, 2, \ldots, t. \tag{1.3.19}$$

Then, if $\hat{\mathbf{d}}^T \mathbf{G}(\mathbf{x}) \hat{\mathbf{d}}$ *is negative,* $\mathbf{x}$ *does not solve the constrained minimization problem.*

Proof. Condition (1.3.19) implies that there exists a positive number, $\bar{\alpha}$ say, such that the points $(\mathbf{x} - \alpha\hat{\mathbf{d}})$ and $(\mathbf{x} + \alpha\hat{\mathbf{d}})$ are feasible for all α in the range $0 \leqslant \alpha \leqslant \bar{\alpha}$. Therefore, if $\mathbf{g}(\mathbf{x})^T\hat{\mathbf{d}}$ is not zero, Theorem 1.1 implies that $\mathbf{x}$ does not solve the constrained minimization problem.

Alternatively, when $\mathbf{g}(\mathbf{x})^T\hat{\mathbf{d}}$ is zero, we may define $\mathbf{d} = \alpha\hat{\mathbf{d}}$ in expression (1.3.4) for a sequence of positive values of α that tends to zero. Thus we obtain the equation

$$\lim_{\alpha \to 0} \frac{F(\mathbf{x} + \alpha\hat{\mathbf{d}}) - F(\mathbf{x})}{\alpha^2 \|\hat{\mathbf{d}}\|^2} = \frac{\tfrac{1}{2}\hat{\mathbf{d}}^T \mathbf{G}(\mathbf{x})\, \hat{\mathbf{d}}}{\|\hat{\mathbf{d}}\|^2}, \tag{1.3.20}$$

and the right-hand side is negative by hypothesis. It follows that $F(\mathbf{x} + \alpha\hat{\mathbf{d}})$ is less than $F(\mathbf{x})$ for some feasible values of $(\mathbf{x} + \alpha\hat{\mathbf{d}})$, which proves the theorem. ▮

So far in this section we have given theorems only when the constraints are linear, and we have treated this case quite thoroughly. Therefore now we turn to second-order conditions when there are some nonlinear constraints.

If the constraint functions $c_i(\mathbf{x})$ are concave, then every vector $\mathbf{d}$ that satisfies the inequality

$$c_i(\mathbf{x} + \mathbf{d}) - c_i(\mathbf{x}) \geqslant 0 \tag{1.3.21}$$

also satisfies the condition

$$\mathbf{a}_i(\mathbf{x})^T \mathbf{d} \geqslant 0, \tag{1.3.22}$$

where $\mathbf{a}_i(\mathbf{x})$ is the gradient vector of the function $c_i(\mathbf{x})$. Therefore, in the statement of Theorem 1.5 we may replace the linear constraints (1.2.13) by the nonlinear constraints (1.2.1), and, throughout the statement and proof of the theorem, all other occurrences of the vectors $\mathbf{a}_i$ may be replaced by the vectors $\mathbf{a}_i(\mathbf{x})$. Thus we obtain a sufficient condition for $\mathbf{x}$ to be a strong local minimum that is useful when the feasible region is convex. However, Theorem 1.6 does not generalize in this way, and, when the feasible region is not convex, the second-order conditions have to take account of, not only the second derivatives of $F(\mathbf{x})$, but also the second derivatives of the constraint functions $c_i(\mathbf{x})$.

The following example shows the influence of the curvature of the constraint functions quite well. Minimize the function

$$F(x_1, x_2) = 3x_2 + {x_1}^2 + {x_2}^2 \tag{1.3.23}$$

subject to the constraint

$$c_1(\mathbf{x}) = {x_1}^2 + (x_2 + 1)^2 \geqslant 1. \tag{1.3.24}$$

We consider whether the point $\mathbf{x} = \mathbf{0}$ is a local minimum. Because the equation

$$\mathbf{g}(\mathbf{0}) = 1.5\,\mathbf{a}_1(\mathbf{0}) \tag{1.3.25}$$

is satisfied, and because the second-derivative matrix of $F(\mathbf{x})$ is positive definite, Theorem 1.4 indicates that we may have a local minimum. However the purpose of the example is to show that this suggestion is false. The point $(\sin\theta, \cos\theta - 1)$ is feasible for all values of θ, and the dependence of the objective function on θ is given by the equation

$$\begin{aligned} F(\sin\theta, \cos\theta - 1) &= 3(\cos\theta - 1) + \sin^2\theta + (\cos\theta - 1)^2 \\ &= \cos\theta - 1. \end{aligned} \tag{1.3.26}$$

Therefore, although the second-derivative matrix of $F(\mathbf{x})$ is positive definite, and although equation (1.3.25) is satisfied, the objective function becomes smaller when the vector of variables is moved away from $\mathbf{x} = \mathbf{0}$ around the boundary of the feasible region.

This behaviour occurs because the curvature of the constraint function is so severe that it brings the constraint boundary inside the surface of points $(\mathbf{x} + \mathbf{d})$, defined by the values of $\mathbf{d}$ satisfying the equation

$$F(\mathbf{x} + \mathbf{d}) = F(\mathbf{x}), \tag{1.3.27}$$

where $\mathbf{x}$ is the point under consideration as a local minimum. Theoretical second-order conditions for nonlinear constraints can be obtained by using "Lagrangian functions". Some theorems are given in Section 1.5.

1.4. Some Active Set Strategies and Quadratic Programming

In this section we continue the study of descent methods for minimization begun in Section 1.1, in the case when all the constraints are linear. In particular we consider the problem of selecting a search direction $\mathbf{p}^{(k)}$ at $\mathbf{x}^{(k)}$. Let the linear constraints on $\mathbf{x}$ be given by expression (1.1.1), and let just the first t constraints be satisfied as equalities at the point $\mathbf{x}^{(k)}$. Then we require $\mathbf{p}^{(k)}$ to satisfy the conditions

$$\mathbf{g}^{(k)T}\mathbf{p}^{(k)} < 0 \tag{1.4.1}$$

and

$$\mathbf{a}_i{}^T\mathbf{p}^{(k)} \geqslant 0, \qquad i = 1, 2, \ldots, t, \tag{1.4.2}$$

in order that it is a feasible descent direction. Thus we find that "active set strategies" are an important part of algorithms for constrained minimization, and we note some of the difficulties that occur from active sets.

The Farkas Lemma, proved in Section 1.2, shows that a suitable search direction $\mathbf{p}^{(k)}$ exists if and only if $\mathbf{g}^{(k)}$ is not in the convex cone spanned by the vectors $\mathbf{a}_i$ $(i = 1, 2, \ldots, t)$. Therefore throughout this section we suppose that $\mathbf{g}^{(k)}$ is not in this cone. Otherwise we expect the descent algorithm to accept $\mathbf{x}^{(k)}$ as the required solution to the constrained minimization problem.

One method suggested by Zoutendijk (1960) for specifying $\mathbf{p}^{(k)}$ is to calculate it to minimize the left-hand side of inequality (1.4.1), subject to expression (1.4.2) and to a normalization condition that fixes the Euclidean length (1.1.10) of $\mathbf{p}^{(k)}$. We now prove that this choice of $\mathbf{p}^{(k)}$ is identical to the vector (1.2.8).

THEOREM 1.7. *Let $\mathbf{h}^{(k)}$ be the point of the convex cone spanned by the vectors $\mathbf{a}_i$ $(i = 1, 2, \ldots, t)$ that is closest to $\mathbf{g}^{(k)}$ and let $\mathbf{p}^{(k)}$ be the vector*

$$\mathbf{p}^{(k)} = \mathbf{h}^{(k)} - \mathbf{g}^{(k)}. \tag{1.4.3}$$

If $\mathbf{p}$ is any other feasible direction satisfying the normalization condition

$$\|\mathbf{p}\| = \|\mathbf{p}^{(k)}\|, \tag{1.4.4}$$

then the inequality

$$\mathbf{g}^{(k)T}\,\mathbf{p}^{(k)} < \mathbf{g}^{(k)T}\,\mathbf{p} \tag{1.4.5}$$

holds.

Proof. Since $\mathbf{h}^{(k)}$ is in the convex cone spanned by the vectors $\mathbf{a}_i$ $(i = 1, 2, \ldots, t)$, it satisfies an equation of the form

$$\mathbf{h}^{(k)} = \sum_{i=1}^{t} \eta_i \mathbf{a}_i, \qquad \eta_i \geqslant 0. \tag{1.4.6}$$

Thus expressions (1.4.3) and (1.2.5) imply the inequality

$$(\mathbf{p}^{(k)} + \mathbf{g}^{(k)})^T \mathbf{p} = \mathbf{h}^{(k)T} \mathbf{p} \geqslant 0. \tag{1.4.7}$$

Moreover the derivation of equations (1.2.8) and (1.2.9) provides the identity

$$\mathbf{g}^{(k)T} \mathbf{p}^{(k)} = -\|\mathbf{p}^{(k)}\|^2. \tag{1.4.8}$$

Therefore, by using expressions (1.4.7), (1.4.4) and (1.4.8) and also the Schwarz inequality, we deduce the bound

$$\begin{aligned} \mathbf{g}^{(k)T} \mathbf{p} &\geqslant -\mathbf{p}^{(k)T} \mathbf{p} \\ &> -\|\mathbf{p}^{(k)}\| \, \|\mathbf{p}\| \\ &= -\|\mathbf{p}^{(k)}\|^2 \\ &= \mathbf{g}^{(k)T} \mathbf{p}^{(k)}, \end{aligned} \tag{1.4.9}$$

which proves the theorem. ∎

This theorem provides a nice geometric interpretation of the steepest feasible direction at $\mathbf{x}^{(k)}$. Also it implies that $\mathbf{p}^{(k)}$ is the vector (1.4.3), where $\mathbf{h}^{(k)}$ has the form (1.4.6), the values of the non-negative multipliers η_i $(i = 1, 2, \ldots, t)$ being calculated to minimize the quadratic function

$$\|\mathbf{g}^{(k)} - \mathbf{h}^{(k)}\|^2 = \left\| \mathbf{g}^{(k)} - \sum_{i=1}^{t} \eta_i \mathbf{a}_i \right\|^2. \tag{1.4.10}$$

Thus the calculation of the steepest feasible descent direction is reduced to a quadratic programming problem in t variables, namely η_i $(i = 1, 2, \ldots, t)$, which are subject to non-negativity constraints.

A different quadratic programming problem that yields the same vector $\mathbf{p}^{(k)}$ is as follows. Let $\mathbf{p}^{(k)}$ be the vector $\mathbf{p}$ that minimizes the function $\|\mathbf{p} + \mathbf{g}^{(k)}\|^2$ subject to the inequality constraints (1.2.5). Note that now there are n variables, namely the components of $\mathbf{p}$, instead of t variables. The equivalence of these two problems is an example of duality theory. For more information on this subject see Mangasarian (1969).

However these remarks do not help the calculation of $\mathbf{p}^{(k)}$ yet, because algorithms for quadratic programming also require the calculation of feasible directions. Thus we have replaced the feasible direction problem when $F(\mathbf{x})$ is a general function by the feasible direction problem when $F(\mathbf{x})$ is a quadratic function. Therefore in the next few paragraphs we consider quadratic programming algorithms, and we derive a method of solution.

Quadratic programming algorithms are iterative methods that use an "active set strategy". Let the objective function be the quadratic

$$F(\mathbf{x}) = \tfrac{1}{2}\mathbf{x}^T\mathbf{Q}\mathbf{x} + \mathbf{q}^T\mathbf{x} + \text{const}, \tag{1.4.11}$$

and let the constraints be the linear constraints (1.1.1). We continue to use the notation $\mathbf{x}^{(k)}$ $(k = 0, 1, \ldots)$ for the sequence of points calculated by the iterative method. The idea of an active set strategy is that the active set is a list of those constraints that are satisfied as equalities during an iteration. For instance if just the first t of the constraints (1.2.13) are satisfied as equalities at $\mathbf{x}^{(k)}$, these t constraints may constitute the active set, in which case we force them to be satisfied at $\mathbf{x}^{(k+1)}$ also, by imposing the condition

$$\mathbf{a}_i{}^T\mathbf{p}^{(k)} = 0, \qquad i = 1, 2, \ldots, t. \tag{1.4.12}$$

This condition replaces inequality (1.4.2), so we now have less freedom in the choice of $\mathbf{p}^{(k)}$.

An excellent choice of $\mathbf{p}^{(k)}$ is to let $(\mathbf{x}^{(k)} + \mathbf{p}^{(k)})$ be the vector $\mathbf{x}$ that minimizes the function (1.4.11) subject to the constraints (1.4.12). The next theorem gives a formula for this choice of $\mathbf{p}^{(k)}$ in the case that the matrix $\mathbf{Q}$ is positive definite. In fact, because of the constraints (1.4.12), the definition of $\mathbf{p}^{(k)}$ remains unchanged if $\mathbf{Q}$ is replaced by the matrix

$$\hat{\mathbf{Q}} = \mathbf{Q} + \sum_{i=1}^{t} \sigma_i \mathbf{a}_i \mathbf{a}_i{}^T, \qquad \sigma_i \geqslant 0, \tag{1.4.13}$$

where the values of σ_i $(i = 1, 2, \ldots, t)$ are arbitrary. Therefore the theorem is useful when $\mathbf{Q}$ is not positive definite, provided that we can choose the values of σ_i $(i = 1, 2, \ldots, t)$ so that $\hat{\mathbf{Q}}$ is positive definite.

THEOREM 1.8. *Let* $\hat{\mathbf{A}}$ *be the matrix whose columns are* $\mathbf{a}_i$ $(i = 1, 2, \ldots, t)$ *when these vectors are independent, and whose columns provide a basis of the space spanned by* $\mathbf{a}_i$ $(i = 1, 2, \ldots, t)$ *when these vectors are not independent. Then, if the matrix* $\mathbf{Q}$ *is positive definite and if* $\mathbf{x}^{(k)}$ *is given, the function* $F(\mathbf{x}^{(k)} + \mathbf{p}^{(k)})$, *defined by equation* (1.4.11), *is least, subject to the conditions* (1.4.12), *when* $\mathbf{p}^{(k)}$ *is the vector*

$$\mathbf{p}^{(k)} = \{\mathbf{Q}^{-1}\hat{\mathbf{A}}(\hat{\mathbf{A}}^T\mathbf{Q}^{-1}\hat{\mathbf{A}})^{-1}\hat{\mathbf{A}}^T\mathbf{Q}^{-1} - \mathbf{Q}^{-1}\}\mathbf{g}^{(k)}, \tag{1.4.14}$$

where $\mathbf{g}^{(k)}$ *is the gradient vector*

$$\mathbf{g}^{(k)} = \mathbf{Q}\mathbf{x}^{(k)} + \mathbf{q}. \tag{1.4.15}$$

Proof. The constraints on $\mathbf{p}^{(k)}$ may be written in the form

$$\hat{\mathbf{A}}^T\mathbf{p}^{(k)} = \mathbf{0}, \tag{1.4.16}$$

so Theorem 1.4 implies that there is a vector $\boldsymbol{\lambda}$, having as many components as the number of columns of $\hat{\mathbf{A}}$, such that the equation

$$\begin{aligned}\text{grad}\, F(\mathbf{x}^{(k)} + \mathbf{p}^{(k)}) &= \mathbf{Q}\{\mathbf{x}^{(k)} + \mathbf{p}^{(k)}\} + \mathbf{q} \\ &= \hat{\mathbf{A}}\boldsymbol{\lambda}\end{aligned} \tag{1.4.17}$$

is satisfied. In fact the components of $\boldsymbol{\lambda}$ may be negative because the constraints (1.4.16) are equalities. We write equation (1.4.17) in the form

$$\mathbf{Q}\mathbf{p}^{(k)} = \hat{\mathbf{A}}\boldsymbol{\lambda} - \mathbf{g}^{(k)} \tag{1.4.18}$$

in order to deduce the identity

$$\hat{\mathbf{A}}^T\mathbf{p}^{(k)} = \hat{\mathbf{A}}^T\mathbf{Q}^{-1}\hat{\mathbf{A}}\boldsymbol{\lambda} - \hat{\mathbf{A}}^T\mathbf{Q}^{-1}\mathbf{g}^{(k)}. \tag{1.4.19}$$

From equation (1.4.16) it follows that $\boldsymbol{\lambda}$ is the vector

$$\boldsymbol{\lambda} = (\hat{\mathbf{A}}^T\mathbf{Q}^{-1}\hat{\mathbf{A}})^{-1}\hat{\mathbf{A}}^T\mathbf{Q}^{-1}\mathbf{g}^{(k)}, \tag{1.4.20}$$

so by using equation (1.4.18) again we obtain the required result (1.4.14). Theorem 1.8 is proved. ∎

If we always make this choice of $\mathbf{p}^{(k)}$, we may begin the quadratic programming algorithm in the following way. We let $\mathbf{x}^{(0)}$ be any point that satisfies the constraints (1.1.1), and we let the active set be composed of all constraints that are satisfied as equalities at $\mathbf{x}^{(0)}$. We calculate $\mathbf{p}^{(0)}$ by the method just described. We let $\mathbf{x}^{(1)}$ be the point $\mathbf{x}^{(0)} + \mathbf{p}^{(0)}$, unless this point is infeasible, in which case we let $\mathbf{x}^{(1)}$ be the point

$$\mathbf{x}^{(1)} = \mathbf{x}^{(0)} + \alpha^{(0)}\mathbf{p}^{(0)}, \tag{1.4.21}$$

where the value of $\alpha^{(0)}$, which must be in the interval $0 < \alpha^{(0)} < 1$, is as large as possible subject to feasibility of $\mathbf{x}^{(1)}$. In this case another constraint is satisfied as an equality at $\mathbf{x}^{(1)}$. It is added to the active set and we repeat the procedure. Thus eventually we reach a point $\mathbf{x}^{(k)}$ where the vector (1.4.14) is zero, and where the number of elements in the active set has increased on every iteration except probably the last one. At this point the quadratic function (1.4.11) is least subject to the condition that every member of the active set is an equality constraint. We suppose as usual that just the first t constraints are members of the active set.

However the constraints are inequality constraints, so often we may reduce $F(\mathbf{x})$ further by deleting elements from the active set. We consider this problem only in the case when the vectors $\mathbf{a}_i$ $(i = 1, 2, \ldots, t)$ are linearly independent. If there is linear dependence, then it may be treated by deleting dependent constraints from the active set, imagining that they are no longer satisfied as equalities; instead we assume that the values of $(\mathbf{a}_i^T\mathbf{x} - b_i)$ are very small positive quantities.

When the constraints are independent and $\mathbf{p}^{(k)}$ is zero, we may write equation (1.4.18) in the form

$$\mathbf{g}^{(k)} = \sum_{i=1}^{t} \lambda_i \mathbf{a}_i, \tag{1.4.22}$$

where $\boldsymbol{\lambda}$ is the vector (1.4.20). Therefore Theorem 1.4 implies that $\mathbf{x}^{(k)}$ solves the quadratic programming problem if and only if the multipliers λ_i $(i = 1, 2, \ldots, t)$ are all non-negative. Otherwise we delete one constraint from the active set, and continue the iterative procedure described above, until we reach another point $\mathbf{x}^{(k)}$ at which the vector (1.4.14) is zero. The following theorem shows that we may delete any constraint for which λ_i is negative.

THEOREM 1.9. *Let* $\mathbf{x}^{(k)}$ *be a feasible point at which equation* (1.4.22) *is valid, where just the first* t *of the constraints* (1.2.13) *are satisfied as equalities. If the vectors* $\mathbf{a}_i$ $(i = 1, 2, \ldots, t)$ *are linearly independent, if* $\lambda_t < 0$, *and if we replace* t *by* $t - 1$ *in the statement of Theorem* 1.8 *in order to define the vector* $\mathbf{p}^{(k)}$, *then* $\mathbf{p}^{(k)}$ *is a feasible descent direction, because the conditions*

$$\mathbf{a}_t^T\{\mathbf{x}^{(k)} + \alpha\mathbf{p}^{(k)}\} > b_t, \qquad \alpha > 0, \tag{1.4.23}$$

and

$$\mathbf{g}^{(k)T}\mathbf{p}^{(k)} < 0 \tag{1.4.24}$$

are satisfied.

Proof. The linear independence of the vectors $\mathbf{a}_i$ $(i = 1, 2, \ldots, t)$, the fact that λ_t is non-zero, and equation (1.4.22), imply that $\mathbf{g}^{(k)}$ is not a linear combination of the vectors $\mathbf{a}_i$ $(i = 1, 2, \ldots, t-1)$. Therefore Theorem 1.4 implies that $F(\mathbf{x}^{(k)} + \mathbf{p}^{(k)})$ is less than $F(\mathbf{x}^{(k)})$. Since $F(\mathbf{x})$ is a positive-definite quadratic function it follows that the condition (1.4.24) holds. By substituting expression (1.4.22) in place of $\mathbf{g}^{(k)}$ in inequality (1.4.24) and by using the fact that $\mathbf{p}^{(k)}$ is subject to the conditions

$$\mathbf{a}_i^T\mathbf{p}^{(k)} = 0, \qquad i = 1, 2, \ldots, t-1, \tag{1.4.25}$$

we deduce the inequality

$$\lambda_t \mathbf{a}_t^T\mathbf{p}^{(k)} < 0. \tag{1.4.26}$$

Therefore, because λ_t is negative and because $\mathbf{a}_t^T\mathbf{x}^{(k)} = b_t$, expression (1.4.23) is true. Theorem 1.9 is proved. ∎

Note that if two of the multipliers λ_i $(i = 1, 2, \ldots, t)$ occurring in equation (1.4.22) are negative, it may not be possible to delete both the corresponding constraints from the active set, because the resultant vector $\mathbf{p}^{(k)}$ may be infeasible. Therefore, instead of calculating whether two constraints may be removed from the active set simultaneously, it is usual to delete only one constraint at a time. One method of choosing this constraint is to normalize the constraints initially so that every vector $\mathbf{a}_i$ $(i = 1, 2, \ldots, m)$ has unit length, and to delete the constraint whose multiplier λ_i is most negative.

The procedure, described immediately before Theorem 1.9, is repeated, deleting a constraint from the active set when equation (1.4.22) holds and at least one of the multipliers λ_i $(i = 1, 2, \ldots, t)$ is negative, until we reach a point where equation (1.4.22) is satisfied, and where every multiplier λ_i $(i = 1, 2, \ldots, t)$ is positive or zero. This point is the required solution to the quadratic programming problem.

It is very easy to prove that this method converges when, for every active set, the corresponding vectors $\mathbf{a}_i$ are linearly independent. In this case, immediately before a constraint is deleted, we have calculated the least value of $F(\mathbf{x})$ subject to the active constraints being satisfied as equalities, and then the next iteration reduces the value of $F(\mathbf{x})$. Therefore we cannot return to the set of constraints that was active immediately before the deletion. Since there are only a finite number of combinations of the constraints, it follows that the process must terminate.

This method is very similar to the quadratic programming algorithm described by Fletcher (1971), the main difference being that he includes some refinements for the frequently occurring case when the second-derivative matrix of the quadratic function is not positive definite.

We return to the case when $F(\mathbf{x})$ is a general function. We may now let the descent direction at $\mathbf{x}^{(k)}$ be the vector $\mathbf{p}^{(k)}$ that is the subject of Theorem 1.7. In this case it is appropriate to let the steplength $\alpha^{(k)}$ of equation (1.1.4) have the value that minimizes $F(\mathbf{x}^{(k+1)})$ subject to the condition that $\mathbf{x}^{(k+1)}$ is feasible. If $\mathbf{p}^{(k)}$ and $\alpha^{(k)}$ are chosen in this way on every iteration, then the algorithm is the extension of the well-known steepest-descent method for unconstrained minimization to the case when there are linear constraints on the variables.

Unfortunately this method not only shares the rather slow convergence of the steepest-descent method for unconstrained minimization, but also the presence of constraints can cause zigzagging. The following example due to Wolfe (1966) shows very clearly what is meant by zigzagging.

Minimize the function of three variables

$$F(\mathbf{x}) = \tfrac{4}{3}(x_1^2 - x_1 x_2 + x_2^2)^{\frac{3}{4}} + x_3, \qquad (1.4.27)$$

subject to the constraints

$$x_i \geqslant 0, \qquad i = 1, 2, 3, \tag{1.4.28}$$

starting at the point

$$\mathbf{x}^{(0)} = (\beta, 0, \gamma)^T, \tag{1.4.29}$$

where β and γ satisfy the conditions

$$\left.\begin{aligned} 0 < \beta \leqslant \tfrac{1}{4}\sqrt{2} \\ \gamma > (1 + \tfrac{1}{2}\sqrt{2})\sqrt{\beta} \end{aligned}\right\}. \tag{1.4.30}$$

At $\mathbf{x}^{(0)}$ the gradient is the vector

$$\mathbf{g}^{(0)} = (2\sqrt{\beta}, -\sqrt{\beta}, 1)^T, \tag{1.4.31}$$

so we let $\mathbf{p}^{(0)} = -\mathbf{g}^{(0)}$, because this direction is feasible. Then $F(\mathbf{x}^{(0)} + \alpha\mathbf{p}^{(0)})$ is the function

$$F(\mathbf{x}^{(0)} + \alpha\mathbf{p}^{(0)}) = \tfrac{4}{3}(\beta^2 - 5\alpha\beta^{\frac{3}{2}} + 7\alpha^2\beta)^{\frac{3}{4}} - \alpha, \tag{1.4.32}$$

which decreases monotonically for $0 \leqslant \alpha \leqslant \frac{1}{2}\sqrt{\beta}$, because of condition (1.4.30). Therefore the value $\alpha^{(0)} = \frac{1}{2}\sqrt{\beta}$ is determined by the constraint $x_1 \geqslant 0$, and it gives the point

$$\mathbf{x}^{(1)} = (0, \tfrac{1}{2}\beta, \gamma - \tfrac{1}{2}\sqrt{\beta})^T. \tag{1.4.33}$$

By symmetry the next vector of variables is the point

$$\mathbf{x}^{(2)} = \left(\tfrac{1}{4}\beta, 0, \gamma - \tfrac{1}{2}\sqrt{\beta} - \frac{1}{2\sqrt{2}}\sqrt{\beta}\right)^T. \tag{1.4.34}$$

Equations (1.4.29), (1.4.33) and (1.4.34) show that, if we continue this process inductively, then the sequence $\mathbf{x}^{(k)}$ converges to the point

$$\begin{aligned} &\left(0, 0, \gamma - \tfrac{1}{2}\sqrt{\beta} - \frac{1}{2\sqrt{2}}\sqrt{\beta} - \tfrac{1}{4}\sqrt{\beta} - \ldots\right) \\ &\qquad = (0, 0, \gamma - \{1 + \tfrac{1}{2}\sqrt{2}\}\sqrt{\beta}). \end{aligned} \tag{1.4.35}$$

Thus the zigzagging between the constraints has made the convergence rather slow, and, more seriously, it has caused convergence to a point that is not the solution to the optimization problem.

In theory, a way round this difficulty is to follow the active set strategy that is used by the quadratic programming method described earlier in this section. In this case we do not delete any constraints from the active set until the least value of $F(\mathbf{x})$ is calculated subject to the constraints in the set being satisfied as equalities, and then we delete only one constraint at a time, corresponding to a negative value of λ_i in equation (1.4.22). Constraints are added to the active set whenever they limit the steplength along a descent direction.

Unfortunately this method is not really practicable, because to minimize a general function subject to linear constraints is an infinite calculation. Therefore it is wasteful to attempt such a minimization before every deletion from the list of active constraints. Instead other techniques have been proposed to avoid the zigzagging problem, for instance by Rosen (1960) and by McCormick (1969).

Rosen suggests methods of the following type. Let $\mathbf{p}^{(k)}$ be the steepest downhill direction at $\mathbf{x}^{(k)}$ subject to the equality constraints (1.4.12), and let $\hat{\mathbf{p}}^{(k)}$ be the steepest downhill direction at $\mathbf{x}^{(k)}$ subject to the inequality constraints (1.4.2). Then a constraint is deleted from the active set if the condition

$$\hat{\mathbf{p}}^{(k)T}\mathbf{g}^{(k)}/\|\hat{\mathbf{p}}^{(k)}\| \leqslant \mu\, \mathbf{p}^{(k)T}\mathbf{g}^{(k)}/\|\mathbf{p}^{(k)}\| \tag{1.4.36}$$

is satisfied, where μ is a suitable constant, for example $\mu = 2$. Thus constraints are deleted from the active set if and only if this yields a good improvement in the derivative of the objective function along the search direction.

The other question that must be solved to provide efficient descent algorithms is that we must improve on the rather slow rate of convergence that is usually obtained by the steepest-descent algorithm for unconstrained optimization. In Chapters II, III and IV suitable methods are described by Gill and Murray, based on second derivatives of the objective function. We make only one remark to introduce this work. It is that the results of this section, which depend on Euclidean concepts of "distance" and "steepest", could equally well have been derived using the norm

$$\|\mathbf{x}\| = (\mathbf{x}^T\mathbf{N}\mathbf{x})^{\frac{1}{2}}, \tag{1.4.37}$$

where $\mathbf{N}$ is a suitable positive-definite matrix, which may be varied from iteration to iteration. Many of the methods that will be described later can be viewed as methods for making good choices of the matrices $\mathbf{N}$.

1.5. Lagrangian Functions

Theorems 1.2 and 1.3 show that it is usual for the equation

$$\mathbf{g}(\mathbf{x}) = \sum_{i=1}^{t} \lambda_i\, \mathbf{a}_i(\mathbf{x}), \qquad \lambda_i \geqslant 0, \tag{1.5.1}$$

to hold when $F(\mathbf{x})$ is least subject to the constraints (1.2.1). In this section we assume that the vectors $\mathbf{a}_i(\mathbf{x})$ $(i = 1, 2, \ldots, t)$ are linearly independent, in order that the parameters λ_i are determined uniquely by equation (1.5.1), and in order that Theorem 1.3 is valid. Since $\mathbf{g}(\mathbf{x})$ and $\mathbf{a}_i(\mathbf{x})$ are the first derivative vectors of the functions $F(\mathbf{x})$ and $c_i(\mathbf{x})$ respectively, it follows from equation (1.5.1) that the solution of the constrained problem is a stationary point, with respect to $\mathbf{x}$, of the function

$$L(\mathbf{x}, \boldsymbol{\lambda}) = F(\mathbf{x}) - \sum_{i=1}^{t} \lambda_i c_i(\mathbf{x}), \tag{1.5.2}$$

for the appropriate value of $\boldsymbol{\lambda}$. The function $L(\mathbf{x}, \boldsymbol{\lambda})$ is called the Lagrangian function, and the parameters λ_i are called Lagrangian parameters. This section gives some properties of Lagrangian functions that are useful to the constrained minimization algorithms that are described in Chapters VIII and VI by Fletcher and by Ryan. Note that a more usual form of the Lagrangian function is the expression

$$L(\mathbf{x}, \boldsymbol{\lambda}) = F(\mathbf{x}) - \sum_{i=1}^{m} \lambda_i c_i(\mathbf{x}), \tag{1.5.3}$$

where, in accordance with equations (1.2.19) and (1.2.20), the values of λ_i should be zero for $i = t+1, t+2, \ldots, m$.

The Lagrangian parameter λ_i is non-negative in equation (1.5.1) because it corresponds to the constraint $c_i(\mathbf{x}) \geqslant 0$. If instead we have the equivalent constraint

$$\bar{c}_i(\mathbf{x}) = -c_i(\mathbf{x}) \leqslant 0, \tag{1.5.4}$$

then we may replace the term $\{\lambda_i \mathbf{a}_i(\mathbf{x})\}$ of equation (1.5.1) by the equal term $\{(-\lambda_i)\,\bar{\mathbf{a}}_i(\mathbf{x})\}$, where $\bar{\mathbf{a}}_i(\mathbf{x})$ is the gradient vector of $\bar{c}_i(\mathbf{x})$. It follows that the Lagrangian parameters of any constraints of the form $\bar{c}_i(\mathbf{x}) \leqslant 0$ are non-positive. We make this comment to justify the statement that if there is an equality constraint, say $c_i(\mathbf{x}) = 0$, then we include the term $\lambda_i c_i(\mathbf{x})$ in the Lagrangian function with no restriction on the sign of λ_i.

Because this section is an introduction to Lagrangian functions, we consider only the case when the constraints on $\mathbf{x}$ are all equality constraints,

$$c_i(\mathbf{x}) = 0, \qquad i = 1, 2, \ldots, t, \tag{1.5.5}$$

say. This case is directly relevant to the active set strategies described in the previous section, where the minimization is carried out subject to the constraints being maintained as equalities. Also it is closely related to the inequality problem, because the constraint $c_i(\mathbf{x}) \geqslant 0$ may be written in the form $c_i(\mathbf{x})_- = 0$, where $c_i(\mathbf{x})_-$ is the function

$$c_i(\mathbf{x})_- = \begin{cases} c_i(\mathbf{x}), & c_i(\mathbf{x}) \leqslant 0 \\ 0, & c_i(\mathbf{x}) \geqslant 0. \end{cases} \tag{1.5.6}$$

However the results of this section do not apply directly to $c_i(\mathbf{x})_-$, because we assume that the constraint functions (1.5.5) have continuous first derivatives.

The main relation between the Lagrangian function and the minimization problem subject to equality constraints is given by the following theorem.

THEOREM 1.10. *Let* $\mathbf{x}^*$ *give the least value of* $F(\mathbf{x})$ *subject to the constraints (1.5.5). Then, if the gradient vectors* $\mathbf{a}_i(\mathbf{x}^*)$ *are linearly independent, there exist multipliers* λ_i^* $(i = 1, 2, \ldots, t)$ *such that the equation*

$$\mathbf{g}(\mathbf{x}^*) = \sum_{i=1}^{t} \lambda_i^* \mathbf{a}_i(\mathbf{x}^*) \tag{1.5.7}$$

is satisfied. Further $\mathbf{x}^*$ *is a stationary point with respect to* $\mathbf{x}$ *of the Lagrangian function* $L(\mathbf{x}, \boldsymbol{\lambda}^*)$.

Proof. This theorem is not an immediate consequence of Theorem 1.3, because Theorem 1.3 depends on the use of feasible search directions, and in general, when there are curved equality constraints, there are no straight feasible search directions.

Therefore we make a change of variables so that the constraints become linear. We may suppose without loss of generality that the first t rows of the matrix whose columns are $\mathbf{a}_i(\mathbf{x}^*)$ $(i = 1, 2, \ldots, t)$ are linearly independent, in which case by continuity there is a closed neighbourhood of $\mathbf{x}^*$, $N(\mathbf{x}^*)$ say, such that these rows are independent for all $\mathbf{x}$ in $N(\mathbf{x}^*)$. For $\mathbf{x}$ in $N(\mathbf{x}^*)$ we make the change of variables

$$\left.\begin{aligned} y_i &= c_i(\mathbf{x}), & i &= 1, 2, \ldots, t \\ y_i &= x_i, & i &= t+1, t+2, \ldots, n \end{aligned}\right\}, \tag{1.5.8}$$

which is a homeomorphism by the inverse function theorem (see Ortega and Rheinboldt, 1970, for instance). Thus there is an inverse transformation

$$\mathbf{x} = X(\mathbf{y}), \tag{1.5.9}$$

which is differentiable. We let its Jacobian matrix be $\mathbf{J}(X)$.

Now in y-space the constraints may be written as the linear inequalities

$$\left.\begin{aligned} y_i \geqslant 0 \\ -y_i \geqslant 0 \end{aligned}\right\}, \quad i = 1, 2, \ldots, t, \tag{1.5.10}$$

so Theorem 1.2 implies that there exist parameters λ_i^* $(i = 1, 2, \ldots, t)$, such that the equation

$$\nabla_y F(X(\mathbf{y})) = \sum_{i=1}^{t} \lambda_i^* \nabla_y c_i(X(\mathbf{y})) \tag{1.5.11}$$

is satisfied at the constrained minimum. The fact that $\nabla_y c_i(X(\mathbf{y}))$ is the ith co-ordinate vector in y-space is not relevant. What is relevant is that the differential operator ∇_y is related to ∇_x by the equation

$$\nabla_y = \mathbf{J}(X)^T \nabla_x. \tag{1.5.12}$$

We substitute this expression into equation (1.5.11) to obtain the identity

$$\mathbf{J}(X)^T \mathbf{g}(\mathbf{x}^*) = \sum_{i=1}^{t} \lambda_i^* \mathbf{J}(X)^T \mathbf{a}_i(\mathbf{x}^*). \tag{1.5.13}$$

Since $\mathbf{J}(X)$ is non-singular, equation (1.5.7) is true. Moreover the statement that $\mathbf{x}^*$ is a stationary point of the Lagrangian is an immediate consequence of the definition of $L(\mathbf{x}, \boldsymbol{\lambda}^*)$. Theorem 1.10 is proved. ∎

The Lagrangian function can be used to derive some second-order conditions for the solution of the constrained minimization problem, which are valid for nonlinear constraints. The following two theorems, which correspond to Theorems 1.6 and 1.5, are useful examples. More general theorems, which take account of inequality constraints, are given by Fiacco and McCormick (1968).

THEOREM 1.11. *Let the conditions of Theorem* 1.10 *be satisfied, and let the functions $F(\mathbf{x})$ and $c_i(\mathbf{x})$ $(i = 1, 2, \ldots, t)$ be twice differentiable at* $\mathbf{x}^*$. *Further let the matrix*

$$\mathbf{W} = \mathbf{G} + \sum_{i=1}^{t} \lambda_i^* \mathbf{G}_i \tag{1.5.14}$$

be the second-derivative matrix of the Lagrangian function $L(\mathbf{x}, \boldsymbol{\lambda}^*)$ at $\mathbf{x}^*$, *where* $\mathbf{G}$ *and* $\mathbf{G}_i$ *are the second-derivative matrices of* $F(\mathbf{x})$ *and* $c_i(\mathbf{x})$ *respectively. Then, if* $\hat{\mathbf{d}}$ *is any direction satisfying the equations*

$$\hat{\mathbf{d}}^T\mathbf{a}_i(\mathbf{x}^*) = 0, \qquad i = 1, 2, \ldots, t, \tag{1.5.15}$$

the inequality

$$\hat{\mathbf{d}}^T\mathbf{W}\hat{\mathbf{d}} \geqslant 0 \tag{1.5.16}$$

is true.

Proof. We consider a sequence of positive values of α, tending to zero, such that the points $\mathbf{x}^* + \alpha\hat{\mathbf{d}}$ are in the neighbourhood $N(\mathbf{x}^*)$, defined in the proof of Theorem 1.10, where $\hat{\mathbf{d}}$ is any vector satisfying the conditions (1.5.15). By applying expression (1.3.4) to the function $c_i(\mathbf{x}^* + \alpha\hat{\mathbf{d}})$ we obtain the equation

$$\lim_{\alpha\to 0} \frac{c_i(\mathbf{x}^* + \alpha\hat{\mathbf{d}}) - \frac{1}{2}\alpha^2\hat{\mathbf{d}}^T\mathbf{G}_i\hat{\mathbf{d}}}{\alpha^2\|\hat{\mathbf{d}}\|^2} = 0, \tag{1.5.17}$$

because condition (1.5.15) is satisfied and because $c_i(\mathbf{x}^*)$ is zero. We write this equation in the form

$$c_i(\mathbf{x}^* + \alpha\hat{\mathbf{d}}) = O(\alpha^2), \qquad i = 1, 2, \ldots, t. \tag{1.5.18}$$

Now let the change of variables (1.5.8) be expressed by the operator

$$\mathbf{y} = Y(\mathbf{x}), \tag{1.5.19}$$

so Y is the inverse of the operator (1.5.9). Further let the operator

$$\mathbf{z} = Z(\mathbf{y}) \tag{1.5.20}$$

be defined by the equations

$$\left.\begin{aligned} z_i &= 0, \qquad i = 1, 2, \ldots, t \\ z_i &= y_i, \qquad i = t + 1, t + 2, \ldots, n \end{aligned}\right\}. \tag{1.5.21}$$

Then equation (1.5.18) is equivalent to the expression

$$Y(\mathbf{x}^* + \alpha\hat{\mathbf{d}}) = Z(\mathbf{x}^* + \alpha\hat{\mathbf{d}}) + O(\alpha^2). \tag{1.5.22}$$

We operate on this equation with the differentiable operator X, and re-arrange terms, to obtain the relation

$$\begin{aligned} X[Z(\mathbf{x}^* + \alpha\hat{\mathbf{d}})] &= \mathbf{x}^* + \alpha\hat{\mathbf{d}} + O(\alpha^2) \\ &= \mathbf{x}^* + \bar{\mathbf{d}}, \end{aligned} \tag{1.5.23}$$

say, where $\bar{\mathbf{d}}$ depends on α and tends to zero as α tends to zero. Because the definition of X and Z imply that the point $(\mathbf{x}^* + \bar{\mathbf{d}})$ is feasible, and because $\mathbf{x}^*$ is the solution of the constrained minimization problem, we have the inequality

$$L(\mathbf{x}^* + \bar{\mathbf{d}}, \boldsymbol{\lambda}^*) - L(\mathbf{x}^*, \boldsymbol{\lambda}^*) = F(\mathbf{x}^* + \bar{\mathbf{d}}) - F(\mathbf{x}^*) \geqslant 0. \tag{1.5.24}$$

Therefore, using the fact that the gradient of the Lagrangian function is zero at $\mathbf{x}^*$, we find by applying equation (1.3.4) to $L(\mathbf{x}, \boldsymbol{\lambda}^*)$ that the inequality

$$\lim_{\alpha \to 0} - \tfrac{1}{2} \bar{\mathbf{d}}^T \mathbf{W} \bar{\mathbf{d}} / \|\bar{\mathbf{d}}\|^2 \leqslant 0, \tag{1.5.25}$$

is true. Therefore, by expressing $\bar{\mathbf{d}}$ in terms of $\hat{\mathbf{d}}$ through the right-hand sides of expression (1.5.23), it follows that the bound (1.5.16) is satisfied, which proves the theorem. ∎

THEOREM 1.12. *Let $\mathbf{x}^*$ be a point that satisfies the equality constraints* (1.5.5), *and let the functions $F(\mathbf{x})$ and $c_i(\mathbf{x})$ $(i = 1, 2, \ldots, t)$ be twice differentiable at $\mathbf{x}^*$. If the constraint gradients $\mathbf{a}_i(\mathbf{x}^*)$ $(i = 1, 2, \ldots, t)$ are linearly independent, if there exist Lagrangian parameters λ_i^* $(i = 1, 2, \ldots, t)$ such that equation* (1.5.7) *is satisfied, and if there exists a positive constant ε such that for every vector $\hat{\mathbf{d}}$ satisfying conditions* (1.5.15) *the inequality*

$$\hat{\mathbf{d}}^T \mathbf{W} \hat{\mathbf{d}} \geqslant \varepsilon \|\hat{\mathbf{d}}\|^2 \tag{1.5.26}$$

holds, where $\mathbf{W}$ is the second-derivative matrix of $L(\mathbf{x}, \boldsymbol{\lambda}^*)$ at $\mathbf{x}^*$, then $\mathbf{x}^*$ is a strong local minimum of $F(\mathbf{x})$.

Proof. We follow the techniques used to prove Theorems 1.5 and 1.11, except that we replace the operators X and Y by operators that are appropriate to the linear approximations to the constraints at $\mathbf{x}^*$. Specifically, instead of expression (1.5.8) we make the change of variables

$$\left.\begin{aligned} y_i &= (\mathbf{x} - \mathbf{x}^*)^T \mathbf{a}_i(\mathbf{x}^*), \qquad i = 1, 2, \ldots, t \\ y_i &= x_i, \qquad i = t+1, t+2, \ldots, n \end{aligned}\right\}, \tag{1.5.27}$$

which we write in the form $\mathbf{y} = \overline{Y}(\mathbf{x})$, and we let $\mathbf{x} = \overline{X}(\mathbf{y})$ be the inverse transformation. We continue to use the operator Z defined by equations (1.5.20) and (1.5.21). Because the quantity y_i, defined by the first line of equation (1.5.27), differs from $c_i(\mathbf{x})$ by a term that is $O(\|\mathbf{x} - \mathbf{x}^*\|^2)$, the equation

$$\overline{Y}(\mathbf{x}^* + \mathbf{d}) = Z(\mathbf{x}^* + \mathbf{d}) + O(\|\mathbf{d}\|)^2 \tag{1.5.28}$$

holds when the point $(\mathbf{x}^* + \mathbf{d})$ is feasible. We operate on this equation with $\bar{X}$ to obtain the relation

$$\begin{aligned} \bar{X}Z(\mathbf{x}^* + \mathbf{d}) &= \mathbf{x}^* + \mathbf{d} + O(\|\mathbf{d}\|^2) \\ &= \mathbf{x}^* + \hat{\mathbf{d}}, \end{aligned} \tag{1.5.29}$$

say, which is useful because the definitions of Z and $\bar{X}$ imply that $\hat{\mathbf{d}}$ satisfies the conditions (1.5.15). Moreover we note that equation (1.5.7) implies the equation

$$\nabla_x L(\mathbf{x}^*, \boldsymbol{\lambda}^*) = \mathbf{0}. \tag{1.5.30}$$

To prove the theorem we establish a contradiction if $\mathbf{x}^*$ is not a strong local minimum. Therefore let us suppose that there is a sequence of vectors $\mathbf{d}$, converging to the zero vector, such that the points $(\mathbf{x}^* + \mathbf{d})$ are all feasible, and such that inequality (1.3.3) is satisfied. Because the feasibility of $(\mathbf{x}^* + \mathbf{d})$ gives the equation

$$L(\mathbf{x}^* + \mathbf{d}, \boldsymbol{\lambda}^*) = F(\mathbf{x}^* + \mathbf{d}), \tag{1.5.31}$$

the inequality

$$L(\mathbf{x}^* + \mathbf{d}, \boldsymbol{\lambda}^*) \leqslant L(\mathbf{x}^*, \boldsymbol{\lambda}^*) \tag{1.5.32}$$

holds. We apply equation (1.3.4) to the Lagrangian function, to deduce from expressions (1.5.30) and (1.5.32) the inequality

$$\lim_{\|\mathbf{d}\| \to 0} -\tfrac{1}{2}\mathbf{d}^T W\mathbf{d}/\|\mathbf{d}\|^2 \geqslant 0. \tag{1.5.33}$$

Therefore the right-hand sides of expression (1.5.29) imply the bound

$$\lim_{\|\hat{\mathbf{d}}\| \to 0} \hat{\mathbf{d}}^T W\hat{\mathbf{d}}/\|\hat{\mathbf{d}}\|^2 \leqslant 0, \tag{1.5.34}$$

but this contradicts inequality (1.5.26). Theorem 1.12 is proved. ∎

Theorem 1.10 indicates that, if by some means we can obtain values of the Lagrangian parameters λ_i, that are good estimates of λ_i^* $(i = 1, 2, \ldots, t)$, then among the stationary points with respect to $\mathbf{x}$ of the Lagrangian function (1.5.2), there should be a good estimate of the solution to the constrained minimization problem. The appropriate stationary point will be characterized by the constraint functions $c_i(\mathbf{x})$ $(i = 1, 2, \ldots, t)$ being close to zero, and by the objective function $F(\mathbf{x})$ being small. Also we expect the second-order condition (1.5.16) to be satisfied by all directions $\hat{\mathbf{d}}$ that are orthogonal to the gradient vectors of the constraint functions.

Unfortunately in general we cannot calculate the required stationary point of the Lagrangian by applying an algorithm for unconstrained minimization to $L(\mathbf{x}, \boldsymbol{\lambda})$, because usually the required point is a saddle point of $L(\mathbf{x}, \boldsymbol{\lambda})$. Therefore it is useful to note that the solution to the constrained problem is also a stationary point of the "augmented Lagrangian function"

$$L(\mathbf{x}, \boldsymbol{\lambda}^*, r) = F(\mathbf{x}) - \sum_{i=1}^{t} \lambda_i^* c_i(\mathbf{x}) + r \sum_{i=1}^{t} [c_i(\mathbf{x})]^2, \tag{1.5.35}$$

where r is a parameter. Under rather mild conditions it may be proved that there is a threshold value of r, $\bar{r}$ say, such that for all $r > \bar{r}$ the required solution $\mathbf{x}^*$ is a strong local minimum of $L(\mathbf{x}, \boldsymbol{\lambda}^*, r)$. Therefore techniques for unconstrained minimization can be applied to the augmented Lagrangian function, instead of having to consider all stationary points of $L(\mathbf{x}, \boldsymbol{\lambda})$. Thus some very effective algorithms for constrained minimization are obtained, which are described in Chapter VIII.

Chapter II

Newton-type Methods for Linearly Constrained Optimization

PHILIP E. GILL AND WALTER MURRAY

Division of Numerical Analysis and Computing, National Physical Laboratory

2.1. Introduction

In the next three chapters we shall be concerned with the subclass of constrained nonlinear problems in which the constraints are linear in the variables. Unlike the general nonlinear case, where there is still some debate as to which is the most promising approach, it is widely accepted that the most effective methods for the solution of linearly constrained problems have been identified. However, apart from being somewhat more straightforward than their nonlinear counterparts, linearly constrained problems have received considerable attention over the past few years for the following reasons.

(i) Linearly constrained problems form a significant class of their own. The problem of maximizing or minimizing a linear function subject to linear constraints on the variables is known as the linear programming (*LP*) problem and the majority of the problems solved commercially fall into this class.

(ii) Recently several methods have been proposed in which a general nonlinear problem is solved as a sequence of linearly constrained problems. Under these circumstances it is essential that each of the subproblems be solved as efficiently as possible. In addition the method should be guaranteed to be convergent and numerically reliable, otherwise we cannot ensure the convergence of the outer iterations.

(iii) When solving a problem in which both linear and nonlinear constraints occur it may be advantageous to treat those constraints which are linear separately, and not as part of the general problem.

As in unconstrained optimization, information about the objective function can be obtained from subroutines which compute the function value $F(\mathbf{x})$, gradient vector $\mathbf{g}(\mathbf{x})$, and Hessian matrix $\mathbf{G}(\mathbf{x})$, of $F(\mathbf{x})$ at a given point. We shall be concerned throughout this chapter with methods which require the provision of a subroutine for the computation of the gradient vector, although much of the discussion assumes that the Hessian matrix of second derivatives is available also. All methods considered are "descent methods" (see Chapter I), that is, the algorithm will generate a sequence of points $\{\mathbf{x}^{(k)}\}$ such that

$$\mathbf{x}^{(k+1)} = \mathbf{x}^{(k)} + \alpha^{(k)}\mathbf{p}^{(k)} \quad \text{and} \quad F(\mathbf{x}^{(k+1)}) < F(\mathbf{x}^{(k)}),$$

where $\mathbf{p}^{(k)}$ is known as the direction of search and $\alpha^{(k)}$ the steplength. The epithet "Newton-type" applies to all those techniques for which the vector $\mathbf{p}^{(k)}$ is determined from derivative information *computed in the immediate neighbourhood of* $\mathbf{x}^{(k)}$.

An important point must be emphasized. Of all the computations required for a typical descent method, that of the steplength might appear to be the simplest. Unfortunately this is not the case since it is important to obtain a new point $F(\mathbf{x}^{(k+1)})$ which is *sufficiently lower* than the current point $F(\mathbf{x}^{(k)})$ for overall convergence of the descent method to be guaranteed. Often an algorithm requires $\alpha^{(k)}$ to minimize $F(\mathbf{x})$ along the vector $\mathbf{p}^{(k)}$. Our experience is that exact univariate minimization is almost as difficult as its multi-dimensional counterpart. An inadequate choice of step will either give slow convergence or cause the algorithm to fail completely. Methods for computing $\alpha^{(k)}$ will not be considered in any detail in this volume and the reader is referred to alternative sources for further information—see for example Armijo (1966), Brent (1973), Elkin (1968), Gill and Murray (1974) and Ortega and Rheinboldt (1970).

It is not our intention in this chapter to consider directly problems which have a significant number of zero elements in the matrix of second derivatives or matrix of constraints. This will be done in Chapter IV, where selected theoretical and computational results of this chapter are utilized.

2.2. Geometrical Considerations and Conditions for a Solution

In general mathematical terms the problem of concern is

LCP: minimize $F(\mathbf{x})$ subject to the linear constraints $\mathbf{A}^T\mathbf{x} \geqslant \mathbf{b}$,

where $\mathbf{A}^T$ is an $m \times n$ matrix.

Each constraint $\mathbf{a}_j{}^T\mathbf{x} \geqslant b_j$ can be viewed as defining a hyperplane in E^n with equation $\mathbf{a}_j{}^T\mathbf{x} = b_j$. The vector $\mathbf{a}_i/\|\mathbf{a}_i\|_2$ is the unit normal of the hyperplane pointing into the feasible region and is consequently orthogonal to any vector parallel to the hyperplane. A point $\mathbf{x}$ is defined as being a feasible point of *LCP* if $\mathbf{x}$ satisfies all the constraints, that is, $\mathbf{A}^T\mathbf{x} \geqslant \mathbf{b}$. We shall define Π as the set of all feasible points

$$\Pi = \{\mathbf{x} : \mathbf{A}^T\mathbf{x} \geqslant \mathbf{b}\}.$$

An important property of linearly constrained optimization problems is that we can assert *a priori* that the feasible region Π is *convex*, i.e. any point $\mathbf{y}$ on the line segment joining two feasible points $\mathbf{x}_1$ and $\mathbf{x}_2$ is also feasible. This is easily shown if $\mathbf{y}$ is written in the form

$$\mathbf{y} = (1-\theta)\,\mathbf{x}_1 + \theta\mathbf{x}_2 \quad \text{for} \quad 0 \leqslant \theta \leqslant 1$$

in which case

$$\begin{aligned}\mathbf{A}^T\mathbf{y} &= (1-\theta)\,\mathbf{A}^T\mathbf{x}_1 + \theta\mathbf{A}^T\mathbf{x}_2\\ &\geqslant (1-\theta)\,\mathbf{b} + \theta\mathbf{b} = \mathbf{b}.\end{aligned}$$

The convexity of Π implies that if we compute a point $\bar{\mathbf{x}} = \mathbf{x}^{(k)} + \bar{\alpha}\mathbf{p}^{(k)}$ on the boundary of Π then we can assert that $\bar{\alpha}$ is the largest α giving a feasible value of $\mathbf{x}^{(k)} + \alpha\mathbf{p}^{(k)}$.

In this chapter we shall be particularly concerned with strong local minima of *LCP*, a strong local minimum being defined as a point $\overset{*}{\mathbf{x}}$ which is strictly lower than all other feasible points in a sufficiently small neighbourhood of $\overset{*}{\mathbf{x}}$. In mathematical terms $\overset{*}{\mathbf{x}}$ is such that there exists a positive scalar δ such that

$$F(\mathbf{x}) - F(\overset{*}{\mathbf{x}}) > 0 \quad \text{for all} \quad \mathbf{x} \in N(\overset{*}{\mathbf{x}}, \delta) \cap \Pi$$

where $N(\overset{*}{\mathbf{x}}, \delta)$ is the neighbourhood

$$N(\overset{*}{\mathbf{x}}, \delta) = \{\mathbf{x} : \|\mathbf{x} - \overset{*}{\mathbf{x}}\| \leqslant \delta,\ \mathbf{x} \neq \overset{*}{\mathbf{x}}\}.$$

Let $\mathbf{x}$ be any feasible point. A constraint will be defined as *active* at $\mathbf{x}$ if $\mathbf{a}_j{}^T\mathbf{x} = b_j$. Using this definition we shall restate the result of Theorem 1.5 which gives the conditions for $\overset{*}{\mathbf{x}}$ to be a strong local minimum of *LCP*. Let $\overset{*}{\mathbf{A}}{}^T$ be the $t \times n$ matrix of constraints active at a point $\overset{*}{\mathbf{x}}$, if the following conditions hold then $\overset{*}{\mathbf{x}}$ is a strong local minimum of *LCP*;

(i) there exist non-negative scalars λ_j, $j = 1, 2, \ldots, t$ such that

$$\mathbf{g}(\overset{*}{\mathbf{x}}) = \overset{*}{\mathbf{A}}\boldsymbol{\lambda};$$

(ii) $\mathbf{v}^T\mathbf{G}(\mathbf{\mathring{x}})\,\mathbf{v} > 0$, where $\mathbf{v}$ is any non-zero vector which satisfies the relation $\mathbf{a}_j{}^T\mathbf{v} = 0$ for active constraints $\mathbf{a}_j{}^T\mathbf{x} = b_j$ with a strictly positive Lagrange multiplier.

If there are no constraints active at $\mathbf{\mathring{x}}$ and if δ can be chosen such that $N(\mathbf{\mathring{x}}, \delta) \subset \Pi$ then Theorem 1.5 gives the conditions for $\mathbf{\mathring{x}}$ to be an unconstrained strong local minimum, viz: $\mathbf{g}(\mathbf{\mathring{x}}) = \mathbf{0}$ and $\mathbf{G}(\mathbf{\mathring{x}})$ positive definite.

These are not the weakest conditions on $\mathbf{\mathring{x}}$ since functions exist which have positive curvature along the constraints $\mathbf{\mathring{A}}^T$ but which are such that $\mathbf{G}(\mathbf{\mathring{x}})\,\mathbf{v} = \mathbf{0}$ for some $\mathbf{v}$ parallel to the active constraint hyperplanes. However, we have given those second-order conditions which can be verified numerically using the matrix of constraints and the first and second derivatives of $F(\mathbf{x})$, The nature of the local curvature when $\mathbf{G}$ is singular with respect to vectors parallel to the constraints can only be investigated using higher derivatives and we shall not consider these functions further apart from remarking that they occur rarely in practice.

Of course, we do not know *a priori* which constraints are active at a strong local minimum. However, since $\mathbf{\mathring{x}}$ must be a strong local minimum of $F(\mathbf{x})$ for all $\mathbf{x} \in \Pi$ such that $\mathbf{\mathring{A}}^T\mathbf{x} = \mathbf{\mathring{b}}$, we can proceed to minimize $F(\mathbf{x})$ on any given set of constraints and compute the quantities λ_j to see whether an optimal point has been located. If we encounter the boundary of Π during the course of this minimization, the corresponding constraint (or constraints) are added to the active set. Similarly at a minimum on a set of constraints we can consider a constraint with a negative Lagrange multiplier as being inactive. It must be possible to obtain a lower point in subsequent iterations since otherwise the second-order conditions of Theorem 1.5 would be contradicted.

The active constraint strategy just outlined has two major implications. Firstly the signs of λ_j may imply that no constraints should be regarded as active. In this case any algorithm should constitute an efficient method for unconstrained minimization. Secondly, we must be able to efficiently minimize the objective function subject to the linear *equality* constraints defined by the active constraints. In the next three sections (2.3, 2.4 and 2.5) we shall consider in detail methods for solving these two types of problems, before considering methods of general applicability for choosing the set of active constraints in Sections 2.6 and 2.7, and an initial feasible point in Section 2.9.

2.3. Newton-type Methods for Unconstrained Minimization

Assume for the moment that $\mathbf{G}^{(k)}$, the Hessian matrix at $\mathbf{x}^{(k)}$, is known and *that it is positive definite*. We shall show in the following that $\mathbf{p}^{(k)}$ can be defined as the minimum of a quadratic function.

Consider the Taylor expansion of $F(\mathbf{x})$ about the point $\mathbf{x}^{(k)}$

$$F(\mathbf{x}^{(k)} + \mathbf{p}) = F^{(k)} + \mathbf{g}^{(k)T}\mathbf{p} + \tfrac{1}{2}\mathbf{p}^T\mathbf{G}^{(k)}\mathbf{p} + O(\|\mathbf{p}\|^3)$$
$$= Q(\mathbf{p}) + O(\|\mathbf{p}\|^3),$$

where

$$Q(\mathbf{p}) = F^{(k)} + \mathbf{g}^{(k)T}\mathbf{p} + \tfrac{1}{2}\mathbf{p}^T\mathbf{G}^{(k)}\mathbf{p}.$$

The contours of $Q(\mathbf{p})$ are ellipsoids whose principal axes are the eigenvectors of $\mathbf{G}^{(k)}$ with lengths proportional to the reciprocals of the eigenvalues of $\mathbf{G}^{(k)}$. The function $Q(\mathbf{p})$ can be regarded as a quadratic approximation to $F(\mathbf{x})$ at $\mathbf{x}^{(k)}$ and we can choose $\mathbf{p}^{(k)}$ as the solution of the problem

$$\underset{\mathbf{p}}{\text{minimize}}\, Q(\mathbf{p}) \text{ for } \mathbf{p} \in E^n. \tag{2.3.1}$$

The gradient vector of this function is $\mathbf{g}^{(k)} + \mathbf{G}^{(k)}\mathbf{p}$ and its minimum is at the point $\mathbf{p}^{(k)}$ which satisfies the equations

$$\mathbf{G}^{(k)}\mathbf{p}^{(k)} = -\,\mathbf{g}^{(k)}. \tag{2.3.2}$$

These are the equations defining Newton's method. Note that the condition that $\mathbf{G}^{(k)}$ is positive definite ensures that $\mathbf{p}^{(k)}$ always exists.

Although $\mathbf{G}$ is usually positive definite in a region of a strong local minimum there is no way of choosing $\mathbf{x}^{(0)}$ so that $\mathbf{G}^{(k)}$ will be positive definite at all succeeding points $\{\mathbf{x}^{(k)}\}$. Since $\mathbf{G}^{(k)}$ cannot be guaranteed to be positive definite or even non-singular, the quadratic subproblem (2.3.1) may not have a bounded minimum. In the following theorem we summarize the possible situations that can arise for a general quadratic function.

THEOREM 2.1. *If $Q(\mathbf{p})$ is a general quadratic function with $Q(\mathbf{p}) = \mathbf{g}^T\mathbf{p} + \tfrac{1}{2}\mathbf{p}^T\mathbf{G}\mathbf{p}$, then*

(i) *if $\mathbf{G}$ is positive definite, a unique strong local minimum $\mathbf{\overset{*}{p}}$ is given by the solution of the equations $\mathbf{G}\mathbf{\overset{*}{p}} = -\mathbf{g}$;*

(ii) *if $\mathbf{G}$ is indefinite, $Q(\mathbf{p})$ does not possess a bounded minimum;*

(iii) *if $\mathbf{G}$ is positive semi-definite, $Q(\mathbf{p})$ has a bounded weak minimum only if $\mathbf{g}$ is orthogonal to all vectors $\mathbf{v}$ such that $\mathbf{G}\mathbf{v} = \mathbf{0}$ (i.e. all eigenvectors with zero eigenvalues).* ▮

In Figs 2.1, 2.2 and 2.3 we plot the contours of $Q(\mathbf{p})$ in the two-dimensional case for each of the three cases discussed in Theorem 2.1. We have denoted the eigenvalues and eigenvectors of $\mathbf{G}$ as μ_1, μ_2 and $\mathbf{v}_1$, $\mathbf{v}_2$

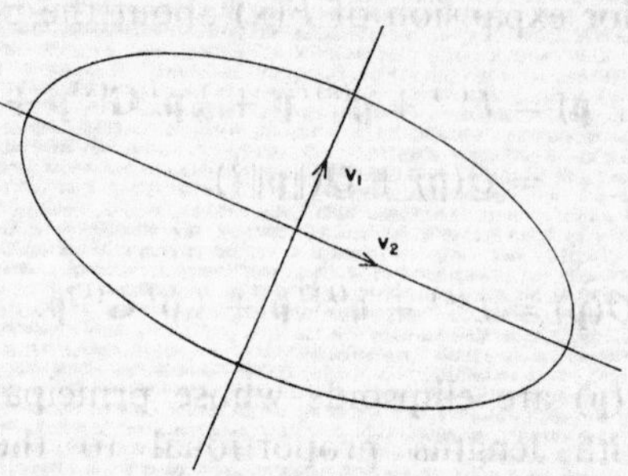

FIG. 2.1. G positive definite, eigenvalues $\mu_1 > 0, \mu_2 > 0$.

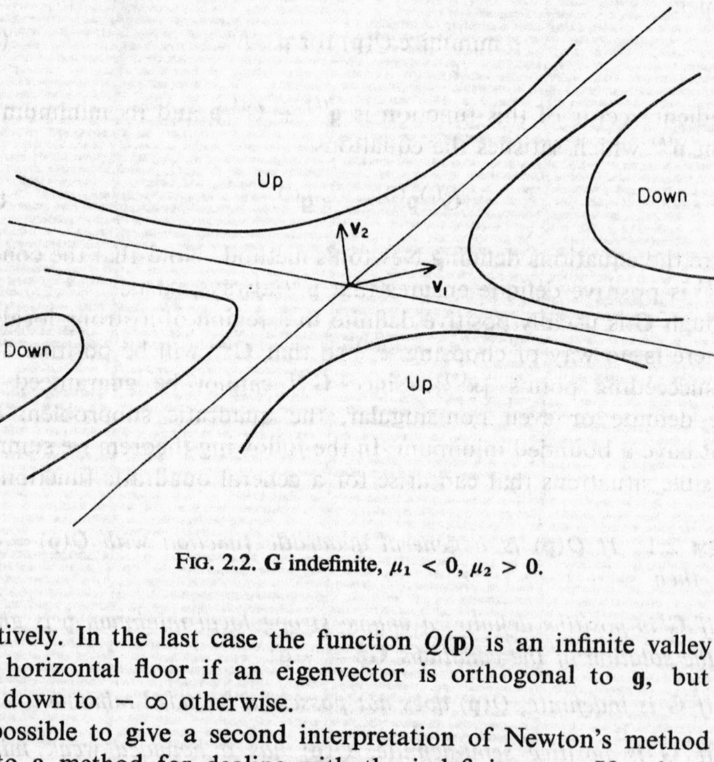

FIG. 2.2. G indefinite, $\mu_1 < 0, \mu_2 > 0$.

respectively. In the last case the function $Q(\mathbf{p})$ is an infinite valley which has a horizontal floor if an eigenvector is orthogonal to $\mathbf{g}$, but which slopes down to $-\infty$ otherwise.

It is possible to give a second interpretation of Newton's method which leads to a method for dealing with the indefinite case. If only the first-order terms of the expansion (2.3.1) are considered, we have

$$F(\mathbf{x}^{(k)} + \mathbf{p}) = F^{(k)} + \mathbf{g}^{(k)T}\mathbf{p} + O(\|\mathbf{p}\|^2).$$

If we attempt to minimize the linear function $F^{(k)} + \mathbf{g}^{(k)T}\mathbf{p}$ as a function of $\mathbf{p}$ we find that no bounded solution exists. However, we can pose the

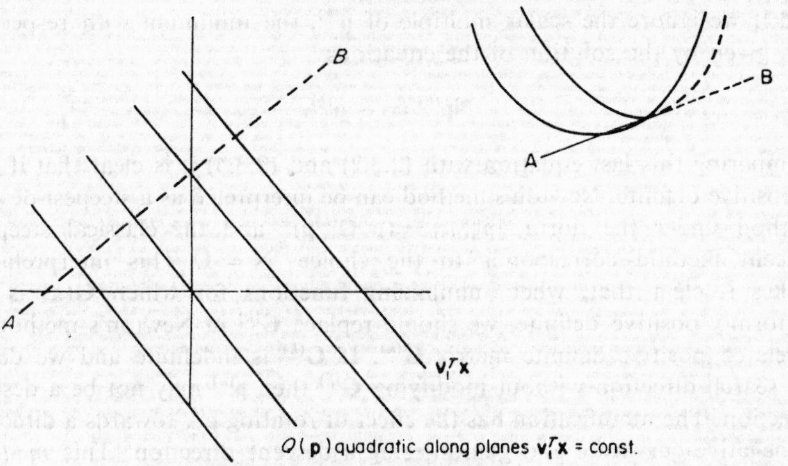

FIG. 2.3. G singular, $\mu_1 = 0$, $\mu_2 > 0$.

problem: *which direction* **p** *is such that the maximum decrease in the function* $F^{(k)} + \mathbf{g}^{(k)T}\mathbf{p}$ *is obtained for a unit step?* In mathematical terms this gives the constrained problem

$$\underset{\mathbf{p}}{\text{minimize}}\ \{F^{(k)} + \mathbf{g}^{(k)T}\mathbf{p}\}$$

subject to the constraint $\|\mathbf{p}\|_2 = 1$, where $\|\mathbf{p}\|_2$ denotes the vector norm $(\sum_{j=1}^{n} p_j{}^2)^{\frac{1}{2}}$. The solution can be found by minimizing with respect to **p** the Lagrangian function

$$F^{(k)} + \mathbf{g}^{(k)T}\mathbf{p} + \lambda(\|\mathbf{p}\|_2^2 - 1). \tag{2.3.3}$$

If the derivative with respect to **p** of this function is set equal to zero we obtain

$$\mathbf{p}^{(k)} = -\frac{1}{2\lambda}\mathbf{g}^{(k)} = -\mathbf{g}^{(k)}/\|\mathbf{g}^{(k)}\|_2, \tag{2.3.4}$$

the value of λ following from the condition that $\|\mathbf{p}^{(k)}\|_2 = 1$. Since we are concerned only with the *direction* of search we generally use $\mathbf{p}^{(k)} = -\mathbf{g}^{(k)}$; the value of λ will be implicitly defined by the steplength algorithm. This definition of $\mathbf{p}^{(k)}$ is the classical method of steepest descent.

In fact, this definition of $\mathbf{p}^{(k)}$ depends upon the norm used to constrain **p**. If **N** is any positive definite symmetric matrix then the quantity $\|\mathbf{p}\|_{\mathbf{N}} = (\mathbf{p}^T\mathbf{N}\mathbf{p})^{\frac{1}{2}}$ also defines a norm on E^n. In terms of this norm the Lagrangian (2.3.3) becomes

$$F^{(k)} + \mathbf{g}^{(k)T}\mathbf{p} + \lambda(\mathbf{p}^T\mathbf{N}\mathbf{p} - 1), \tag{2.3.5}$$

and if we ignore the scalar multiple of $\mathbf{p}^{(k)}$, the minimum with respect to $\mathbf{p}$ is given by the solution of the equations

$$\mathbf{N}\mathbf{p}^{(k)} = -\mathbf{g}^{(k)}.$$

Comparing this last equation with (2.3.2) and (2.3.4) it is clear that if $\mathbf{G}^{(k)}$ is positive definite, Newton's method can be interpreted as a steepest-descent method under the norm $\|\mathbf{p}\|_{\mathbf{G}^{(k)}} = (\mathbf{p}^T\mathbf{G}^{(k)}\mathbf{p})^{\frac{1}{2}}$ and the classical steepest-descent method corresponds to the choice $\mathbf{N} = \mathbf{I}$. This interpretation makes it clear that, when minimizing functions for which $\mathbf{G}(\mathbf{x})$ is not uniformly positive definite, we should replace $\mathbf{G}^{(k)}$ in Newton's method by a related positive definite matrix $\overline{\mathbf{G}}^{(k)}$. If $\mathbf{G}^{(k)}$ is indefinite and we define the search direction without modifying $\mathbf{G}^{(k)}$ then $\mathbf{p}^{(k)}$ may not be a descent direction. The modification has the effect of rotating $\mathbf{p}^{(k)}$ towards a direction of negative curvature and guaranteeing a descent direction. This *modified* Newton method is a steepest-descent method under the norm

$$\|\mathbf{p}\|_{\overline{\mathbf{G}}^{(k)}} = (\mathbf{p}^T\overline{\mathbf{G}}^{(k)}\mathbf{p})^{\frac{1}{2}}.$$

The matrix $\overline{\mathbf{G}}^{(k)}$ should be such that if $\mathbf{G}^{(k)}$ is sufficiently positive definite then $\overline{\mathbf{G}}^{(k)} = \mathbf{G}^{(k)}$ and on the occasions when $\mathbf{G}^{(k)}$ is indefinite and bounded then $\|\mathbf{G}^{(k)} - \overline{\mathbf{G}}^{(k)}\|$ is bounded. It is essential that the algorithm be numerically stable, for otherwise rounding errors could cause $\|\mathbf{G}^{(k)} - \overline{\mathbf{G}}^{(k)}\|$ to be unbounded and/or $\mathbf{p}^{(k)}$ not to be a descent direction.

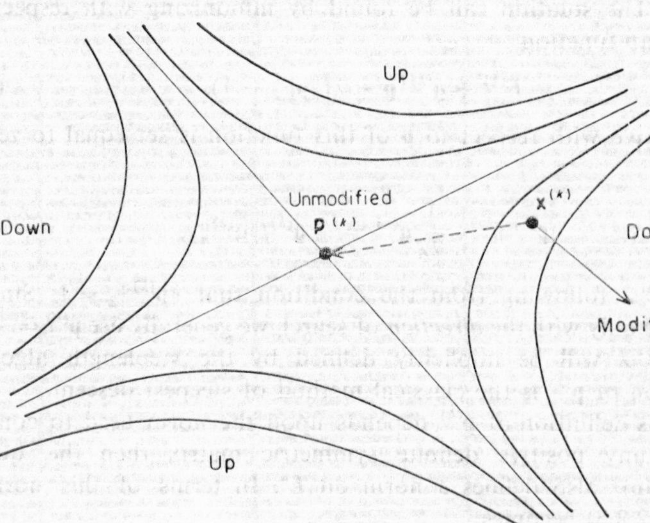

FIG. 2.4.

Several modified Newton methods have been proposed and we shall review the best five of them briefly (see Murray, 1972a for a more detailed survey).

(a) In a method due originally to Greenstadt (1967) $\overline{\mathbf{G}}^{(k)}$ is found by computing the eigenvalues $\mu_1, \mu_2, \ldots, \mu_n$ ($\mu_i \leqslant \mu_j$ if $i \leqslant j$) and eigenvectors $\mathbf{v}_1, \ldots, \mathbf{v}_n$ of $\mathbf{G}^{(k)}$, and setting

$$\overline{\mathbf{G}}^{(k)} = \sum_{j=1}^{n} \bar{\mu}_j \mathbf{v}_j \mathbf{v}_j^T$$

where

$$\bar{\mu}_j = \max \{\delta, |\mu_j|\}.$$

The parameter δ is introduced to avoid numerical difficulties in evaluating $\mathbf{p}^{(k)}$ when $\mathbf{G}^{(k)}$ is positive definite but very ill-conditioned. A suitable choice of δ on a computer with a mantissa of t bits is

$$\delta = \max \{2^{-t} \| \mathbf{G}^{(k)} \|_\infty, 2^{-t}\}.$$

(b) A more efficient method of modifying $\mathbf{G}^{(k)}$ (Gill and Murray, 1972b) can be used by attempting to compute the Cholesky factorization $\mathbf{G}^{(k)} = \mathbf{L}^{(k)}\mathbf{D}^{(k)}\mathbf{L}^{(k)T}$. During the computation, the diagonals of $\mathbf{D}^{(k)}$ are increased in size by an amount that is sufficient to ensure a stable factorization. Eventually a factorization

$$\mathbf{L}^{(k)} \mathbf{D}^{(k)} \mathbf{L}^{(k)T} = \mathbf{G}^{(k)} + \mathbf{E}^{(k)} = \overline{\mathbf{G}}^{(k)}$$

is obtained, where $\overline{\mathbf{G}}^{(k)}$ is positive definite and $\mathbf{E}^{(k)}$ is a diagonal matrix which is equal to zero if $\mathbf{G}^{(k)}$ is sufficiently positive definite.

(c) A slightly different approach from that used in (a) and (b) was suggested by Levenberg (1944) in the context of minimizing a sum of squares and popularized by Marquardt (1963). The basis of the method is to avoid the calculation of the steplength $\alpha^{(k)}$ by always taking a *unit* step along $\mathbf{p}^{(k)}$ and altering $\mathbf{p}^{(k)}$ if $F(\mathbf{x}^{(k)} + \mathbf{p}^{(k)})$ is not sufficiently lower than $F(\mathbf{x})$. This can be done by choosing a scalar $\gamma^{(k)}$ such that $\mathbf{G}^{(k)} + \gamma^{(k)}\mathbf{I}$ is positive definite and the solution of the equations

$$(\mathbf{G}^{(k)} + \gamma^{(k)}\mathbf{I})\, \mathbf{p}^{(k)} = -\,\mathbf{g}^{(k)} \tag{2.3.6}$$

is such that $\|\mathbf{p}^{(k)}\|_2 \leqslant h^{(k)}$, where $h^{(k)}$ is a scalar which varies from iteration to iteration. In this case the parameters $\gamma^{(k)}$ and $h^{(k)}$ must be determined rather than the steplength $\alpha^{(k)}$. Any method using (2.3.6) must include some rule for increasing or decreasing $h^{(k)}$ depending upon whether or not $F(\mathbf{x}^{(k)} + \mathbf{p}^{(k)})$ is sufficiently lower than $F(\mathbf{x}^{(k)})$.

It is easily shown that $\mathbf{p}^{(k)}$ is the solution of the problem

$$\underset{\mathbf{p}}{\text{minimize}} \{Q(\mathbf{p}) = F^{(k)} + \mathbf{g}^{(k)T}\mathbf{p} + \tfrac{1}{2}\mathbf{p}^T\mathbf{G}^{(k)}\mathbf{p}\} \tag{2.3.7}$$

subject to the constraint $\|\mathbf{p}\|_2 \leqslant \|\mathbf{p}^{(k)}\|_2$ and that in imposing the condition $\|\mathbf{p}^{(k)}\|_2 \leqslant h^{(k)}$ we are attempting to restrict $\mathbf{x}^{(k+1)}$ to lie in a region in which the quadratic approximation is expected to be valid.

(d) Goldfeld, Quandt and Trotter (1966) recommend computing $\gamma^{(k)}$ by an iterative method based upon a complete eigenvalue analysis of $\mathbf{G}^{(k)}$. This method is both very expensive computationally and can have the disadvantage of possibly having a slower rate of convergence than methods (a) and (b) since $\gamma^{(k)}$ may be non-zero when $\mathbf{G}^{(k)}$ is positive definite. A possible superlinear rate of convergence will only be achieved if $\gamma^{(k)} = 0$.

(e) In an attempt to overcome these difficulties, a version of (c) based upon triangular factorizations has been suggested by Murray (1972a) and Hebden (1973). The latter method is based upon attempting to form the LDL^T factorization of $\mathbf{G}^{(k)} + \gamma\mathbf{I}$, but whenever possible a trial value of $\gamma = 0$ is made.

If $\mathbf{G}^{(k)}$ is sufficiently positive definite and we are sufficiently close to the solution, algorithms (b) and (e) are identical, being just Newton's method implemented using the LDL^T factorization. It is difficult to draw further numerical comparisons since Hebden publishes only a single numerical example, but the justification for using (2.3.6) appears questionable. Firstly, in practice we avoid an algorithm for computing $\alpha^{(k)}$ only by requiring a similar one for computing $h^{(k)}$ and $\gamma^{(k)}$. Secondly, we only want the constraint $\|\mathbf{p}^{(k)}\| \leqslant h^{(k)}$ to be active *away* from a strong local minimum, since otherwise the rate of convergence is impaired, but when $\mathbf{x}^{(k)}$ is far away from the solution it is less important that $\mathbf{x}^{(k+1)}$ lies in the region for which (2.3.7) is an adequate quadratic approximation. This implies that we could dispense with the requirement $\|\mathbf{p}^{(k)}\|_2 \leqslant h^{(k)}$ altogether. Finally, if the function value $F(\mathbf{x}^{(k)} + \mathbf{p}^{(k)})$ is not sufficiently lower than $F(\mathbf{x}^{(k)})$ then at least one more LDL^T factorization and function evaluation must be made in order to obtain a lower function value, whereas only function evaluations are used to obtain $\alpha^{(k)}$ in the Gill–Murray algorithm.

In addition to the possibility that $\mathbf{G}^{(k)}$ may be indefinite, a difficulty with Newton's method is that at a saddle point the search direction defined by equation (2.3.2) is zero, since the gradient vanishes. In this situation we must have an alternative method of defining the direction of search. In practice this alternative direction should be used whenever $\mathbf{x}^{(k)}$ is in the immediate neighbourhood of a stationary point—for example, whenever $\|\mathbf{g}^{(k)}\|_2$ is less than some preassigned tolerance ε.

If $\mathbf{x}^{(k)}$ is a saddle point, the Taylor expansion becomes

$$F(\mathbf{x}^{(k)} + \mathbf{p}) = F^{(k)} + \tfrac{1}{2}\mathbf{p}^T\mathbf{G}^{(k)}\mathbf{p} + O(\|\mathbf{p}\|^3).$$

If $\mathbf{p}$ is chosen such that $\mathbf{p}^T\mathbf{G}^{(k)}\mathbf{p} < 0$, then for $\|\mathbf{p}\|$ sufficiently small we have $F(\mathbf{x}^{(k)} + \mathbf{p}) < F(\mathbf{x}^{(k)})$. Such a vector $\mathbf{p}$ is called a *direction of negative curvature.* The problem is to identify this direction in a numerically stable way, preferably using information already available from the process of modifying the Hessian matrix to be positive definite.

The modified methods (a), (b), (d) and (e) provide a means of identifying directions of negative curvature. In Greenstadt's method we can form $\mathbf{p}$ as a linear combination of eigenvectors associated with eigenvalues which are negative. For example if λ_s is an eigenvalue with eigenvector $\mathbf{v}_s$,

$$\begin{aligned}\mathbf{v}_s{}^T\mathbf{G}^{(k)}\mathbf{v}_s &= \sum_{j=1}^{n} \lambda_j \mathbf{v}_s{}^T\mathbf{v}_j\mathbf{v}_j{}^T\mathbf{v}_s \\ &= \lambda_s < 0, \quad \text{since} \quad \mathbf{v}_j{}^T\mathbf{v}_s = 0,\ j \neq s,\ \|\mathbf{v}_s\|_2 = 1.\end{aligned}$$

Again, a more efficient method is to use the Cholesky factors of $\overline{\mathbf{G}}^{(k)}$. Gill and Murray (1972b) have shown that a direction of negative curvature can be found by solving the equations

$$\mathbf{L}^{(k)T}\mathbf{p} = \mathbf{e}_s$$

where s is the index such that,

$$d_s{}^{(k)} - E_s{}^{(k)} \leqslant d_j{}^{(k)} - E_j{}^{(k)}, \qquad j = 1, 2, \ldots, n.$$

and $d_j{}^{(k)}$ and $E_j{}^{(k)}$ are the jth diagonal elements of the matrices $\mathbf{D}^{(k)}$ and $\mathbf{E}^{(k)}$ respectively. A similar scheme is suggested by Hebden in his implementation of the Levenberg–Marquardt algorithm.

A way of eliminating the need to provide analytical second derivatives of $F(\mathbf{x})$ is to approximate them by finite differences. The finite-difference approximation to the Hessian matrix is found by first forming the matrix $\mathbf{Y}$ whose jth column is given by

$$\mathbf{y}_j = (\mathbf{g}(\mathbf{x}^{(k)} + h_j\mathbf{e}_j) - \mathbf{g}^{(k)})/h_j,$$

where $\mathbf{e}_j$ is the jth column of the identity matrix, and h_j is the finite-difference interval. The symmetric approximation $\mathbf{G}_h{}^{(k)}$ to $\mathbf{G}^{(k)}$ is then given by

$$\mathbf{G}_h{}^{(k)} = \tfrac{1}{2}(\mathbf{Y} + \mathbf{Y}^T).$$

It is possible to construct this approximation in such a way that the maximum storage required is $n(n + 1)/2 + n$.

The use of finite differences has been suggested by many other authors for both minimization and the solution of nonlinear equations (see for example Goldstein and Price, 1967; Brown and Dennis, 1972) but generally the method has not been popular. There are two main reasons for this. Firstly, it would appear that the algorithm might be very sensitive to the choice of the steplength $\mathbf{h}$. Secondly, known theoretical results concerning the ultimate rate of convergence of finite difference methods indicate that if a Newton-like rate of convergence is to be achieved, then $\|\mathbf{h}\|_\infty$ must tend to zero as k tends to infinity. Clearly this is not possible numerically since cancellation would soon have a serious effect upon the computation of the direction of search. However, numerical experience reported by Gill, Murray and Picken (1972) suggests the surprising result that, provided a ridiculous choice of $\mathbf{h}$ is avoided, the results are almost independent of $\mathbf{h}$ and that the number of iterations required is almost identical to Newton's method. The general conclusion is that discrete Newton methods are more robust than quasi-Newton methods and will converge to a solution for a wider class of problems—for example when the Hessian matrix is very ill-conditioned. A disadvantage of the method with respect to quasi-Newton methods is the need for n additional gradient evaluations to compute $\mathbf{G}_h^{(k)}$; however, we note that if $\mathbf{G}^{(k)}$ is known to be sparse and has structure, then the number of gradient evaluations can be reduced (see Chapter IV).

When finite differences are used it is essential that the method used should modify the discrete Hessian matrix when this is indefinite; even if $\mathbf{G}(\mathbf{x})$ is globally positive definite, $\mathbf{G}_h(\mathbf{x})$ need not possess the same property.

2.4. Minimization with Linear Equality Constraints—a Survey

The second requirement of any active constraint method is that it should be effective for the problem with linear *equality* constraints

$$LECP: \qquad \underset{\mathbf{x}}{\text{minimize}}\, F(\mathbf{x}) \quad \text{subject to } \hat{\mathbf{A}}^T\mathbf{x} = \hat{\mathbf{b}},$$

where $\hat{\mathbf{A}}^T$ is a $t \times n$ matrix with $t \leqslant n$. We shall assume that initially we know a feasible point $\mathbf{x}^{(0)}$; methods for obtaining such a point will be considered in Section 2.9. Associated with a stationary point $\hat{\mathbf{x}}$ of the equality-constraint problem is a set of Lagrange multipliers $\boldsymbol{\lambda}$ such that

$$\hat{\mathbf{A}}\boldsymbol{\lambda} = \mathbf{g}(\hat{\mathbf{x}}), \tag{2.4.1}$$

the signs of each λ_j being unrestricted. Of these n equations any t are linearly independent, the remaining $n - t$ being linear combinations of these since $\mathbf{g}(\hat{\mathbf{x}})$ lies in the range of $\hat{\mathbf{A}}$ by Theorem 1.5. Hence (2.4.1) has the unique solution

$$\boldsymbol{\lambda} = \hat{\mathbf{A}}^+\mathbf{g}(\hat{\mathbf{x}}),$$

where $\hat{\mathbf{A}}^+ = (\hat{\mathbf{A}}^T\hat{\mathbf{A}})^{-1}\hat{\mathbf{A}}^T$ is the pseudo-inverse of $\hat{\mathbf{A}}$. At points other than stationary points of *LECP* there is no vector $\boldsymbol{\lambda}^{(k)}$ such that $\mathbf{g}(\mathbf{x}^{(k)}) - \hat{\mathbf{A}}\boldsymbol{\lambda}^{(k)} = \mathbf{0}$

and we can only compute *estimates* of the vector $\boldsymbol{\lambda}$. An estimate often used in practice is the vector $\boldsymbol{\lambda}^{(k)} = \hat{\mathbf{A}}^{+}\mathbf{g}^{(k)}$ which minimizes $\|\mathbf{g}^{(k)} - \hat{\mathbf{A}}\boldsymbol{\lambda}\|_2$ and $\|\boldsymbol{\lambda}\|_2$ with respect to $\boldsymbol{\lambda}$ (see Peters and Wilkinson, 1970). It is easily shown that $\|\boldsymbol{\lambda} - \boldsymbol{\lambda}^{(k)}\| = O(\|\mathbf{h}\|)$ where $\mathbf{h}$ is the vector such that $\hat{\mathbf{x}} = \mathbf{x}^{(k)} + \mathbf{h}$. Vectors which satisfy this property are defined as *first-order estimates* of the Lagrange multipliers.

It was shown in the previous section that the direction of search associated with Newton's method for unconstrained minimization is defined by the unconstrained minimum of a quadratic function. As might be expected the direction of search in the linearly constrained case can be viewed as the minimum of a quadratic function subject to linear equality constraints.

Consider again the quadratic approximation $Q(\mathbf{p})$ defined by (2.3.7). If the point $\mathbf{x}^{(k+1)} = \mathbf{x}^{(k)} + \alpha^{(k)}\mathbf{p}^{(k)}$ is to satisfy the constraints which are active at $\mathbf{x}^{(k)}$, $\mathbf{p}^{(k)}$ must be restricted to be orthogonal to the constraint normals. In this case $\mathbf{p}^{(k)}$ is the solution of the problem

$$\underset{\mathbf{p}}{\text{minimize}}\ Q(\mathbf{p}) \tag{2.4.2}$$

subject to the constraints $\hat{\mathbf{A}}^T\mathbf{p} = \mathbf{0}$.

The problem analogous to (2.3.5) with $\mathbf{N} = \mathbf{G}^{(k)}$ is

$$\underset{\mathbf{p}}{\text{minimize}}\ \{F^{(k)} + \mathbf{g}^{(k)T}\mathbf{p} + \lambda(\mathbf{p}^T\mathbf{G}^{(k)}\mathbf{p} - 1)\} \tag{2.4.3}$$

subject to the constraints $\hat{\mathbf{A}}^T\mathbf{p} = \mathbf{0}$.

The direction $\mathbf{p}^{(k)}$ can thus be interpreted as a direction of steepest descent selected from those vectors which are orthogonal to the constraint normals.

The properties of the two quadratic programming problems (2.4.2) and (2.4.3) can be determined by considering the following problem

QP: $\quad \underset{\mathbf{p}}{\text{minimize}}\ \{\tfrac{1}{2}\,\mathbf{p}^T\mathbf{G}\mathbf{p} + \mathbf{g}^T\mathbf{p}\}$ subject to the constraints $\hat{\mathbf{A}}^T\mathbf{p} = \mathbf{0}$.

The constant term has been omitted since it does not alter the solution and we have dropped the superscript k since the Hessian $\mathbf{G}^{(k)}$ and gradient $\mathbf{g}^{(k)}$ are constant with respect to $\mathbf{p}$.

From Theorem 1.5, at a stationary point $\mathring{\mathbf{p}}$ of QP there must exist Lagrange multipliers $\mathring{\boldsymbol{\omega}}$ such that

$$\hat{\mathbf{A}}\mathring{\boldsymbol{\omega}} = \text{grad}\, Q(\mathring{\mathbf{p}}) = \mathbf{G}\mathring{\mathbf{p}} + \mathbf{g}, \tag{2.4.4}$$

or equivalently

$$\mathring{\boldsymbol{\omega}} = \hat{\mathbf{A}}^{+}(\mathbf{G}\mathring{\mathbf{p}} + \mathbf{g}).$$

The vector $\mathring{\boldsymbol{\omega}}$ is unique (since $\mathbf{G}\mathring{\mathbf{p}} + \mathbf{g}$ lies in the range of $\hat{\mathbf{A}}$, by Theorem 1.5) and has the property that $\|\boldsymbol{\lambda} - \mathring{\boldsymbol{\omega}}\| = O(\|\mathbf{h}\|^2)$. Hence $\mathring{\boldsymbol{\omega}}$ is a *second-order* estimate of λ. It is a feature of second-order estimates of the Lagrange multipliers that they are invariant under a linear transformation of the variables.

All active constraint methods for the solution of linearly constrained minimization problems are based upon one of two alternative methods for solving *QP*. We now consider these methods in detail.

Method I (*Solution of the Primal Quadratic Program*)

Consider the set of vectors orthogonal to $\hat{\mathbf{A}}^T$

$$M_0 = \{\mathbf{y}: \hat{\mathbf{A}}^T\mathbf{y} = \mathbf{0}\}.$$

M_0 is a linear vector subspace of E^n parallel to the manifold

$$M = \{\mathbf{x}: \hat{\mathbf{A}}^T\mathbf{x} = \hat{\mathbf{b}}\},$$

and if the rows of $\hat{\mathbf{A}}^T$ are linearly independent, which we shall assume hereafter, M_0 is of dimension $n - t$. Every vector in M_0 can be expressed as a linear combination of $n - t$ basis vectors $\{\mathbf{z}_j\}_{j=1}^{n-t}$. This implies that if $\mathbf{Z}$ is the matrix with columns $\mathbf{z}_j$ then for any $\mathbf{y} \in M_0$ there exist $n - t$ scalars v_j such that

$$\mathbf{y} = \mathbf{Z}\mathbf{v}.$$

If we express $\mathbf{p}$ in this form and substitute in *QP* we have

$$\underset{\mathbf{v}}{\text{minimize}} \{\tfrac{1}{2}\,\mathbf{v}^T(\mathbf{Z}^T\mathbf{G}\mathbf{Z})\,\mathbf{v} + \mathbf{g}^T\mathbf{Z}\mathbf{v}\},$$

which is now an *unconstrained* problem in the $n - t$ variables $\mathbf{v}$. If the matrix $\mathbf{Z}^T\mathbf{G}\mathbf{Z}$ is positive definite Theorem 2.1 can be used and yields the solution $\overset{*}{\mathbf{v}}$ as the solution of the equations

$$(\mathbf{Z}^T\mathbf{G}\mathbf{Z})\,\overset{*}{\mathbf{v}} = -\,\mathbf{Z}^T\mathbf{g};$$

we recover the solution $\overset{*}{\mathbf{p}}$ of *QP* as

$$\overset{*}{\mathbf{p}} = \mathbf{Z}\overset{*}{\mathbf{v}}. \tag{2.4.5}$$

The n-vector $\overset{*}{\mathbf{p}}$ is clearly feasible; this can be verified by computing $\hat{\mathbf{A}}^T\overset{*}{\mathbf{p}} = \hat{\mathbf{A}}^T\mathbf{Z}\overset{*}{\mathbf{v}} = \mathbf{0}$, since we have $\hat{\mathbf{A}}^T\mathbf{Z} = \mathbf{0}$.

In terms of finding a feasible descent direction of the linearly constrained problem, the matrix $\mathbf{Z}^T\mathbf{G}^{(k)}\mathbf{Z}$, which is the matrix of second derivatives with respect to the linear space M_0, is defined as the *projected Hessian matrix* and written as $\mathbf{G}_A{}^{(k)}$. Similarly the $n - t$ vector $\mathbf{g}_A{}^{(k)} = \mathbf{Z}^T\mathbf{g}^{(k)}$ is defined as the *projected gradient*. At present we require that $\mathbf{Z}^T\mathbf{G}^{(k)}\mathbf{Z}$ be positive definite but we shall relax this condition in the final version of the method given in Section 2.5.

At a point $\mathbf{x}^{(k)}$ the method of computing $\boldsymbol{\omega}^{(k)}$, the second-order estimate of $\boldsymbol{\lambda}$, depends upon the method used to define $\mathbf{Z}$ (see Section 2.8). It is often more convenient, however, to use the first-order estimate $\boldsymbol{\lambda}^{(k)} = \hat{\mathbf{A}}^{+}\mathbf{g}^{(k)}$. Fortunately this is no disadvantage when minimizing nonlinear functions. In order to compute a value of $\boldsymbol{\omega}^{(k)}$ which satisfies (2.4.4) we must know the value of $\mathbf{p}^{(k)}$; we may just as well step to the point $\mathbf{x}^{(k+1)}$ and evaluate $\mathbf{g}^{(k+1)}$ since this should be close to $\mathbf{G}^{(k)}\mathbf{p}^{(k)} + \mathbf{g}^{(k)}$ when $F(\mathbf{x})$ is near quadratic.

It is a feature of this method that the greater the number of constraints active at $\mathbf{x}^{(k)}$, the smaller the dimension of the system of equations to be solved for $\mathbf{p}^{(k)}$. This is in contrast to the alternative method of solving QP considered next, which is such that the fewer the number of constraints active, the fewer the number of equations that must be solved.

Method II (Solution of the Dual Program)

The solution of QP is defined by two vectors, the solution $\overset{*}{\mathbf{p}}$, and $\overset{*}{\boldsymbol{\omega}}$ the vector of Lagrange multipliers associated with the constraints $\hat{\mathbf{A}}^T$ which satisfy $\hat{\mathbf{A}}\overset{*}{\boldsymbol{\omega}} = \mathbf{g} + \mathbf{G}\overset{*}{\mathbf{p}}$. We refer to $(\overset{*}{\mathbf{p}}, \overset{*}{\boldsymbol{\omega}})$ as a *solution pair* to QP. The basis of Method II is to pose and solve an alternative quadratic programming problem called the *dual*, having as solution a pair $(\overset{*}{\mathbf{y}}, \overset{*}{\mathbf{u}})$ for which, under certain conditions, $\overset{*}{\mathbf{y}} = \overset{*}{\mathbf{p}}$ and $\overset{*}{\mathbf{u}} = \overset{*}{\boldsymbol{\omega}}$. The dual problem for QP is as follows

$$DQP: \qquad \underset{\mathbf{y},\mathbf{u}}{\text{minimize}} \{D(\mathbf{y}, \mathbf{u}) = \tfrac{1}{2}\mathbf{y}^T\mathbf{G}\mathbf{y}\}$$

subject to the constraints

$$\hat{\mathbf{A}}\mathbf{u} - \mathbf{G}\mathbf{y} = \mathbf{g}.$$

The notation $D(\mathbf{y}, \mathbf{u})$ has been used since the objective function is implicitly dependent upon $\mathbf{u}$. In order to make use of this dual we must first determine the conditions under which a unique solution $(\overset{*}{\mathbf{y}}, \overset{*}{\mathbf{u}})$ of DQP exists and then determine whether this solution is a strong local minimum of QP.

LEMMA 2.1. *Let $(\overset{*}{\mathbf{y}}, \overset{*}{\mathbf{u}})$ be a solution of DQP. If $\overset{*}{\mathbf{y}} = \overset{*}{\mathbf{p}}$, a solution of QP, then* $\mathbf{G}$ *must be non-singular.*

Proof. If $\mathbf{G}$ has rank r $(r < n)$, then there exists a vector $\mathbf{v}$, $\|\mathbf{v}\| > 0$ such that $\mathbf{G}\mathbf{v} = \mathbf{0}$. Clearly if $(\overset{*}{\mathbf{y}}, \overset{*}{\mathbf{u}})$ is a solution of DQP then so is $(\overset{*}{\mathbf{y}} + \mathbf{v}, \overset{*}{\mathbf{u}})$ but since this is not necessarily a solution of QP, $\mathbf{G}$ must be non-singular. ▮

THEOREM 2.2. *Let* $\mathbf{G}$ *be non-singular and the matrix* $\hat{\mathbf{A}}^T\mathbf{G}^{-1}\hat{\mathbf{A}}$ *be positive definite; then a bounded solution* $(\overset{*}{\mathbf{y}}, \overset{*}{\mathbf{u}})$ *of DQP exists and if* $\mathbf{Z}^T\mathbf{G}\mathbf{Z}$ *is positive* *definite and* $\overset{*}{\mathbf{p}}$ *is the strong local minimum of QP with multipliers* $\overset{*}{\boldsymbol{\omega}}$, *then* $\overset{*}{\mathbf{p}} = \overset{*}{\mathbf{y}}$ *and* $\overset{*}{\boldsymbol{\omega}} = \overset{*}{\mathbf{u}}$.

Proof. Since $\mathbf{G}$ is non-singular we can solve for $\mathbf{y}$ using the constraints of *DQP* to obtain

$$\mathbf{y} = \mathbf{G}^{-1}(\hat{\mathbf{A}}\mathbf{u} - \mathbf{g}). \tag{2.4.6}$$

Substituting for $\mathbf{y}$ in the objective function we obtain the modified problem

$$\underset{\mathbf{u}}{\text{minimize}} \, \{\tfrac{1}{2}\mathbf{u}^T(\hat{\mathbf{A}}^T\mathbf{G}^{-1}\hat{\mathbf{A}})\,\mathbf{u} - \mathbf{g}^T\mathbf{G}^{-1}\hat{\mathbf{A}}\mathbf{u} + \tfrac{1}{2}\mathbf{g}^T\mathbf{G}^{-1}\mathbf{g}\}.$$

The assumption that $\hat{\mathbf{A}}^T\mathbf{G}^{-1}\hat{\mathbf{A}}$ is positive definite enables us to apply Theorem 2.1 case (i), to give the vector $\overset{*}{\mathbf{u}}$ as the solution of the set of equations

$$(\hat{\mathbf{A}}^T\mathbf{G}^{-1}\hat{\mathbf{A}})\overset{*}{\mathbf{u}} = \hat{\mathbf{A}}^T\mathbf{G}^{-1}\mathbf{g}. \tag{2.4.7}$$

This value of $\overset{*}{\mathbf{u}}$, when substituted in (2.4.6), gives $\overset{*}{\mathbf{y}}$ as

$$\overset{*}{\mathbf{y}} = \mathbf{G}^{-1}(\hat{\mathbf{A}}(\hat{\mathbf{A}}^T\mathbf{G}^{-1}\hat{\mathbf{A}})^{-1}\hat{\mathbf{A}}^T\mathbf{G}^{-1} - \mathbf{I})\,\mathbf{g}. \tag{2.4.8}$$

If we multiply this last equation by $\hat{\mathbf{A}}^T$ we see that $\overset{*}{\mathbf{y}}$ satisfies the identity

$$\hat{\mathbf{A}}^T\overset{*}{\mathbf{y}} = \mathbf{0},$$

and consequently can be written in the form

$$\overset{*}{\mathbf{y}} = \mathbf{Z}\bar{\mathbf{v}}$$

for some vector $\bar{\mathbf{v}}$. Premultiplying this last equation by $\mathbf{Z}^T\mathbf{G}$ we have

$$\mathbf{Z}^T\mathbf{G}\overset{*}{\mathbf{y}} = \mathbf{Z}^T\mathbf{G}\mathbf{Z}\bar{\mathbf{v}}.$$

Substituting for $\overset{*}{\mathbf{y}}$ from equation (2.4.8) gives

$$\begin{aligned}\mathbf{Z}^T\mathbf{G}\mathbf{Z}\bar{\mathbf{v}} &= \mathbf{Z}^T\hat{\mathbf{A}}\overset{*}{\mathbf{u}} - \mathbf{Z}^T\mathbf{g}\\ &= -\,\mathbf{Z}^T\mathbf{g},\end{aligned}$$

since we have $\mathbf{Z}^T\hat{\mathbf{A}} = \mathbf{0}$. This last equation implies that $\bar{\mathbf{v}} = \overset{*}{\mathbf{v}}$ and is unique, since $\mathbf{Z}^T\mathbf{G}\mathbf{Z}$ is positive definite, and consequently $\overset{*}{\mathbf{p}} = \overset{*}{\mathbf{y}}$. The theorem is complete if it can be shown that $\overset{*}{\mathbf{u}}$ are the Lagrange multipliers for *QP*, $\overset{*}{\boldsymbol{\omega}}$.

From the definition of *DQP* we have

$$\hat{\mathbf{A}}\overset{*}{\mathbf{u}} - \mathbf{G}\mathbf{y} = \mathbf{g}.$$

Consequently at $\overset{*}{\mathbf{y}} = \overset{*}{\mathbf{p}}$,

$$\hat{\mathbf{A}}\overset{*}{\mathbf{u}} - \mathbf{G}\overset{*}{\mathbf{p}} = \mathbf{g},$$

or equivalently

$$\hat{\mathbf{A}}\overset{*}{\mathbf{u}} = \mathbf{g} + \mathbf{G}\overset{*}{\mathbf{p}} = \hat{\mathbf{A}}\overset{*}{\boldsymbol{\omega}}.$$

Since $\hat{\mathbf{A}}$ is of full column rank, $\overset{*}{\boldsymbol{\omega}} = \overset{*}{\mathbf{u}}$ as required. ▮

In terms of the kth step of an algorithm for minimization subject to linear constraints the dual method becomes

I. compute $\mathbf{G}^{(k)-1}$ and the $t \times t$ matrix $\hat{\mathbf{A}}^T\mathbf{G}^{(k)-1}\hat{\mathbf{A}}$;

II. evaluate the vector $\boldsymbol{\omega}^{(k)}$ by solving the set of equations

$$(\hat{\mathbf{A}}^T\mathbf{G}^{(k)-1}\hat{\mathbf{A}})\,\boldsymbol{\omega}^{(k)} = \hat{\mathbf{A}}^T\mathbf{G}^{(k)-1}\mathbf{g}^{(k)} \tag{2.4.9}$$

and set

$$\mathbf{p}^{(k)} = \mathbf{G}^{(k)-1}(\hat{\mathbf{A}}\boldsymbol{\omega}^{(k)} - \mathbf{g}^{(k)}). \tag{2.4.10}$$

We note that, in contrast to Method I, the Lagrange multipliers are obtained in the process of computing $\mathbf{p}^{(k)}$.

An alternative way of deriving the equations defining Method II is by solving

$$\begin{pmatrix} \mathbf{G}^{(k)} & -\hat{\mathbf{A}} \\ -\hat{\mathbf{A}}^T & \mathbf{0} \end{pmatrix} \begin{pmatrix} \mathbf{p}^{(k)} \\ \boldsymbol{\omega}^{(k)} \end{pmatrix} = \begin{pmatrix} -\mathbf{g}^{(k)} \\ \mathbf{0} \end{pmatrix}.$$

It can be shown that the inverse of the coefficient matrix is given by

$$\begin{pmatrix} \mathbf{W}^{(k)}\mathbf{G}^{(k)-1} & -\mathbf{G}^{(k)-1}\hat{\mathbf{A}}(\hat{\mathbf{A}}^T\mathbf{G}^{(k)-1}\hat{\mathbf{A}})^{-1} \\ -(\hat{\mathbf{A}}^T\mathbf{G}^{(k)-1}\hat{\mathbf{A}})^{-1}\hat{\mathbf{A}}^T\mathbf{G}^{(k)-1} & -(\hat{\mathbf{A}}^T\mathbf{G}^{(k)-1}\hat{\mathbf{A}})^{-1} \end{pmatrix},$$

where $\mathbf{W}^{(k)} = \mathbf{I} - \mathbf{G}^{(k)-1}\hat{\mathbf{A}}(\hat{\mathbf{A}}^T\mathbf{G}^{(k)-1}\hat{\mathbf{A}})^{-1}\hat{\mathbf{A}}^T$. The reader is referred to Fletcher (1972b) for further details.

2.5. A Projected Newton-type Method for the Equality-constraint Problem

As in the unconstrained case, if we are intending to solve general problems, we cannot expect $\mathbf{G}^{(k)}$ to be positive definite everywhere. In the linearly constrained case, however, the situation is more serious since *we cannot expect* $\mathbf{G}^{(k)}$ *to be positive definite or even non-singular at a strong local minimum.* The following example illustrates this point.

Example

Consider the minimization of the quadratic function

$$Q(\mathbf{p}) = \tfrac{1}{2}p_1^{\,2} + \tfrac{3}{2}p_2^{\,2} + \sqrt{3}\,p_1 p_2 - p_1 + 3\sqrt{3}\,p_2$$

subject to the constraint $p_2 = 0$. In the notation of the problem *QP* we have

$$\mathbf{G} = \begin{pmatrix} 1 & \sqrt{3} \\ \sqrt{3} & 3 \end{pmatrix} \quad \text{and} \quad \mathbf{g} = \begin{pmatrix} -1 \\ 3\sqrt{3} \end{pmatrix}.$$

The matrix $\mathbf{G}$ is singular, having a zero eigenvalue with corresponding eigenvector $\mathbf{v} = [\sqrt{3}/2, -\tfrac{1}{2}]^T$ but it is easily verified that the problem has a strong local minimum at the point $[1, 0]^T$. The unconstrained quadratic function $Q(\mathbf{p})$ is of the form considered in case (iii) of Theorem 2.1 and does not possess an unbounded solution, but along the plane $p_2 = 0$ the function is quadratic (see Fig. 2.5).

This phenomenon contrasts with the unconstrained case where $\mathbf{G}(\mathbf{x})$ is generally positive definite in the neighbourhood of a strong local minimum. If we are to use a modified Newton method we must ensure that no modification takes place in the immediate neighbourhood of a strong local minimum, lest the rate of convergence deteriorate. Method II is unsuitable because it is not an easy matter to modify $\mathbf{G}^{(k)}$ without impairing the rate of convergence. An additional difficulty occurs with Method II if $\hat{\mathbf{A}}^T\mathbf{G}^{(k)-1}\hat{\mathbf{A}}$ turns out to be indefinite. This matrix does not appear at all in the conditions for a point to be a strong local minimum of the overall problem, and the interpretation of a set of multipliers obtained by forcing $\hat{\mathbf{A}}^T\mathbf{G}^{(k)-1}\hat{\mathbf{A}}$ to be positive definite is not obvious.

These problems do not arise with Method I since Theorem 1.5 applied to the equality constrained problem states that if $\mathbf{g}_A(\mathbf{\mathring{x}}) = \mathbf{0}$ and $\mathbf{G}_A(\mathbf{\mathring{x}})$ is positive definite then $\mathbf{\mathring{x}}$ is a strong local minimum. This implies that the rate of convergence near $\mathbf{\mathring{x}}$ will not be impaired by modification of the matrix $\mathbf{G}_A(\mathbf{x})$.

If the Lagrange multipliers are computed for every iteration, Methods I and II both require the solution of two sets of linear equations. These comprise an $n \times t$ under-determined system and an $(n - t) \times (n - t)$ system for Method I and an $n \times n$ and $t \times t$ system for Method II. Thus Method I always requires less work per iteration than Method II. The most complicated system of equations, namely that involving the coefficient matrix $\hat{\mathbf{A}}^T\mathbf{G}^{(k)-1}\hat{\mathbf{A}}$ in Method II could be of low order if the number of active constraints is low throughout the computation. However, it is difficult to identify these cases *a priori*; the converse occurs with Method I, where it can often be asserted before the solution commences that a large number of constraints will be active for all iterations (see for example Chapter IV, Section 4.6).

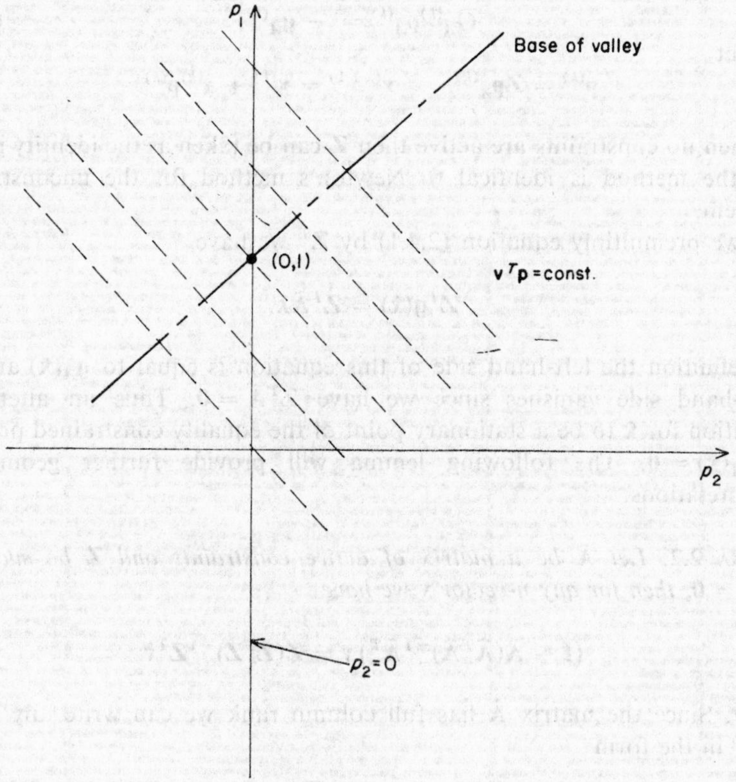

FIG. 2.5.

The basic superiority of Method I leads us not to consider Method II further here, although it will be discussed in the next chapter on quasi-Newton methods.

We are now ready to recommend a modified Newton method for linearly constrained optimization in which $\mathbf{G}_A^{(k)}$ is modified to be positive definite by one of the methods given in Section 2.3. The iteration is summarized as follows.

Let $\hat{\mathbf{A}}^T$ be the matrix of constraints active at $\mathbf{x}^{(k)}$ and $\mathbf{Z}$ the matrix such that $\hat{\mathbf{A}}^T\mathbf{Z} = \mathbf{0}$. A method for computing $\mathbf{Z}$ is given in Section 2.8.

(I) Form the matrix $\bar{\mathbf{G}}_A{}^{(k)}$ which is equal to $\mathbf{G}_A{}^{(k)} = \mathbf{Z}^T\mathbf{G}^{(k)}\mathbf{Z}$ if $\mathbf{G}_A{}^{(k)}$ is sufficiently positive definite, and $\mathbf{g}_A{}^{(k)} = \mathbf{Z}^T\mathbf{g}^{(k)}$.

(II) Solve the set of equations

$$\bar{\mathbf{G}}_A{}^{(k)}\mathbf{p}_A{}^{(k)} = -\mathbf{g}_A{}^{(k)}, \tag{2.5.1}$$

and set

$$\mathbf{p}^{(k)} = \mathbf{Z}\mathbf{p}_A{}^{(k)}, \qquad \mathbf{x}^{(k+1)} = \mathbf{x}^{(k)} + \alpha^{(k)}\mathbf{p}^{(k)}.$$

When no constraints are active then $\mathbf{Z}$ can be taken as the identity matrix and the method is identical to Newton's method for the unconstrained problem.

If we premultiply equation (2.4.1) by $\mathbf{Z}^T$ we have

$$\mathbf{Z}^T\mathbf{g}(\hat{\mathbf{x}}) = \mathbf{Z}^T\hat{\mathbf{A}}\boldsymbol{\lambda}.$$

By definition the left-hand side of this equation is equal to $\mathbf{g}_A(\hat{\mathbf{x}})$ and the right-hand side vanishes since we have $\mathbf{Z}^T\hat{\mathbf{A}} = \mathbf{0}$. Thus an alternative condition for $\hat{\mathbf{x}}$ to be a stationary point of the equality constrained problem is $\mathbf{g}_A(\hat{\mathbf{x}}) = \mathbf{0}$. The following lemma will provide further geometrical interpretations.

LEMMA 2.2. *Let $\hat{\mathbf{A}}$ be a matrix of active constraints and $\mathbf{Z}$ be such that $\hat{\mathbf{A}}^T\mathbf{Z} = \mathbf{0}$, then for any n-vector $\mathbf{v}$ we have*

$$(\mathbf{I} - \hat{\mathbf{A}}(\hat{\mathbf{A}}^T\hat{\mathbf{A}})^{-1}\hat{\mathbf{A}}^T)\,\mathbf{v} = \mathbf{Z}(\mathbf{Z}^T\mathbf{Z})^{-1}\mathbf{Z}^T\mathbf{v}.$$

Proof. Since the matrix $\hat{\mathbf{A}}$ has full column rank we can write any vector $\mathbf{v} \in E^n$ in the form

$$\mathbf{v} = \hat{\mathbf{A}}\mathbf{u}_1 + \mathbf{Z}\mathbf{u}_2 \tag{2.5.2}$$

where $\mathbf{u}_1$ is a t-vector and $\mathbf{u}_2$ an $(n-t)$-vector. Pre-multiplying this expression by $\hat{\mathbf{A}}^T$ and using the orthogonality of $\hat{\mathbf{A}}^T$ and $\mathbf{Z}$ we have

$$\hat{\mathbf{A}}^T\mathbf{v} = \hat{\mathbf{A}}^T\hat{\mathbf{A}}\mathbf{u}_1.$$

Since the rows of $\hat{\mathbf{A}}^T$ are linearly independent the matrix $\hat{\mathbf{A}}^T\hat{\mathbf{A}}$ is of full rank and we can write

$$\mathbf{u}_1 = (\hat{\mathbf{A}}^T\hat{\mathbf{A}})^{-1}\hat{\mathbf{A}}^T\mathbf{v}. \tag{2.5.3}$$

If (2.5.2) is now pre-multiplied by $\mathbf{Z}^T$ we obtain the similar expression

$$\mathbf{u}_2 = (\mathbf{Z}^T\mathbf{Z})^{-1}\mathbf{Z}^T\mathbf{v}$$

and hence

$$\mathbf{Z}\mathbf{u}_2 = \mathbf{Z}(\mathbf{Z}^T\mathbf{Z})^{-1}\mathbf{Z}^T\mathbf{v}.$$

Substituting for $\mathbf{Z}\mathbf{u}_2$ in this equation from equation (2.5.2) gives

$$\mathbf{v} - \hat{\mathbf{A}}\mathbf{u}_1 = \mathbf{Z}(\mathbf{Z}^T\mathbf{Z})^{-1}\mathbf{Z}^T\mathbf{v},$$

or, from (2.5.3)

$$(\mathbf{I} - \hat{\mathbf{A}}(\hat{\mathbf{A}}^T\hat{\mathbf{A}})^{-1}\hat{\mathbf{A}}^T)\,\mathbf{v} = \mathbf{Z}(\mathbf{Z}^T\mathbf{Z})^{-1}\mathbf{Z}^T\mathbf{v}. \tag{2.5.4}$$

This completes the proof. ∎

The matrix $\mathbf{P} = \hat{\mathbf{A}}(\hat{\mathbf{A}}^T\hat{\mathbf{A}})^{-1}\hat{\mathbf{A}}^T$ is a projection matrix which projects vectors on to the space spanned by the columns of $\hat{\mathbf{A}}$, and $\overline{\mathbf{P}} = \mathbf{I} - \mathbf{P}$ projects vectors so that they are orthogonal to these columns and hence lie in the intersection of the constraint hyperplanes.

If we choose the norm matrix $\mathbf{N}$ to be the identity for every iteration of the quadratic subproblem, equation (2.5.1) gives the direction of search for Method I as

$$\begin{aligned}\mathbf{p}^{(k)} &= -\,\mathbf{Z}(\mathbf{Z}^T\mathbf{Z})^{-1}\mathbf{Z}^T\mathbf{g}^{(k)} \qquad (2.5.5)\\ &= -\,\overline{\mathbf{P}}\mathbf{g}^{(k)}, \text{ from (2.5.4).}\end{aligned}$$

This is the direction of search suggested by Rosen (1960) in his gradient-projection method, and is the direct generalization of the classical method of steepest descent to the linearly constrained problem.

THEOREM 2.3. *Let* $\hat{\mathbf{A}}^T$ *be the matrix of constraints active at the point* $\hat{\mathbf{x}}$ *(not a stationary point) with* $\hat{\mathbf{A}}^T\mathbf{Z} = \mathbf{0}$; *then the gradient at* $\hat{\mathbf{x}}$ *can be written in the form*

$$\mathbf{g}(\hat{\mathbf{x}}) = \hat{\mathbf{A}}\boldsymbol{\lambda}_L + \mathbf{Z}(\mathbf{Z}^T\mathbf{Z})^{-1}\mathbf{g}_A(\hat{\mathbf{x}})$$

where $\boldsymbol{\lambda}_L$ *is the estimate of the Lagrange multipliers for which the residual* $\mathbf{g}(\hat{\mathbf{x}}) - \hat{\mathbf{A}}\boldsymbol{\lambda}$ *is minimal in the least squares sense.*

Proof. The gradient vector $\mathbf{g}(\hat{\mathbf{x}})$ can be written in the form

$$\mathbf{g}(\hat{\mathbf{x}}) = \mathbf{P}\mathbf{g}(\hat{\mathbf{x}}) + (\mathbf{I} - \mathbf{P})\,\mathbf{g}(\hat{\mathbf{x}}),$$

where $\mathbf{P}$ is the projection matrix defined earlier. Using Lemma 2.2 we can write

$$\begin{aligned} \mathbf{g}(\hat{\mathbf{x}}) &= \mathbf{P}\mathbf{g}(\hat{\mathbf{x}}) + \mathbf{Z}(\mathbf{Z}^T\mathbf{Z})^{-1}\mathbf{Z}^T\mathbf{g}(\hat{\mathbf{x}}) \\ &= \hat{\mathbf{A}}(\hat{\mathbf{A}}^T\hat{\mathbf{A}})^{-1}\hat{\mathbf{A}}^T\mathbf{g}(\hat{\mathbf{x}}) + \mathbf{Z}(\mathbf{Z}^T\mathbf{Z})^{-1}\mathbf{g}_A(\hat{\mathbf{x}}). \end{aligned} \tag{2.5.6}$$

The vector $\boldsymbol{\lambda}_L = \hat{\mathbf{A}}^+\mathbf{g}(\hat{\mathbf{x}})$ is the solution of the normal equations $(\hat{\mathbf{A}}^T\hat{\mathbf{A}})\boldsymbol{\lambda}_L = \hat{\mathbf{A}}^T\mathbf{g}(\hat{\mathbf{x}})$, consequently equation (2.5.6) can be written in the form

$$\mathbf{g}(\hat{\mathbf{x}}) = \hat{\mathbf{A}}\boldsymbol{\lambda}_L + \mathbf{Z}(\mathbf{Z}^T\mathbf{Z})^{-1}\mathbf{g}_A(\hat{\mathbf{x}}),$$

which proves the theorem. ∎

COROLLARY 1. *If $\bar{\boldsymbol{\lambda}}$ is any estimate of the Lagrange multipliers with corresponding residual vector $\boldsymbol{\mu} = \mathbf{g}(\hat{\mathbf{x}}) - \hat{\mathbf{A}}\bar{\boldsymbol{\lambda}}$, then*

$$\boldsymbol{\mu} = \hat{\mathbf{A}}(\boldsymbol{\lambda}_L - \bar{\boldsymbol{\lambda}}) + \mathbf{Z}(\mathbf{Z}^T\mathbf{Z})^{-1}\mathbf{g}_A(\hat{\mathbf{x}}).$$

COROLLARY 2. *If $\boldsymbol{\mu}_L$ is the residual corresponding to $\boldsymbol{\lambda}_L$, the least-squares estimate of $\boldsymbol{\lambda}$ at $\hat{\mathbf{x}}$, and if the columns of $\mathbf{Z}$ are orthogonal, then $\|\boldsymbol{\mu}_L\|_2 = \|\mathbf{g}_A(\hat{\mathbf{x}})\|_2$.*

From Theorem 2.3, the condition $\mathbf{g}_A(\hat{\mathbf{x}}) = \mathbf{0}$ is equivalent to the statement that the component of $\mathbf{g}(\hat{\mathbf{x}})$ in M_0 is zero and its component in the range of $\hat{\mathbf{A}}$ is $\hat{\mathbf{A}}\boldsymbol{\lambda}$ where $\boldsymbol{\lambda}$ are the Lagrange multipliers.

An analogue of the discrete Newton algorithm can be constructed for the linearly constrained case. Instead of forming finite differences of the gradient for the Hessian directly and projecting it onto the set of active constraints, it is advantageous to utilize the differences of the gradient along the columns of the matrix $\mathbf{Z}$. If the columns of the matrix $\mathbf{V}$ are calculated by the rule

$$\mathbf{v}_j = (\mathbf{g}(\mathbf{x}^{(k)} + h_j\mathbf{z}_j) - \mathbf{g}^{(k)})/h_j \quad \text{for} \quad j = 1, 2, \ldots, n - t,$$

then the matrix $\frac{1}{2}[\mathbf{Z}^T\mathbf{V} + \mathbf{V}^T\mathbf{Z}]$ is the forward-difference approximation to $\mathbf{G}_A{}^{(k)}$ and can be modified using one of the techniques described earlier. With this scheme the number of gradient evaluations required decreases with the number of constraints active.

2.6. Determination of the Set of Active Constraints

We turn now to the inequality constrained problem where some decision must be made as to which constraints should be regarded as active. Assume for the moment that all the constraints which make up $\hat{\mathbf{A}}^T$ are linearly independent and let t constraints be satisfied exactly at a point $\mathbf{x}^{(k)}$. If all but one of these constraints, say $\mathbf{a}_s^T\mathbf{x} = b_s$, are regarded as being active for the purposes of defining $\mathbf{Z}$ and we ensure that the subsequent direction of search $\mathbf{p}^{(k)}$ is such that $\mathbf{a}_s^T\mathbf{p}^{(k)} > 0$ then $\mathbf{x}^{(k+1)}$ will be interior to the region with respect to this constraint.

The strategy for adding constraints to the basis is fixed by the choice of $\mathbf{p}^{(k)}$ and the steplength algorithm. If the predicted step $\bar{\alpha}$ violates the nearest constraint $\mathbf{a}_r^T\mathbf{x} = b_r$ and $F(\mathbf{x}^{(k)} + \alpha\mathbf{p}^{(k)})$ is decreasing with respect to α at the boundary, this constraint is added to the basis and $\mathbf{x}^{(k+1)}$ is set equal to the point at which $\mathbf{p}^{(k)}$ intersects the boundary. If $F(\mathbf{x}^{(k)} + \alpha\,\mathbf{p}^{(k)})$ is increasing at the boundary we can avoid adding a constraint by decreasing $\bar{\alpha}$ so that a lower function value is obtained and $\mathbf{x}^{(k+1)}$ is not on the boundary of Π. It is advisable not to add a constraint unnecessarily since the housekeeping necessary to update the matrix $\mathbf{Z}$ is thereby avoided.

The step to the nearest constraint is the smallest positive value of α such that for all the inactive constraints $\mathbf{a}_j^T\mathbf{x} = b_j$, $\mathbf{a}_j^T(\mathbf{x}^{(k)} + \alpha\,\mathbf{p}^{(k)}) - b_j = 0$. This gives the distance to the boundary, θ_r say, as

$$\theta_r = \min_j \{-r_j^{(k)}/\mathbf{a}_j^T\,\mathbf{p}^{(k)}:\ \ \mathbf{a}_j^T\,\mathbf{p}^{(k)} < 0\},$$

$r_j^{(k)}$ being the residual $\mathbf{a}_j^T\mathbf{x}^{(k)} - b_j$ of the inactive constraint $\mathbf{a}_j^T\mathbf{x} = b_j$ at $\mathbf{x}^{(k)}$. If there are several constraints which are satisfied exactly at $\mathbf{x}^{(k+1)}$ these are generally added to the basis one at a time. For this reason several "iterations" may be required in which hyperplanes are added to the constraint set and the point $\mathbf{x}^{(k)}$ remains fixed although our linear independence assumption implies that this can only occur a finite number of times.

When zero steps are being taken it is useful to define the order in which constraints are to be added to the basis. Let S be the set of indices

$$S = \{j : \mathbf{a}_j^T\,\mathbf{p}^{(k)} < 0,\quad \theta_r = \theta_j),$$

and σ_j the cosine of the angle between the normal to the constraint $\mathbf{a}_j^T\,\mathbf{x} = b_j$ and $-\,\mathbf{p}^{(k)}$, that is

$$\sigma_j = -\,\mathbf{a}_j^T\,\mathbf{p}^{(k)}/\|\mathbf{a}_j\|_2\,\|\mathbf{p}^{(k)}\|_2,\qquad j \in S.$$

The first constraint to be added to the active basis is that for which σ_j is smallest. In the case where the constraint normals are normalized to be of unit length, σ_j can be interpreted as identifying the constraint giving the most negative residual if a unit step were taken along the direction $\mathbf{p}^{(k)}$.

Strategies for determining which constraint to delete present more problems than do strategies for adding constraints The simplest strategy is to retain all the current constraints until a minimum is found with respect to the subspace so defined. During this process it may be necessary to add to the basis constraints which are encountered during the minimization. Let $\hat{\mathbf{x}}$ be a minimum over the subspace defined by $\hat{\mathbf{A}}^T$, and let $\boldsymbol{\lambda}$ be the Lagrange multipliers defined by (2.4.1). (We assume for the moment that there are no zero Lagrange multipliers.) If a constraint $\mathbf{a}_s$ has a negative Lagrange multiplier (i.e. $\lambda_s < 0$) it must be possible to obtain a lower point by deleting this constraint from the basis in the next iteration—for otherwise the condition for a point to be a strong local minimum would be violated. On the assumption that there are only a finite number of stationary points and that the constraints are linearly independent it is easy to show that this scheme will terminate at a strong local minimum after only a finite number of basis changes. (A particular basis which yields one local minimum of the function can recur only at a point with a lower function value. Consequently succeeding points must converge to an alternative minimum and the algorithm must terminate after a finite number of basis changes since there are only a finite number of strong local minima and possible constraint configurations.) The disadvantage of this strategy is that we may be using a lot of computation in order to compute the minimum on a subspace which is far from the solution.

An alternative strategy is to compute estimates of the Lagrange multipliers every iteration and move off constraints for which the value of λ_j is negative. However, since the condition $\mathbf{g}_A(\hat{\mathbf{x}}) = \mathbf{0}$ is not satisfied, in general these estimates tend to be very inaccurate (see the corollary to Theorem 2.3); consequently a constraint may be repeatedly dropped at one iteration only to be brought in again later, and progress to the solution can be very slow. Indeed it is not possible generally to prove that this type of strategy will terminate after a finite number of basis changes. This is the phenomena of "zigzagging", of which an example is given in Chapter I.

In practice nearly all methods for deleting constraints from the basis are some form of compromise between the above two strategies of minimizing on a subspace and deleting a constraint at the earliest opportunity. Zoutendijk (1960) proposed a strategy whereby a constraint that has previously been dropped and returned to is kept in the constraint basis until a minimal solution is obtained on a subspace. In this way we are effectively defining a set of "eligible" constraints from whose elements we can select one for deletion. This algorithm also will terminate in a finite number of basis changes.

In a paper presented by McCormick (1969) zigzagging is avoided by projecting the direction of search on to the successive active sets formed by incorporating each new constraint as it is encountered. This "bending" of the current direction of search continues until either an unconstrained minimum is found with respect to α, or the matrix of constraints defines a subspace containing a local minimum. Only at this point is the gradient information recomputed and a new direction of search defined. Another, more complex version of this method has been presented (McCormick, 1970) and a proof is included that zigzagging cannot occur.

In practice, it is relatively simply to deal with the zigzagging phenomenon once it has been recognized, since merely being more accurate in the minimization on a subspace will ensure convergence. Unfortunately, the same basis could recur after several iterations and it is not easy to remember all combinations of constraints that have been active.

Another technique often used in practice is to drop a constraint only if it is estimated that this will result in a sufficient decrease in the function. This is not an anti-zigzagging rule but a criterion for deciding whether or not to delete a particular constraint. A more detailed discussion of this and other rules will be given in Section 3.5 of the next chapter.

Our experience is that the Zoutendijk rule is the most effective guarantee against zigzagging, but instead of minimizing the function exactly on a subspace it is preferable to minimize the function to within a fairly slack tolerance before examining the Lagrange multipliers. For example, we could require $\|\mathbf{g}_A^{(k)}\|$ not to exceed a preassigned positive scalar ε. If it transpires that all the Lagrange multipliers are positive, the tolerance is refined and the minimization on the subspace is continued.

In practice, the occurrence of a zero or near-zero Lagrange multiplier can cause considerable computational problems; since this matter is rarely discussed we shall complete this section by considering the problem in some detail. We have seen in Theorem 2.3 that the vector of Lagrange multipliers at a stationary point is given by

$$\boldsymbol{\lambda} = \hat{\mathbf{A}}^+\mathbf{g}(\hat{\mathbf{x}}),$$

where $\hat{\mathbf{A}}^+$ is the pseudo-inverse of $\hat{\mathbf{A}}$. The sth row of $\hat{\mathbf{A}}^+$, $\mathbf{v}^T$ say, is such that $\mathbf{g}^T\mathbf{v} = \mathbf{g}^T(\hat{\mathbf{A}}^+)^T\mathbf{e}_s = \lambda_s$ and $\mathbf{a}_s^T\,\mathbf{v} = \mathbf{e}_s^T\,\hat{\mathbf{A}}^T(\hat{\mathbf{A}}^+)^T\mathbf{e}_s = 1$. These properties imply that $\mathbf{v}$ is a descent direction which lies within the the feasible space and in Fig. 2.6 the graph of $F(\mathbf{x})$ along $\mathbf{v}$ is shown with the value of $\alpha = 0$ defining the boundary of the constraint $\mathbf{a}_s^T\mathbf{x} = b_s$.

If λ_s is zero any one of the situations depicted in Fig. 2.7 could occur and $\mathbf{v}$ is a descent direction only in case (c).

If $\boldsymbol{\lambda}$ is computed exactly the curvature of the function can be investigated by dropping $\mathbf{a}_s^T\,\mathbf{x} = b_s$ from the active basis and determining whether or not the projected Hessian matrix is positive definite. If all the constraints which correspond to zero Lagrange multipliers are dropped, and the projected Hessian in the remaining subspace is positive definite, then $\hat{\mathbf{x}}$ is a strong local minimum; otherwise we compute a descent direction in the normal way.

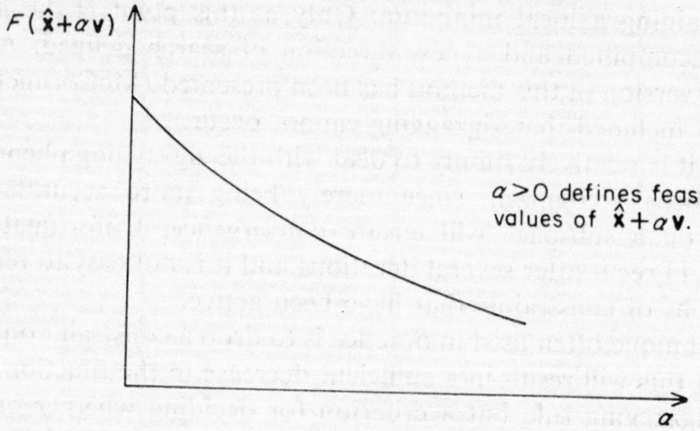

FIG. 2.6.

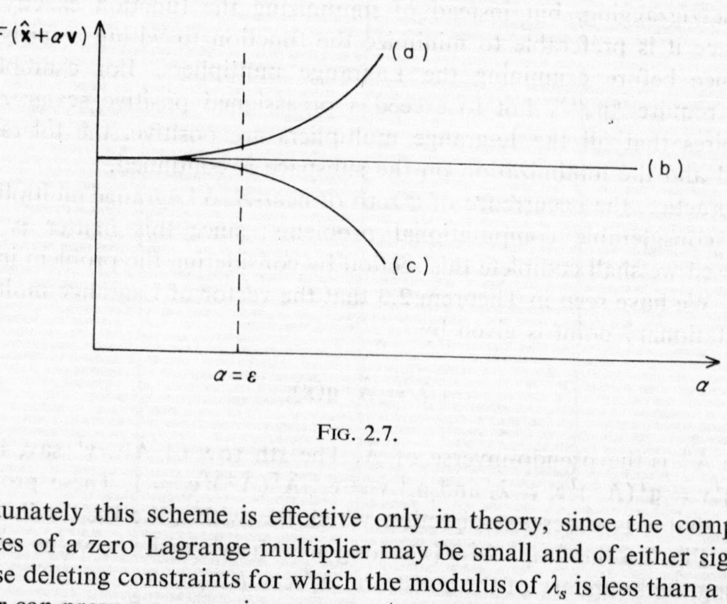

FIG. 2.7.

Unfortunately this scheme is effective only in theory, since the computed estimates of a zero Lagrange multiplier may be small and of either sign. In this case deleting constraints for which the modulus of λ_s is less than a small number can prove an expensive process. A practical method for determining which constraints to delete when there are several Lagrange multipliers near zero is given in the following.

There is no loss of generality in assuming that the point $\hat{\mathbf{x}}$ where near-zero Lagrange multipliers occur is a minimum on the current active set and all the remaining Lagrange multipliers are positive. If this were not the case either $F(\mathbf{x})$ could be further reduced, giving multipliers which are no longer near zero, or a constraint with a large negative multiplier could be deleted from the basis. (In most algorithms the constraint with the most negative Lagrange multiplier is automatically dropped from the basis.) Let J_0 be the set of indices of constraints with near-zero multipliers. If each constraint $\mathbf{a}_s{}^T\mathbf{x} = b_s$, $s \in J_0$ is perturbed by a small positive scalar ε and the Lagrange multipliers are *recomputed* it is possible to determine the nature of the curvature in the neighbourhood of $\hat{\mathbf{x}}$ (see Fig. 2.7). The following theorem will enable us to gauge the effect of this perturbation on the equations for the Lagrange multipliers.

THEOREM 2.4. *Let* $\mathbf{x}(\varepsilon)$ *be such that*

$$\mathbf{a}_j{}^T\mathbf{x}(\varepsilon) = \begin{cases} b_j + \varepsilon, & j \in J_0, \\ b_j, & j \notin J_0, \end{cases}$$

then

$$\mathbf{x}(\varepsilon) = \hat{\mathbf{x}} + \mathbf{p}(\varepsilon)$$

where

$$\mathbf{p}(\varepsilon) = \varepsilon \sum_{s \in J_0} (\hat{\mathbf{A}}^+)^T \mathbf{e}_s.$$

Proof. From the definition of $\mathbf{p}(\varepsilon)$ for any active constraint we have

$$\begin{aligned} \mathbf{a}_j{}^T\mathbf{x}(\varepsilon) &= \mathbf{a}_j{}^T\hat{\mathbf{x}} + \mathbf{a}_j{}^T\mathbf{p}(\varepsilon) \\ &= b_j + \varepsilon \sum_{s \in J_0} \mathbf{a}_j{}^T(\hat{\mathbf{A}}^+)^T\mathbf{e}_s \\ &= b_j + \varepsilon \sum_{s \in J_0} \mathbf{e}_j{}^T\hat{\mathbf{A}}^T\hat{\mathbf{A}}(\hat{\mathbf{A}}^T\hat{\mathbf{A}})^{-1}\mathbf{e}_s \\ &= b_j + \varepsilon \sum_{s \in J_0} \mathbf{e}_j{}^T\mathbf{e}_s. \end{aligned}$$

The second term of the last expression will be zero or ε depending upon whether or not $j \in J_0$. ∎

This theorem implies that the value of the Lagrange multipliers corresponding to the perturbed constraints can be found by computing an approximate solution of the equations

$$\hat{\mathbf{A}}\boldsymbol{\lambda}_\varepsilon \doteq \mathbf{g}(\hat{\mathbf{x}} + \mathbf{p}(\varepsilon)).$$

The decision to drop or retain a constraint with a near-zero multiplier will depend upon whether the sign of the corresponding element of $\boldsymbol{\lambda}_\varepsilon - \boldsymbol{\lambda}$ is negative or positive. If the Hessian is known, the quantity $\boldsymbol{\lambda}_\varepsilon - \boldsymbol{\lambda}$ can be computed directly by solving the equations

$$\hat{\mathbf{A}}(\boldsymbol{\lambda}_\varepsilon - \boldsymbol{\lambda}) \doteq \mathbf{G}(\hat{\mathbf{x}})\mathbf{p}(\varepsilon).$$

2.7. Degeneracy

If the linear independence condition on the matrix of constraints is relaxed, it is possible that $\mathbf{x}^{(k)}$ could lie in the intersection of a linearly dependent set of hyperplanes. Although the feasible region has a well-defined edge at such a point, some of the constraints there will be redundant. Figure 2.8 depicts an example in which the required vertex is defined by the intersection of the constraints $\mathbf{a}_1$ and $\mathbf{a}_2$ but the constraint $\mathbf{a}_3$ is redundant. If degeneracy occurs

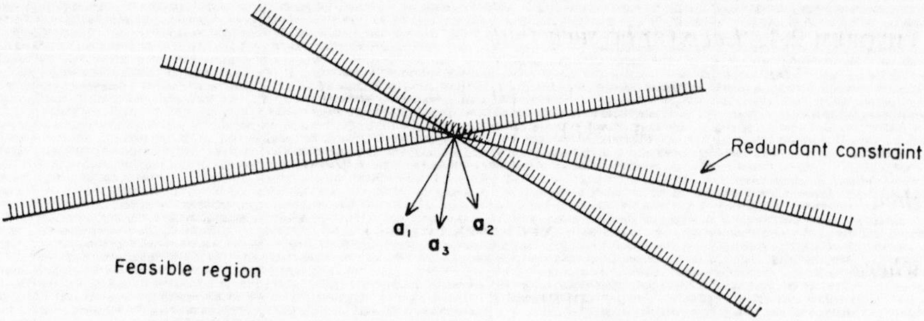

FIG. 2.8. Two-dimensional case of a redundant constraint.

as constraints are being added to the basis it is a non-trivial task to determine the linearly independent constraints which define the boundary of the feasible region. One method is to try different sets of constraints by adding and deleting constraints one at a time, the constraints considered for deletion being those with negative Lagrange multipliers. Unfortunately it is possible for a set of constraints to reappear in the basis and it is not possible to prove that a finite number of basis changes is required to compute a feasible direction. This problem is known as *cycling* and it has received much attention in the literature. The best known method (see Dantzig, 1963, Chapter 10) is to perturb all the linearly dependent constraints so that they become

$$\mathbf{a}_j^T \mathbf{x} \geqslant b_j + \varepsilon_j, \tag{2.7.1}$$

where ε_j is a small positive scalar. This has the effect of separating the constraints defining the degenerate edge or vertex. Unfortunately the algorithm requires each ε_j to be a different power of a fixed number ε in order to be theoretically guaranteed to avoid cycling. If the number of redundant constraints is large, ε needs to be near unity to avoid the possibility of underflow in ε_j.

Fortunately the lack of a guaranteed numerical strategy to deal with cycling is offset by the fact that it virtually never occurs in practice. This is because the rounding error involved in storing and updating the matrix of constraints naturally involves a perturbation of the form (2.7.1) to each constraint. The *ad hoc* strategy given in Section 2.6 for ordering the constraints which are due to be added to the basis has been successful on all the standard examples of cycling given in the literature.

2.8. Computing and Updating the Matrix Z

Algorithms in the literature based on Method I embody methods for computing the columns of the matrix $\mathbf{Z}$ and updating them when active constraints are added to, or deleted from, the basis. However, since existing techniques for handling the linear constraints are generally embedded in a method for minimizing over the set of active constraints or because the matrix $\mathbf{Z}$ may not be stored explicitly, it may not be realized that many of the classical methods for linearly constrained optimization listed in the references are, in fact, based on Method I. For this reason we shall review the two principal methods for computing $\mathbf{Z}$ and suggest possible improvements. First, however, we present some additional theoretical results.

If the rows of the matrix $\hat{\mathbf{A}}^T$ are linearly independent we can add a further $n - t$ linearly independent rows in order to form the non-singular matrix

$$\mathbf{T} = \begin{bmatrix} \hat{\mathbf{A}}^T \\ \mathbf{V}^T \end{bmatrix} \tag{2.8.1}$$

where $\mathbf{V}^T$ is the matrix of $n - t$ rows added to $\hat{\mathbf{A}}^T$. For the moment we shall assume that the rows of $\mathbf{V}$ are completely arbitrary save that the matrix $\mathbf{T}$ is non-singular. The two classical techniques for computing $\mathbf{Z}$ are based on the following theorem, each method being characterized by the particular choice of the matrix $\mathbf{V}^T$.

THEOREM 2.5. *Let* $\mathbf{t}_j$ *be the jth column of* $\mathbf{T}^{-1}$, *then*

$$\hat{\mathbf{A}}^T\mathbf{t}_j = \mathbf{0} \quad \textit{for} \quad j = t+1, t+2, \ldots, n.$$

Proof. By definition we have

$$\begin{bmatrix} \hat{\mathbf{A}}^T \\ \mathbf{V}^T \end{bmatrix} \mathbf{T}^{-1} = \mathbf{I}, \textit{ the identity matrix.}$$

Post-multiplying both sides by $\mathbf{e}_j$, the jth column of $\mathbf{I}$, gives

$$\begin{bmatrix} \hat{\mathbf{A}}^T \\ \mathbf{V}^T \end{bmatrix} \mathbf{t}_j = \mathbf{e}_j,$$

which implies that $\mathbf{t}_j$ is orthogonal to all the rows of $\mathbf{T}$ except the jth. Consequently

$$\hat{\mathbf{A}}^T \mathbf{t}_j = \mathbf{0} \quad \textit{for} \quad j = t+1, t+2, \ldots, n. \quad \blacksquare$$

COROLLARY. *The matrix* $\mathbf{Z}$ *can be chosen as the last* $n - t$ *columns of* $\mathbf{T}^{-1}$, *and we can then write*

$$(\mathbf{T}^T)^{-1} = \begin{bmatrix} \mathbf{S} \\ \mathbf{Z}^T \end{bmatrix}, \quad \textit{say.}$$

The matrix $\mathbf{T}^{-1}$ can be used to compute either second- or first-order estimates of the Lagrange multipliers. In the case where second-order estimates are required, we have from (2.4.4)

$$\hat{\mathbf{A}}\boldsymbol{\omega}^{(k)} = \mathbf{G}^{(k)}\mathbf{p}^{(k)} + \mathbf{g}^{(k)},$$

or equivalently

$$[\hat{\mathbf{A}} \;\; \mathbf{V}] \begin{bmatrix} \boldsymbol{\omega}^{(k)} \\ \mathbf{0} \end{bmatrix} = \mathbf{G}^{(k)}\mathbf{p}^{(k)} + \mathbf{g}^{(k)}.$$

Since the matrix $[\hat{\mathbf{A}} \;\; \mathbf{V}]$ is $\mathbf{T}^T$ we have

$$\begin{bmatrix} \boldsymbol{\omega}^{(k)} \\ \mathbf{0} \end{bmatrix} = [\hat{\mathbf{A}} \;\; \mathbf{V}]^{-1} (\mathbf{G}^{(k)}\mathbf{p}^{(k)} + \mathbf{g}^{(k)}) = (\mathbf{T}^T)^{-1} (\mathbf{G}^{(k)}\mathbf{p}^{(k)} + \mathbf{g}^{(k)}).$$

Similarly first-order estimates (and second-order estimates at a stationary point) are given by

$$\begin{bmatrix} \boldsymbol{\lambda}^{(k)} \\ \mathbf{0} \end{bmatrix} = (\mathbf{T}^T)^{-1}\mathbf{g}^{(k)} = (\mathbf{T}^{-1})^T\mathbf{g}^{(k)} = \begin{bmatrix} \mathbf{S}\mathbf{g}^{(k)} \\ \mathbf{Z}^T\mathbf{g}^{(k)} \end{bmatrix}.$$

We are now ready to review some particular methods for computing $\mathbf{Z}$.

(a) Use of the matrix $\mathbf{T}^{-1}$ to define the columns of $\mathbf{Z}$ was due originally to Wolfe (1967) who used constraints selected from the inactive set to define the matrix $\mathbf{V}^T$ in conjunction with a classical steepest-descent method. This method (which Wolfe calls the "reduced-gradient method") will not generate the same points as the Rosen projected-gradient method of (2.5.5) because Wolfe in effect uses the direction $\mathbf{p}^{(k)} = -\mathbf{Z}\mathbf{Z}^T\mathbf{g}^{(k)}$. Note that the matrix $\mathbf{Z}\mathbf{Z}^T$ will not in general project vectors which are members of the null space of $\hat{\mathbf{A}}^T$ into themselves. As the matrix of active constraints changes we must be able to compute a new $\mathbf{Z}$. Clearly if a constraint is dropped from the basis or a constraint is made active which is already included in $\mathbf{V}^T$ then only a simple interchange of the columns of $\mathbf{T}^{-1}$ is necessary. If a constraint is made active which is not a member of $\mathbf{V}^T$ this constraint is exchanged with a row of $\mathbf{V}^T$. In mathematical terms the new matrix $\bar{\mathbf{T}}$ is given by

$$\bar{\mathbf{T}} = \mathbf{T} + \mathbf{e}_r(\mathbf{a}_r - \mathbf{v}_r)^T$$

where $\mathbf{e}_r$ is the rth column of the identity matrix and $\mathbf{v}_r$ is the out-going column of $\mathbf{V}^T$. Using the Householder modification rule, we can write down $\bar{\mathbf{T}}^{-1}$ directly as

$$\bar{\mathbf{T}}^{-1} = \mathbf{T}^{-1} - \alpha^{-1}\mathbf{T}^{-1}\mathbf{e}_r(\mathbf{a}_r - \mathbf{v}_r)^T\mathbf{T}^{-1}$$

where

$$\alpha = 1 + (\mathbf{a}_r - \mathbf{v}_r)^T\mathbf{T}^{-1}\mathbf{e}_r.$$

(b) The "variable-reduction method" (see McCormick, 1970) is defined by choosing $\mathbf{V}^T$ from rows of the identity matrix. The variables must be reordered so that $\mathbf{T}$ is of the form

$$\mathbf{T} = \begin{bmatrix} \hat{\mathbf{A}}^T \\ \mathbf{0} \quad \mathbf{I} \end{bmatrix} = \begin{bmatrix} \mathbf{B} & \mathbf{D} \\ \mathbf{0} & \mathbf{I} \end{bmatrix},$$

with $\mathbf{B}$ a $t \times t$ non-singular matrix and $\mathbf{D}$ a $t \times (n - t)$ matrix. With this choice of $\mathbf{V}^T$ it is possible to write down explicitly the matrix $\mathbf{T}^{-1}$ in terms of $\mathbf{B}^{-1}$ since

$$\begin{bmatrix} \mathbf{B} & \mathbf{D} \\ \mathbf{0} & \mathbf{I} \end{bmatrix} \begin{bmatrix} \mathbf{B}^{-1} & -\mathbf{B}^{-1}\mathbf{D} \\ \mathbf{0} & \mathbf{I} \end{bmatrix} = \mathbf{I},$$

giving

$$\mathbf{Z} = \begin{bmatrix} -\mathbf{B}^{-1}\mathbf{D} \\ \mathbf{I} \end{bmatrix}.$$

In this case only the inverse of the matrix $\mathbf{B}$ need be recurred and updated. The first-order estimates of the Lagrange multipliers are given by the first t elements of

$$\begin{bmatrix} (\mathbf{B}^{-1})^T & \mathbf{0} \\ -(\mathbf{B}^{-1}\mathbf{D})^T & \mathbf{I} \end{bmatrix} \mathbf{g}^{(k)},$$

or $(\mathbf{B}^{-1})^T\mathbf{g}_1$ where $\mathbf{g}_1$ is the vector of the first t components of $\mathbf{g}^{(k)}$. If $\boldsymbol{\mu}$ is the residual associated with this estimate we have

$$\begin{aligned}\boldsymbol{\mu} &= \mathbf{g}^{(k)} - \mathbf{T}^T\begin{bmatrix}\boldsymbol{\lambda}^{(k)}\\ \mathbf{0}\end{bmatrix}\\ &= \mathbf{g}^{(k)} - \mathbf{T}^T\begin{bmatrix}(\mathbf{B}^{-1})^T\mathbf{g}_1\\ \mathbf{0}\end{bmatrix}\\ &= \begin{bmatrix}\mathbf{0}\\ \mathbf{Z}^T\mathbf{g}^{(k)}\end{bmatrix} = \begin{bmatrix}\mathbf{0}\\ \mathbf{g}_A{}^{(k)}\end{bmatrix},\end{aligned} \tag{2.8.2}$$

and, as in the least-squares case of Section 2.5, we obtain $\|\boldsymbol{\mu}\|_2 = \|\mathbf{g}_A{}^{(k)}\|_2$. In general, however, $\boldsymbol{\lambda}^{(k)}$ will not be the least squares values defined in Theorem 2.3.

The reduced-gradient and variable-reduction algorithms involve several fundamental difficulties. A poor choice of $\mathbf{V}$ may lead to an ill-conditioned $\mathbf{T}$ and hence to a large $\mathbf{Z}$; in this case $\mathbf{Z}^T\mathbf{g}^{(k)}$ will be large even when $\mathbf{x}^{(k)}$ is close to a stationary point. A large value of $\|\mathbf{g}_A{}^{(k)}\|$ has two ill effects. Firstly from Theorem 2.3 and equation (2.8.2) this can lead to a large residual which in turn implies poor estimates of the Lagrange multipliers. Secondly the Lagrange multipliers could be computed at the wrong time if the criterion as to whether or not to compute them depends upon $\|\mathbf{g}_A{}^{(k)}\|$ (for example, if they are computed in the neighbourhood of a stationary point).

Another difficulty with methods (a) and (b) is that a poor choice of $\mathbf{Z}$ adversely affects the computation of the direction of search. All the modification processes defined in Section 2.3 will modify $\mathbf{G}_A{}^{(k)}$ if it is ill-conditioned. The condition of $\mathbf{G}_A{}^{(k)}$ can be measured by the magnitude of $\kappa(\mathbf{G}^{(k)})$, the condition number of $\mathbf{G}_A{}^{(k)}$, which is defined as

$$\kappa(\mathbf{G}_A{}^{(k)}) = \|\mathbf{G}_A{}^{(k)}\|\,\|\mathbf{G}_A{}^{(k)+}\|,$$

$\mathbf{G}_A{}^{(k)+}$ being the pseudo-inverse of $\mathbf{G}_A{}^{(k)}$. The value of $\kappa(\mathbf{G}_A{}^{(k)})$ depends upon the condition number of $\mathbf{G}^{(k)}$ and the square of the condition number of $\mathbf{Z}$, and it can be shown (J. H. Wilkinson, private communication) that if $\mathbf{G}^{(k)}$ is positive definite then $\kappa(\mathbf{G}_A{}^{(k)}) \leqslant \kappa(\mathbf{G}^{(k)})\,[\kappa(\mathbf{Z})]^2$. Clearly, poor choices of $\mathbf{Z}$ may lead to a very ill-conditioned $\mathbf{G}_A{}^{(k)}$ *even when the original problem is well conditioned.* Thus the matrix $\mathbf{G}_A{}^{(k)}$ may be modified unnecessarily with a consequent deterioration in the rate of convergence. The choice of basis also affects the *accuracy* of the computed direction of search. When the equations (2.5.1) are solved on a computer, rounding error takes place and the computed solution $\bar{\mathbf{p}}_A{}^{(k)}$ generally satisfies a relative error bound of the form

$$\|\bar{\mathbf{p}}_A{}^{(k)} - \mathbf{p}_A{}^{(k)}\|_2/\|\mathbf{p}_A{}^{(k)}\|_2 \leqslant M\,\kappa(\mathbf{G}_A{}^{(k)}),$$

where M is a scalar dependent upon the relative machine precision. Generally if a set of equations with condition number 10^s is solved on a computer with relative machine precision 10^{-t}, then approximately $t - s$ significant figures will be correct in $\bar{\mathbf{p}}_A^{(k)}$. For even moderate values of the condition numbers of $\mathbf{Z}$ and $\mathbf{G}^{(k)}$ there will be very little accuracy in $\bar{\mathbf{p}}_A^{(k)}$.

All the forementioned difficulties are induced by the poor choice of $\mathbf{V}$ in (2.8.1), which should be chosen so that the condition number of $\mathbf{G}_A^{(k)}$ is minimized. In Wolfe's method this implies finding which of the inactive constraints are the least dependent upon $\hat{\mathbf{A}}^T$ and, in the variable-reduction algorithm, finding the most linearly independent set of t columns from $\hat{\mathbf{A}}^T$. Unfortunately the determination of the optimal value of $\mathbf{G}_A^{(k)}$ is a difficult numerical problem, even when the matrix of active constraints is fixed, and as a result ideal versions of (a) and (b) are virtually impossible to implement in a numerically stable and efficient manner. It is possible, however, to attain the optimal choice of $\mathbf{G}_A^{(k)}$ by recurring a specific factorization of $\mathbf{T}$ (rather than recurring the inverse) and choosing $\mathbf{Z}$ in a different way. Consideration of this technique, defining our method (c), leads to a natural choice of $\mathbf{V}^T$ in (2.8.1) giving the method (d), which we shall ultimately recommend for the solution of linearly constrained problems.

(c) Assume that $\mathbf{V}^T$ is arbitrary and that the LQ factorization of $\mathbf{T}$ is known, that is

$$\mathbf{T} = \mathbf{LQ},$$

where $\mathbf{L}$ is a lower-triangular matrix and $\mathbf{Q}$ an orthogonal matrix (i.e. $\mathbf{QQ}^T = \mathbf{Q}^T\mathbf{Q} = \mathbf{I}$). The matrix $\mathbf{Q}$ will be partitioned in the form

$$\mathbf{Q} = \begin{bmatrix} \mathbf{Q}_1 \\ \mathbf{Q}_2 \end{bmatrix}$$

where $\mathbf{Q}_1$ is a $t \times n$ matrix and $\mathbf{Q}_2$ an $(n - t) \times n$ matrix. If $\mathbf{T}$ is post-multiplied by $\mathbf{Q}_2{}^T$ we have

$$\begin{bmatrix} \hat{\mathbf{A}}^T \\ \mathbf{V}^T \end{bmatrix} \mathbf{Q}_2{}^T = \mathbf{TQ}_2{}^T = \mathbf{L} \begin{bmatrix} \mathbf{Q}_1 \\ \mathbf{Q}_2 \end{bmatrix} \mathbf{Q}_2{}^T$$
$$= \mathbf{L} \begin{bmatrix} \mathbf{0} \\ \mathbf{I} \end{bmatrix},$$

since the orthogonality of $\mathbf{Q}$ gives $\mathbf{Q}_2\mathbf{Q}_2{}^T = \mathbf{I}$, $\mathbf{Q}_1\mathbf{Q}_2{}^T = \mathbf{0}$. This implies that $\hat{\mathbf{A}}^T\mathbf{Q}_2{}^T = \mathbf{0}$ since $[\mathbf{0} \quad \mathbf{I}]^T$ is orthogonal to the first t rows of $\mathbf{L}$, and we can take $\mathbf{Q}_2{}^T$ as being the matrix $\mathbf{Z}$. This choice leads to a value of $\mathbf{G}_A^{(k)}$ which has *minimum condition number* and in the positive-definite case we have

$\kappa(\mathbf{G}_A{}^{(k)}) \leqslant \kappa(\mathbf{G}^{(k)})$. The conditioning of Method I is now dependent on the conditioning of the problem and not the implementation. As before, the first-order estimates of the Lagrange multipliers are given by the first t elements of the vector

$$(\mathbf{L}^T)^{-1}\mathbf{Q}\mathbf{g}^{(k)} = (\mathbf{L}^T)^{-1}\begin{bmatrix}\mathbf{Q}_1\mathbf{g}^{(k)}\\ \mathbf{Z}^T\mathbf{g}^{(k)}\end{bmatrix}.$$

Methods for computing the LQ factorization of $\mathbf{T}$ are given by Wilkinson (1965, pp. 233-244) and methods for updating the LQ factorization when rows of $\mathbf{T}$ are added and deleted are discussed by Gill, Golub, Murray and Saunders (1974).

(d) Minimizing $\kappa(\mathbf{G}_A{}^{(k)})$ is equivalent to minimizing $\kappa(\mathbf{T})$ and since the matrix $\hat{\mathbf{A}}^T$ is fixed in advance by the active constraint strategy we can only achieve this end by altering the matrix $\mathbf{V}^T$. If the columns of $\mathbf{Z}$ can be chosen such that $\mathbf{Z}^T\mathbf{Z} = \mathbf{I}$ and $\hat{\mathbf{A}}^T$ is augmented by $\mathbf{Z}$ itself, the LQ factorization of $\mathbf{T}$ simplifies to

$$\mathbf{T} = \begin{bmatrix}\hat{\mathbf{A}}^T\\ \mathbf{Z}^T\end{bmatrix} = \begin{bmatrix}\hat{\mathbf{L}} & \mathbf{0}\\ \mathbf{0} & \mathbf{I}\end{bmatrix}\begin{bmatrix}\mathbf{Q}_1\\ \mathbf{Z}^T\end{bmatrix}, \tag{2.8.3}$$

and a natural choice of $\mathbf{Z}$ is the last $n - t$ rows of the orthogonal matrix associated with the LQ factorization of $\hat{\mathbf{A}}^T$, i.e. choose $\mathbf{Z} = \mathbf{Q}_2{}^T$ where

$$\hat{\mathbf{A}}^T = [\hat{\mathbf{L}} \;\; \mathbf{0}]\begin{bmatrix}\mathbf{Q}_1\\ \mathbf{Q}_2\end{bmatrix}. \tag{2.8.4}$$

This is a basis of the method suggested by Gill and Murray (1972b). Using Lemma 2.2 it is easy to verify that

$$(\mathbf{T}^T)^{-1} = [\hat{\mathbf{A}} \quad \mathbf{Z}]^{-1} = \begin{bmatrix}(\hat{\mathbf{A}}^T\hat{\mathbf{A}})^{-1}\hat{\mathbf{A}}^T\\ \mathbf{Z}^T\end{bmatrix}. \tag{2.8.5}$$

If we substitute for $\hat{\mathbf{A}}^T$ and $\mathbf{Z}$ from (2.8.3) and (2.8.4)

$$\begin{bmatrix}\boldsymbol{\lambda}^{(k)}\\ \mathbf{0}\end{bmatrix} = (\mathbf{T}^T)^{-1}\mathbf{g}^{(k)}$$

$$= \begin{bmatrix}\hat{\mathbf{L}}^{-T}\mathbf{Q}_1\mathbf{g}^{(k)}\\ \mathbf{Q}_2\mathbf{g}^{(k)}\end{bmatrix} = \begin{bmatrix}\hat{\mathbf{L}}^{-T}\mathbf{Q}_1\mathbf{g}^{(k)}\\ \mathbf{g}_A{}^{(k)}\end{bmatrix}.$$

In this case it follows from (2.8.5) that the first-order estimate of the Lagrange multipliers is equal to the least-squares estimate $\hat{\mathbf{A}}^+\mathbf{g}^{(k)}$, and from Corollary 2 of Theorem 2.3, since $\mathbf{Z}^T\mathbf{Z} = \mathbf{I}$, we have $\|\boldsymbol{\mu}\|_2 = \|\mathbf{g}_A{}^{(k)}\|$. Since the least-squares solution is also that for which $\|\boldsymbol{\mu}\|_2$ is the smallest, $\mathbf{g}_A^{(k)}$ is the projected gradient with minimum norm and by definition $\boldsymbol{\lambda}^{(k)}$ are the *best* first-order estimates of the Lagrange multipliers.

The methods for updating the *LQ* factors of $\mathbf{T}$ can be used to update the factors of $\hat{\mathbf{A}}^T$ also. When a constraint is added to $\hat{\mathbf{A}}^T$, the new $\mathbf{Z}$ is the old one multiplied by an orthogonal matrix and, when a constraint is deleted, $\mathbf{Z}$ is augmented by a single vector which is the column of a product of two orthogonal matrices. These processes are very stable numerically and it can be shown that, unlike the case of recurring the inverse of $\mathbf{T}$, the *LQ* factorization is always the *exact* factorization of a small perturbation of the current active constraint matrix. Moreover $\|\hat{\mathbf{A}}^T\mathbf{Z}\| \sim O(2^{-t})$ independently of the condition number of $\hat{\mathbf{A}}$ at the current or previous iterations.

Since $\mathbf{Z}^T\mathbf{Z}$ is equal to the identity matrix a vector in the null space of $\hat{\mathbf{A}}^T$ is always mapped into itself by the transformation $\mathbf{Z}(\mathbf{Z}^T\mathbf{Z})^{-1}\mathbf{Z}^T$, hence the methods of matrix reduction and projection merge.

At this point it is beneficial to discuss how Method I can be applied to the special type of linearly constrained problem where the objective function is linear (*LP*) or quadratic (*QP*). It is a feature of *LP*, where m is always greater than n, that the solution lies at a vertex of the feasible region and the simplex method (Dantzig, 1963, pp. 94-119) successively evaluates the objective function at neighbouring vertices until the solution is found. In Method I, Section 2.5, if $\mathbf{x}^{(k)}$ is a vertex and $\mathbf{G}$ is chosen as the identity matrix the direction of search obtained by deleting a single constraint is parallel to the edge defined by the matrix $\hat{\mathbf{A}}^T$ of the remaining $n - 1$ constraints. The point at which a new constraint is encountered defines a neighbouring vertex to $\mathbf{x}^{(k)}$ for which the objective function is reduced. Clearly, under these circumstances Method I is equivalent to the simplex method for linear programming. In the *QP* case the matrix $\mathbf{G}$ is constant and as the basis of active constraints changes it is possible to move from a minimum on one subspace to the minimum on another by updating the matrix $\mathbf{Z}^T\mathbf{G}\mathbf{Z}$. Such an algorithm for indefinite *QP* has been suggested by Murray (1971b) in which the matrix $\mathbf{Z}$ is recurred such that $\mathbf{Z}^T\mathbf{G}\mathbf{Z}$ is a diagonal matrix.

2.9. Finding an Initial Feasible Point

All the algorithms described in this chapter have been "feasible-point" methods in that if the first point $\mathbf{x}^{(0)}$ lies in the feasible region then so will all succeeding points $\mathbf{x}^{(k)}$. Naturally we must have some way of determining an initial feasible point $\mathbf{x}^{(0)}$. Although the complete linearly constrained problem can be regarded as being solved in two phases, phase one being the feasibility algorithm and phase two the solution proper, the method we shall suggest can be regarded as a *single* algorithm in which the objective function is initially linear but changes to the usual nonlinear function $F(\mathbf{x})$ when a point is found which is feasible. The starting conditions for this combined algorithm are exactly those for unconstrained minimization techniques, i.e. the user is free to specify any point $\mathbf{x}^{(0)}$ which is some estimate of the position of the minimum of $F(\mathbf{x})$.

The method of finding a feasible point has been resolved in linear programming by a technique known as *phase I simplex* (Dantzig, 1963, pp. 101–119) and the transition to solving the linear program proper is made in a straightforward and natural way. The basis of the technique is to define an artificial objective function, namely

$$\hat{F}(\mathbf{x}) = -\sum_{j \in J_-(\mathbf{x})} (\mathbf{a}_j{}^T\mathbf{x} - b_j)$$

where $J_-(\mathbf{x})$ is the set of indices of constraints which are violated at the point $\mathbf{x}$, and to minimize this function with respect to $\mathbf{x}$, subject to the constraints $\mathbf{a}_j{}^T\mathbf{x} - b_j \geqslant 0$ for all $j \notin J_-(\mathbf{x})$. The function $\hat{F}(\mathbf{x})$ is linear and is known as the "sum of infeasibilities". If a feasible point exists then the solution $\overset{*}{\mathbf{x}}$ of the artificial problem is such that $\hat{F}(\overset{*}{\mathbf{x}}) = 0$. The usual situation in linear programming (where m always exceeds n) is that a non-feasible vertex is available as an initial feasible point to phase one and the simplex method is applied to minimize $\hat{F}(\mathbf{x})$. This process will ultimately lead to a feasible vertex.

Direct application of this method to finding a feasible point in the case where $F(\mathbf{x})$ is nonlinear and m is less than n is not possible since, although a feasible point may exist, a feasible *vertex* will not. Under these circumstances artificial vertices can be defined by adding simple bounds on the variables, but this could lead to either a poor initial point, since some of these artificial constraints must be active, or exclusion of the feasible region. A way out of this dilemma is to use the non-simplex strategy given below which is based upon an algorithm for linear programming (Gill and Murray, 1973a). The matrices recurred using this algorithm are exactly those required for the solution of *LCP*. Let $\mathbf{x}^{(k)}$ be a point which is not yet completely feasible and as before let $\hat{\mathbf{A}}^T$ be the matrix of constraints which we wish to be active at $\mathbf{x}^{(k+1)}$, with $\mathbf{Z}$ the matrix such that $\hat{\mathbf{A}}^T\mathbf{Z} = \mathbf{0}$ and $\mathbf{Z}^T\mathbf{Z} = \mathbf{I}$. Define

$$\mathbf{p}^{(k)} = -\mathbf{Z}\mathbf{Z}^T\hat{\mathbf{g}}^{(k)},$$

where $\hat{\mathbf{g}}^{(k)}$ is the gradient of the artificial objective function, given by

$$\hat{\mathbf{g}}(\mathbf{x}) = -\sum_{j \in J_-(\mathbf{x})} \mathbf{a}_j.$$

Clearly $\mathbf{p}^{(k)}$ is a descent direction and in the case when $\hat{\mathbf{A}}^T$ involves $n-1$ constraints, $\mathbf{p}^{(k)}$ is identical to the direction defined by the simplex method.

There is some degree of choice open in the step taken along $\mathbf{p}^{(k)}$. One possibility is to take the largest step along $\mathbf{p}^{(k)}$ subject to the restriction that the number of violated constraints is not increased. In this case the step is given by

$$\theta_r = \min_j \{\theta_j: -(\mathbf{a}_j{}^T \mathbf{x}^{(k)} - b_j)/\mathbf{a}_j{}^T \mathbf{p}^{(k)}, \quad \mathbf{a}_j{}^T \mathbf{p}^{(k)} < 0\}.$$

The nearest constraint, which will be denoted by $\mathbf{a}_r{}^T$, can then be added to the basis of active constraints in the normal manner. If, at the boundary point $\tilde{\mathbf{x}} = \mathbf{x}^{(k)} + \theta_r \mathbf{p}^{(k)}$, the quantity

$$-\sum_{j \in J_-(\tilde{\mathbf{x}})} \mathbf{a}_j{}^T \mathbf{p}^{(k)} - \mathbf{a}_r{}^T \mathbf{p}^{(k)}$$

is negative, the objective function is still decreasing at the boundary of $\mathbf{a}_r{}^T$. This suggests another strategy in which we continue along the direction $\mathbf{p}^{(k)}$ until the objective function ceases to be reduced.

In either case several violated constraints may become feasible during a given iteration, and a new constraint will be added to the basis of active constraints. Since zigzagging is not a problem when the objective function is linear, a constraint with a negative Lagrange multiplier can be immediately deleted. Using arguments similar to those given in Section 2.6 the process is convergent if we impose a non-degeneracy condition on the constraints. If a vertex of the artificial problem is found with positive Lagrange multipliers and there are still some constraints violated, the original problem does not possess a feasible point.

If some of the constraints are equalities the resulting under-determined set of equations defined by these constraints can be solved for an initial value of $\mathbf{x}$. However, if degeneracy can occur in the problem it is generally preferable to include these constraints as part of the artificial objective function. If degeneracy is likely, the magnitude of $\mathbf{Z}^T\hat{\mathbf{g}}(\mathbf{x}^{(k)})$ should be checked during the computation of the Lagrange multipliers since the artificial objective function could be parallel to the constraint normals.

Another possibility which will not be considered here in any detail is to use the information concerning the Lagrange multipliers of *LCP* in order to compute which constraints to drop from the basis. In this way the direction of search can be chosen to take the original objective function into account.

2.10. Conclusions

Apart from defining a "prototype" sequence of points which other methods try to emulate with a smaller computational effort, Newton–type methods have several advantages:

(a) they are often effective on highly nonlinear problems which are intractable by other means,

(b) they are especially effective on problems in which a large number of elements of the Hessian matrix are constant,

(c) under mild conditions on the problem they can be shown to be convergent to strong local minima—as opposed to just stationary points,

(d) they require fewer iterations and fewer function evaluations per iteration. These advantages may be outweighed by the increased amount of housekeeping per iteration, and the need to compute the second derivatives, but we have found in practice that if the second derivatives are available they certainly should be used except when their computation time is extremely large compared with that of the function or gradient.

Any combination of the methods for computing the matrix **Z**, choosing the set of active constraints and modifying the matrix $\mathbf{G}_A$ to be positive definite, can be used to form a complete method for the solution of the nonlinear optimization problem with linear constraints.

Two methods have appeared in the literature. The first, suggested by McCormick (1970) uses variable reduction, eigensystem analysis of the projected Hessian matrix and a version of the "bending" algorithm for choosing the set of active constraints. The second, suggested by Gill and Murray (1972b), can be used with any method for choosing the set of active constraints and utilizes the modified Cholesky algorithm to modify the projected Hessian matrix together with the *LQ* factorization of method (d), Section 2.8, to define **Z**. We believe that there is overwhelming evidence supporting the inclusion of the latter algorithm in any software library.

There remains the question of whether to compute the Hessian directly or approximate it by finite differences. Numerical evidence (see Gill, Murray and Picken, 1972) suggests that whatever the value of the finite difference interval, the number of iterations required to find a particular strong local minimum is approximately the same for both the modified Newton method and the discrete modified Newton method. However, every iteration of the discrete modified Newton method involves the additional overhead of $n - t$ gradient subroutine calls, where t is the number of active constraints. Thus if the Hessian matrix is K times more expensive to compute than a single gradient evaluation and it is known that there are going to be on average fewer than $n - K$ constraints active for most iterations, it is better to use the exact Hessian matrix rather than compute its finite-difference approximation. For example, an orthodox projected Newton method would be preferable if the original constraint matrix **A** is such that m is significantly less than n.

This rule may not apply however when **G** has a significant number of constant elements since the gradient vector will not generally have a similar number of constant elements. (See Chapter IV for further details in this situation.)

Chapter III

Quasi-Newton Methods for Linearly Constrained Optimization

PHILIP E. GILL AND WALTER MURRAY

Division of Numerical Analysis and Computing,
National Physical Laboratory

3.1. Introduction

Quasi-Newton methods seek to approximate the Hessian matrix (or its inverse) for the kth step by accumulating information from the preceding steps using only first derivatives (or their finite-difference approximation). This is in contrast to Newton-type methods discussed in the last chapter where the Hessian matrix for the kth step depends on derivative information computed in the immediate neighbourhood of $\mathbf{x}^{(k)}$ alone.

Before describing quasi-Newton methods for the linearly constrained problem we shall first consider a typical iteration of the original algorithm of Davidon (1959) for the unconstrained problem as described by Fletcher and Powell (1963) (hereafter called the DFP algorithm). This is done to introduce the notation and terminology that will be required for the later sections. For a more detailed description the reader is referred to the article by Broyden (1972).

The kth Iteration of the DFP Method for Unconstrained Minimization

Step I

The search direction $\mathbf{p}^{(k)}$ is determined from the matrix-vector multiplication

$$\mathbf{p}^{(k)} = -\mathbf{H}^{(k)}\mathbf{g}^{(k)}, \qquad (3.1.1)$$

where $\mathbf{H}^{(k)}$ is the kth approximation to the inverse Hessian of $F(\mathbf{x})$.

Step II

A steplength $\alpha^{(k)}$ is determined by minimizing $F(\mathbf{x})$ along $\mathbf{p}^{(k)}$. That is, $\alpha^{(k)}$ is the value of α that minimizes the function $F(\mathbf{x}^{(k)} + \alpha\mathbf{p}^{(k)})$ with respect to α.

Step III

The $(k+1)$th estimate of a strong local minimum $\overset{*}{\mathbf{x}}$ is given by

$$\mathbf{x}^{(k+1)} = \mathbf{x}^{(k)} + \alpha^{(k)}\mathbf{p}^{(k)}.$$

Step IV

The $(k+1)$th estimate of the inverse Hessian of $F(\mathbf{x})$ is given by

$$\mathbf{H}^{(k+1)} = \mathbf{H}^{(k)} - \frac{1}{\mathbf{y}^{(k)T}\mathbf{H}^{(k)}\mathbf{y}^{(k)}}\mathbf{H}^{(k)}\mathbf{y}^{(k)}\mathbf{y}^{(k)T}\mathbf{H}^{(k)} + \frac{1}{\mathbf{g}^{(k)T}\mathbf{p}^{(k)}}\alpha^{(k)}\mathbf{p}^{(k)}\mathbf{p}^{(k)T}, \quad (3.1.2)$$

where $\mathbf{y}^{(k)} = \mathbf{g}^{(k+1)} - \mathbf{g}^{(k)}$. (The vector $\mathbf{g}^{(k+1)}$ is usually evaluated in the process of evaluating $\alpha^{(k)}$.) This step completes the basic iteration.

Since the DFP algorithm first appeared, the construction of alternative algorithms by changing the modification formula or the method for computing $\alpha^{(k)}$ has preoccupied many authors. Most modification formulae are similar in that they add a matrix of low rank (usually two) to the approximate inverse Hessian at each iteration and attempt to satisfy the quasi-Newton condition, viz

$$\alpha^{(k)}\mathbf{p}^{(k)} = \mathbf{H}^{(k+1)}\mathbf{y}^{(k)}.$$

This condition is derived from the observation that when $F(\mathbf{x})$ is a strictly convex quadratic function with Hessian matrix $\mathbf{G}$, we have

$$\alpha^{(k)}\mathbf{p}^{(k)} = \mathbf{G}^{-1}\mathbf{y}^{(k)}.$$

Thus the modification formula attempts to force $\mathbf{H}^{(k+1)}$ to have one of the properties which $\mathbf{G}^{-1}$ would possess if $F(\mathbf{x})$ were quadratic. When minimizing general functions one can only expect

$$\alpha^{(k)}\mathbf{p}^{(k)} = \mathbf{G}^{(k+1)-1}\mathbf{y}^{(k)} + O(\alpha^{(k)2}\|\mathbf{p}^{(k)}\|^2), \quad (3.1.3)$$

but if $\alpha^{(k)}\|\mathbf{p}^{(k)}\|$ is small the quasi-Newton condition is approximately true. If $\mathbf{x}^{(k)}$ is converging to $\overset{*}{\mathbf{x}}$ then $\alpha^{(k)}\|\mathbf{p}^{(k)}\|$ will become small for large enough k. (The relation (3.1.3) is simply the backward finite-difference approximation to $\mathbf{G}^{(k+1)}\mathbf{p}^{(k)}$ computed along $\mathbf{p}^{(k)}$. This is illustrated by the fact that if the co-ordinate system is rotated so that $\mathbf{p}^{(k)}$ lies along one of the axes (say $\mathbf{e}_1$), then in the new co-ordinate system the quasi-Newton condition (3.1.3) becomes

$$\mathbf{G}_1^{(k+1)} = (\mathbf{g}(\mathbf{x}^{(k+1)}) - \mathbf{g}(\mathbf{x}^{(k+1)} - h\mathbf{e}_1))/h + O(h),$$

where $\mathbf{G}_1^{(k+1)}$ is the first column of $\mathbf{G}^{(k+1)}$ and $h = x_1^{(k+1)} - x_1^{(k)}$.)

It is necessary to place more conditions on the matrix $\mathbf{H}^{(k+1)}$ if it is to be uniquely defined. These additional conditions are usually introduced to give $\mathbf{H}^{(k)}$ properties of the exact inverse Hessian matrix. For example, we may expect the formula to be such that if $F(\mathbf{x})$ is quadratic then $\mathbf{H}^{(n)} = \mathbf{G}^{-1}$ – the DFP modification formula has this property. Of the many possible updating formulae three have proved to be particularly effective:

(a) *the DFP modification formula*;

(b) *the complementary DFP formula*

$$\mathbf{H}^{(k+1)} = \mathbf{H}^{(k)} + \frac{1}{\mathbf{y}^{(k)T}\mathbf{p}^{(k)}}(\rho^{(k)}\mathbf{p}^{(k)}\mathbf{p}^{(k)T} - \mathbf{p}^{(k)}\mathbf{y}^{(k)T}\mathbf{H}^{(k)} - \mathbf{H}^{(k)}\mathbf{y}^{(k)}\mathbf{p}^{(k)T}), \tag{3.1.4}$$

where $\rho^{(k)} = \alpha^{(k)} + \mathbf{y}^{(k)T}\mathbf{H}^{(k)}\mathbf{y}^{(k)}/\mathbf{y}^{(k)T}\mathbf{p}^{(k)}$; and

(c) *the rank-one modification formula*

$$\mathbf{H}^{(k+1)} = \mathbf{H}^{(k)} + \rho^{(k)}(\alpha^{(k)}\mathbf{p}^{(k)} - \mathbf{H}^{(k)}\mathbf{y}^{(k)})(\alpha^{(k)}\mathbf{p}^{(k)} - \mathbf{H}^{(k)}\mathbf{y}^{(k)})^T,$$

where $\rho^{(k)} = 1/(\alpha^{(k)}\mathbf{p}^{(k)} - \mathbf{H}^{(k)}\mathbf{y}^{(k)})^T\mathbf{y}^{(k)}$. (3.1.5)

3.2. Linearly Constrained Optimization—Historical Developments

In his original paper Davidon envisaged the extension of his algorithm for unconstrained minimization to the case of linear *equality* constraints. He observed that if the initial inverse Hessian approximation $\mathbf{H}^{(0)}$ is orthogonal to the constraint normals then so are all subsequent approximations and consequently all search directions. This is easily demonstrated if the DFP updating formula (3.1.2) is rewritten as

$$\mathbf{H}^{(k+1)} = \mathbf{H}^{(k)} - \mathbf{H}^{(k)}\left(\frac{1}{\mathbf{y}^{(k)T}\mathbf{H}^{(k)}\mathbf{y}^{(k)}}\mathbf{y}^{(k)}\mathbf{y}^{(k)T} - \frac{\alpha^{(k)}}{\mathbf{g}^{(k)T}\mathbf{p}^{(k)}}\mathbf{g}^{(k)}\mathbf{g}^{(k)T}\right)\mathbf{H}^{(k)}. \tag{3.2.1}$$

If, for some matrix $\hat{\mathbf{A}}$, $\hat{\mathbf{A}}^T\mathbf{H}^{(k)} = \mathbf{0}$ then $\hat{\mathbf{A}}^T\mathbf{H}^{(k+1)} = \mathbf{0}$ and it follows from the definition of the direction of search that $\hat{\mathbf{A}}^T\mathbf{p}^{(k)} = \mathbf{0}$.

Consider then, minimizing $F(\mathbf{x})$ subject to the constraints $\hat{\mathbf{A}}^T\mathbf{x} = \hat{\mathbf{b}}$, where $\hat{\mathbf{A}}$ is an $n \times t$ matrix and $\hat{\mathbf{b}}$ a t-vector. We can follow Davidon's suggestion if we can choose a matrix $\mathbf{H}^{(0)}$ such that $\hat{\mathbf{A}}^T\mathbf{H}^{(0)} = \mathbf{0}$ and an initial estimate of the solution $\mathbf{x}^{(0)}$ such that $\hat{\mathbf{A}}\mathbf{x}^{(0)} = \hat{\mathbf{b}}$. To preserve the properties of the DFP algorithm which apply in the unconstrained case it is necessary for $\mathbf{H}^{(0)}$ to be positive definite for all non-zero vectors $\mathbf{v}$ such that $\hat{\mathbf{A}}^T\mathbf{v} = \mathbf{0}$. A suitable initial approximation satisfying these requirements is the projection matrix $\bar{\mathbf{P}}$ associated with $\hat{\mathbf{A}}$ in equations (2.5.4) and (2.5.5), namely

$$\mathbf{H}^{(0)} = \bar{\mathbf{P}} \equiv \mathbf{I} - \hat{\mathbf{A}}(\hat{\mathbf{A}}^T\hat{\mathbf{A}})^{-1}\hat{\mathbf{A}}^T.$$

We have assumed that $\hat{\mathbf{A}}$ has full column rank, for otherwise $\hat{\mathbf{A}}^T\hat{\mathbf{A}}$ will be singular. The matrix $\mathbf{H}^{(0)}$ can be used to generate $\mathbf{x}^{(0)}$ if a suitable initial approximation to $\overset{*}{\mathbf{x}}$ is known. We simply set

$$\mathbf{x}^{(0)} = \mathbf{H}^{(0)}\mathbf{w} + \hat{\mathbf{A}}\mathbf{v},$$

where $\mathbf{w}$ is an arbitrary n-vector and $\mathbf{v}$ is the t-vector $\mathbf{v} = (\hat{\mathbf{A}}^T\hat{\mathbf{A}})^{-1}\hat{\mathbf{b}}$. We note that the matrix $(\hat{\mathbf{A}}^T\hat{\mathbf{A}})^{-1}$ is required for the construction of $\mathbf{H}^{(0)}$.

In his PhD thesis, part of which was subsequently published in 1969, Goldfarb extended the DFP algorithm to the problem of linear *inequality* constraints by utilizing the techniques described by Rosen (1960) in association with his projected-gradient method (see Chapter II, Section 2.5). At each iteration a number of the constraints are regarded as being active and on that set of constraints an equality problem is solved. Some modifications are required to the equality-constraint DFP algorithm just described—we shall denote the matrix recurred in the Goldfarb algorithm as $\mathbf{H}_G{}^{(k)}$ and the matrix of constraints active at the kth iteration as $\hat{\mathbf{A}}^{(k)T}$.

(a) In the course of the linear search a constraint may be violated and consequently a restriction on the maximum step size is needed. This is simply the step along $\mathbf{p}^{(k)}$ to the nearest inactive constraint and this is determined as described in Chapter II, Section 2.6.

(b) If such a step is taken then a non-active constraint, $\mathbf{a}_r{}^T\mathbf{x} = b_r$ say, becomes active and we must modify $\mathbf{H}_G{}^{(k)}$ accordingly. In this case the following updating formula replaces that used in Step IV of the DFP method,

$$\mathbf{H}_G{}^{(k+1)} = \mathbf{H}_G{}^{(k)} - \mathbf{H}_G{}^{(k)}\mathbf{a}_r\mathbf{a}_r{}^T\mathbf{H}_G{}^{(k)}/\mathbf{a}_r{}^T\mathbf{H}_G{}^{(k)}\mathbf{a}_r.$$

We note that $\mathbf{H}_G{}^{(k+1)}$ has the property that $\mathbf{H}_G{}^{(k+1)}\mathbf{a}_r = \mathbf{0}$.

(c) Goldfarb computes the first-order estimates of the Lagrange multipliers given by

$$\boldsymbol{\lambda}^{(k)} = \hat{\mathbf{A}}^{(k)+}\mathbf{g}^{(k)},$$

and stipulates that the sth constraint should be dropped from the basis if

$$\|\mathbf{H}_G{}^{(k)}\mathbf{g}^{(k)}\|_2 \leqslant -\tfrac{1}{2}\lambda_s{}^{(k)}\beta_s{}^{-\frac{1}{2}},$$

where β_s is the sth diagonal element of $(\hat{\mathbf{A}}^{(k)T}\hat{\mathbf{A}}^{(k)})^{-1}$ and s is the integer such that

$$\lambda_s{}^{(k)}\beta_s{}^{-\frac{1}{2}} \leqslant \lambda_j{}^{(k)}\beta_j{}^{-\frac{1}{2}}, \qquad j = 1, 2, \ldots, t.$$

A full discussion of this test is given in Section 3.5. A feasible direction of search which lies interior to the hyperplane $\mathbf{a}_s{}^T\mathbf{x} = b_s$ is found by using a matrix $\mathbf{H}_G{}^{(k+1)}$ in the next iteration which is not orthogonal to $\mathbf{a}_s$. The update suggested by Goldfarb for discarding $\mathbf{a}_s$ is given by

$$\mathbf{H}_G{}^{(k+1)} = \mathbf{H}_G{}^{(k)} + \bar{\mathbf{P}}\mathbf{a}_s\mathbf{a}_s{}^T\bar{\mathbf{P}}/\mathbf{a}_s{}^T\bar{\mathbf{P}}\mathbf{a}_s,$$

where

$$\bar{\mathbf{P}} = \mathbf{I} - \hat{\mathbf{A}}^{(k)}(\hat{\mathbf{A}}^{(k)T}\hat{\mathbf{A}}^{(k)})^{-1}\hat{\mathbf{A}}^{(k)T}. \tag{3.2.2}$$

In the unconstrained case the matrix $\mathbf{H}^{(k)}$ is some approximation to the inverse Hessian $\mathbf{G}^{-1}$ and it is instructive to discuss the significance of the matrix $\mathbf{H}_G{}^{(k)}$ in the linearly constrained case. If $\boldsymbol{\omega}^{(k)}$ is eliminated from equations (2.4.9) and (2.4.10) defining Method II of Chapter II we obtain

$$\mathbf{p}^{(k)} = -\mathbf{W}^{(k)}\mathbf{G}^{(k)-1}\mathbf{g}^{(k)}, \tag{3.2.3}$$

where

$$\mathbf{W}^{(k)} = \mathbf{I} - \mathbf{G}^{(k)-1}\hat{\mathbf{A}}^{(k)}(\hat{\mathbf{A}}^{(k)T}\mathbf{G}^{(k)-1}\hat{\mathbf{A}}^{(k)})^{-1}\hat{\mathbf{A}}^{(k)T}$$

is the projection operator weighted by $\mathbf{G}^{(k)-1}$ which projects vectors of E^n so that they are orthogonal to the space spanned by the columns of $\hat{\mathbf{A}}^{(k)}$ (cf. the matrix $\bar{\mathbf{P}}$ of Section 2.5). Goldfarb has shown that if $F(\mathbf{x})$ is a quadratic function with Hessian $\mathbf{G}$ and if $n - t$ successive iterations are taken with a set of t active constraints $\hat{\mathbf{A}}$, then $\mathbf{H}_G$ will be equal to

$$\mathbf{G}^{-1} - \mathbf{G}^{-1}\hat{\mathbf{A}}(\hat{\mathbf{A}}^T\mathbf{G}^{-1}\hat{\mathbf{A}})^{-1}\hat{\mathbf{A}}^T\mathbf{G}^{-1}$$

within those $n - t$ iterations. The matrix $\mathbf{H}_G{}^{(k)}$ can be considered as an approximation to the matrix $\mathbf{W}^{(k)}\mathbf{G}^{(k)-1}$.

A serious difficulty which occurs with all methods which attempt to approximate the matrix $\mathbf{W}^{(k)}\mathbf{G}^{(k)-1}$ (whatever the updating formula) is that when moving off the constraint $\mathbf{a}_s{}^T\mathbf{x} = b_s$ the rank of $\mathbf{H}_G{}^{(k)}$ increases by one but no information has been accumulated about $\mathbf{H}_G$ in the direction of the constraint normal $\mathbf{a}_s$.

Although Goldfarb suggested the DFP updating formula for his algorithm when no changes of constraint are involved, any one of the other well-known updating formulae could be used. A good reason for using the rank-one formula (3.1.5) is to overcome the disadvantage of the DFP algorithm whereby an exact univariate minimization must be made along $\mathbf{p}^{(k)}$. Such a minimization is not always possible for linearly constrained problems since the minimum along a direction of search may not be a feasible point. A feature of the rank-one updating formula is that it is not necessary to perform an exact univariate minimization for the quasi-Newton condition to hold.

In order to avoid the necessity of an exact univariate minimization and in an attempt to maintain curvature information over the whole of E^n, Murtagh and Sargent (1969) proposed an algorithm in which a *full* $n \times n$ approximation to the inverse Hessian is updated by the rank-one formula (3.1.5). By recurring the matrices $(\hat{\mathbf{A}}^{(k)T}\mathbf{H}^{(k)}\hat{\mathbf{A}}^{(k)})^{-1}$ and $\mathbf{H}^{(k)}$ they are able to compute the direction of search using

$$\mathbf{p}^{(k)} = \mathbf{H}^{(k)}(\hat{\mathbf{A}}^{(k)}\boldsymbol{\omega}^{(k)} - \mathbf{g}^{(k)}), \tag{3.2.4}$$

where

$$\boldsymbol{\omega}^{(k)} = (\hat{\mathbf{A}}^{(k)T}\mathbf{H}^{(k)}\hat{\mathbf{A}}^{(k)})^{-1}\hat{\mathbf{A}}^{(k)T}\mathbf{H}^{(k)}\mathbf{g}^{(k)}. \tag{3.2.5}$$

Due to the similarity of these equations with (2.4.9) and (2.4.10) it may be thought that the $\boldsymbol{\omega}^{(k)}$ of (3.2.5) are "second-order" estimates of the Lagrange multipliers. However, we shall show below that this is rarely the case. We note that $\boldsymbol{\omega}^{(k)}$ is obtained during the process of computing $\mathbf{p}^{(k)}$ but that more storage and work per iteration is required than with the Goldfarb method. Unfortunately, in our view, the benefits obtained by this sacrifice in efficiency are largely illusory. The basic idea of the Murtagh–Sargent algorithm is that information concerning the curvature over the whole of E^n shall be accumulated in the matrix $\mathbf{H}^{(k)}$. However, from the definition of $\mathbf{H}^{(k)}$, information is only added in the space spanned by the search directions and not in the orthogonal space spanned by the constraint normals. For example, if a constraint $\mathbf{a}_j^T\mathbf{x} = b_j$ is active for all iterations, $\mathbf{H}^{(k)}$ will have no curvature information in the direction $\mathbf{a}_j$. It may be argued that if enough iterations are made, $\mathbf{H}^{(k)}$ will ultimately contain curvature information in all directions, but in practice the complete set of search directions rarely span E^n, and even when they do the information gleaned from the earlier iterations ceases to have any significance. The only hope is that fresh information can be obtained during iterations in which movement off a constraint occurs close to the point at which it first becomes active.

With the knowledge that $\mathbf{H}^{(k)}$ may not span E^n as expected, we now investigate the similarity of $\boldsymbol{\omega}^{(k)}$ defined in (3.2.5) to the second-order estimates of the Lagrange multipliers (2.4.10). Since we know that it is impossible to improve $\mathbf{H}^{(k)}$ in certain directions when the active set is constant, the same must apply to the matrix $\hat{\mathbf{A}}^{(k)T}\mathbf{H}^{(k)}\hat{\mathbf{A}}^{(k)}$. In fact, this can be verified directly if the complementary DFP formula (3.1.4) is used, since if $\hat{\mathbf{A}}^{(k+1)} = \hat{\mathbf{A}}^{(k)}$ then

$$\hat{\mathbf{A}}^{(k+1)T}\mathbf{H}^{(k+1)}\hat{\mathbf{A}}^{(k+1)} = \hat{\mathbf{A}}^{(k)T}\mathbf{H}^{(k)}\hat{\mathbf{A}}^{(k)},$$

by virtue of the condition $\hat{\mathbf{A}}^{(k)T}\mathbf{p}^{(k)} = \mathbf{0}$. If we start with an initial approximation $\mathbf{H}^{(0)} = \mathbf{I}$ and always remain on the same set of active constraints then

$$\hat{\mathbf{A}}^{(k)T}\mathbf{H}^{(k)}\hat{\mathbf{A}}^{(k)} = \hat{\mathbf{A}}^{(k)T}\mathbf{H}^{(0)}\hat{\mathbf{A}}^{(k)} = \hat{\mathbf{A}}^{(k)T}\hat{\mathbf{A}}^{(k)}.$$

The reader may well be mystified as to what is being achieved by other modification rules (such as DFP and rank-one) which physically modify the matrix $(\hat{\mathbf{A}}^{(k)T}\mathbf{H}^{(k)}\hat{\mathbf{A}}^{(k)})^{-1}$ during every iteration.

It can be shown that the matrix $\mathbf{W}^{(k)}\mathbf{G}^{(k)-1}$ defined by equation (3.2.3) is positive semi-definite in the neighbourhood of the solution. It is reasonable therefore, to restrict the matrix

$$(\mathbf{I} - \mathbf{H}^{(k)}\hat{\mathbf{A}}^{(k)}(\hat{\mathbf{A}}^{(k)T}\mathbf{H}^{(k)}\hat{\mathbf{A}}^{(k)})^{-1}\hat{\mathbf{A}}^{(k)T})\mathbf{H}^{(k)} \equiv \mathbf{V}^{(k)}\mathbf{H}^{(k)},$$

say, to be positive semi-definite. Unfortunately it is not easy to see how this may be done in the Murtagh–Sargent algorithm without insisting both $\mathbf{H}^{(k)}$ and $\hat{\mathbf{A}}^{(k)T}\mathbf{H}^{(k)}\hat{\mathbf{A}}^{(k)}$ are positive definite. Clearly this is an artificial restriction since neither $\mathbf{G}^{(k)}$ nor $\hat{\mathbf{A}}^{(k)T}\mathbf{G}^{(k)-1}\hat{\mathbf{A}}^{(k)}$ are necessarily positive definite—even in the neighbourhood of the solution. Thus, insisting that $\hat{\mathbf{A}}^{(k)T}\mathbf{H}^{(k)}\hat{\mathbf{A}}^{(k)}$ is positive definite will in general imply that the elements of $\boldsymbol{\omega}^{(k)}$ are poor estimates of the second-order Lagrange multipliers.

A possible danger with both the Goldfarb and the Murtagh–Sargent methods is that the search direction may cease to be orthogonal to the constraint normals due to rounding errors. The feasibility of the direction of search depends upon the relations $\hat{\mathbf{A}}^{(k)T}\mathbf{H}_G{}^{(k)} = \mathbf{0}$ for the Goldfarb algorithm and $\hat{\mathbf{A}}^{(k)T}\mathbf{V}^{(k)} = \mathbf{0}$ for the Murtagh–Sargent method. However, in the situation where the set of active constraints remains constant for a number of iterations these relations are not fulfilled because additional errors are introduced through $\mathbf{H}_G{}^{(k)}$ and $\mathbf{V}^{(k)}$ being modified. Basically, the information concerning the orthogonality of the search directions with respect to the constraint normals, which should be constant while the basis remains fixed, is in fact polluted by the rounding errors produced when the curvature information is amended. Since $\mathbf{H}_G{}^{(k)}$, $\mathbf{V}^{(k)}$ and $\mathbf{p}^{(k)}$ are used to produce $\mathbf{H}_G{}^{(k+1)}$ and $\mathbf{V}^{(k+1)}$, any loss of orthogonality is propagated into the new calculations and can rapidly inflate the magnitude of the error. To illustrate this phenomenon consider a typical iteration of the Goldfarb method with the DFP updating rule (3.1.2). Assume that $\hat{\mathbf{A}}^{(k+1)} = \hat{\mathbf{A}}^{(k)} = \hat{\mathbf{A}}$ and that for the kth iteration the arithmetic is exact. Let $\mathbf{H}_G{}^{(k)}$ be our current approximation which is in error to the extent that

$$\hat{\mathbf{A}}^T\mathbf{H}_G{}^{(k)} = \mathbf{E}^{(k)}.$$

From (3.2.1) we have

$$\hat{\mathbf{A}}^T\mathbf{H}_G{}^{(k+1)} = \mathbf{E}^{(k+1)} = \mathbf{E}^{(k)} - \mathbf{E}^{(k)}\mathbf{Y}\mathbf{H}_G{}^{(k)},$$

where
$$\mathbf{Y} = \frac{1}{\mathbf{y}^{(k)T}\mathbf{H}^{(k)}\mathbf{y}^{(k)}}\mathbf{y}^{(k)}\mathbf{y}^{(k)T} - \frac{\alpha^{(k)}}{\mathbf{g}^{(k)T}\mathbf{p}^{(k)}}\mathbf{g}^{(k)}\mathbf{g}^{(k)T},$$

and consequently $\mathbf{E}^{(k+1)} = \mathbf{E}^{(k)}(\mathbf{I} - \mathbf{Y}\mathbf{H}_G{}^{(k)})$.

Goldfarb recognized that very rapid growth of $\|\mathbf{E}^{(k)}\|$ can occur as k increases. He therefore suggested that the matrix $\mathbf{H}_G{}^{(k)}$ should be reset to

$\mathbf{I} - \hat{\mathbf{A}}^{(k)}(\hat{\mathbf{A}}^{(k)T}\hat{\mathbf{A}}^{(k)})^{-1}\hat{\mathbf{A}}^{(k)}$ and that the value of $\mathbf{x}^{(k)}$ should be refined if the residuals of the active constraints become large. Unfortunately, resetting $\mathbf{H}_G^{(k)}$ implies that all information gleaned from previous iterations is discarded; while refining $\mathbf{x}^{(k)}$ to lie on the constraints usually increases the objective function. In the Murtagh–Sargent and Goldfarb algorithms these difficulties can be eased by refining the direction of search—at each iteration if necessary. Consider, for example, the Goldfarb algorithm. Assume that $\bar{\mathbf{p}}^{(k)}$, the computed direction of search, is such that

$$\|\hat{\mathbf{A}}^{(k)T}\bar{\mathbf{p}}^{(k)}\| = O(\varepsilon).$$

It can be shown that if $\bar{\mathbf{P}}$ is the projection matrix (3.2.2) then $\hat{\mathbf{p}}^{(k)}$, the computed value of $\bar{\mathbf{P}}\bar{\mathbf{p}}^{(k)}$ is such that

$$\|\hat{\mathbf{A}}^{(k)T}\hat{\mathbf{p}}^{(k)}\| = O(\varepsilon^2).$$

Similarly if we reset the approximate Hessian to the computed value of $\bar{\mathbf{P}}\mathbf{H}_G^{(k)}$ we no longer discard all the Hessian information. A similar technique can be applied with the Murtagh–Sargent algorithm using the matrix $\mathbf{V}^{(k)}$.

In Chapter II we have shown that the direction of search can be computed by one of two alternative methods, the value of $\mathbf{p}^{(k)}$ being the solution of a primal or dual quadratic subproblem. The Goldfarb and Murtagh–Sargent methods are based upon the second of these quadratic subproblems in that they both attempt to approximate the matrix $\mathbf{W}^{(k)}\mathbf{G}^{(k)-1}$. The matrix $\mathbf{H}_G^{(k)}$ provides this approximation directly in the Goldfarb method whereas in the Murtagh–Sargent method the approximation is constructed from its component parts. In the following section we shall describe an alternative implementation of the quasi-Newton iteration which can be applied to solve the primal quadratic subproblem.

3.3. Revised Quasi-Newton Methods

Quasi-Newton methods for the unconstrained problem were given a revised format by Gill and Murray (1972a). The basic feature of their implementation was that the approximate Hessian matrix $\mathbf{B}^{(k)}$ should be recurred in place of the approximate inverse Hessian $\mathbf{H}^{(k)}$. In order to expedite the solution of the equations (3.1.1), which become

$$\mathbf{B}^{(k)}\mathbf{p}^{(k)} = -\mathbf{g}^{(k)}.$$

Gill and Murray show how the matrix $\mathbf{B}^{(k)}$ can be recurred in factorized form

$$\mathbf{B}^{(k)} = \mathbf{L}^{(k)}\mathbf{D}^{(k)}\mathbf{L}^{(k)T},$$

where $\mathbf{L}^{(k)}$ is a lower-triangular matrix with unit diagonals and $\mathbf{D}^{(k)}$ is a diagonal matrix. An immediate advantage of this scheme is that $\mathbf{B}^{(k)}$ can be numerically guaranteed to be positive definite by insisting that the diagonal elements of $\mathbf{D}^{(k)}$ are positive. Another advantage is that the matrices $\mathbf{L}^{(k)}$ and $\mathbf{D}^{(k)}$ can easily be altered to give a matrix $\mathbf{L}^{(k)}\mathbf{D}^{(k)}\mathbf{L}^{(k)T}$ with a condition number which is small enough to ensure that the *computed* value of $\mathbf{p}^{(k)}$ is a descent direction.

Every rank-two formula for modifying the approximate inverse Hessian matrix gives a corresponding rank-two rule for the approximate Hessian matrix. The modification formulae corresponding to (3.1.2), (3.1.4) and (3.1.5) are:

(a) *the DFP modification formula*

$$\mathbf{B}^{(k+1)} = \mathbf{B}^{(k)} + \frac{1}{\mu^{(k)}(\mathbf{y}^{(k)T}\mathbf{p}^{(k)})^2}\mathbf{w}^{(k)}\mathbf{w}^{(k)T} - \mu^{(k)}\mathbf{g}^{(k)}\mathbf{g}^{(k)T}$$

where

$$\mu^{(k)} = \alpha^{(k)}/(\mathbf{y}^{(k)T}\mathbf{p}^{(k)} - \alpha^{(k)}\mathbf{g}^{(k)T}\mathbf{p}^{(k)})$$

and

$$\mathbf{w}^{(k)} = \mu^{(k)}\mathbf{y}^{(k)T}\mathbf{p}^{(k)}\mathbf{g}^{(k)} + \mathbf{y}^{(k)};$$

(b) *the complementary DFP formula*

$$\mathbf{B}^{(k+1)} = \mathbf{B}^{(k)} + \frac{1}{\alpha^{(k)}\mathbf{y}^{(k)T}\mathbf{p}^{(k)}}\mathbf{y}^{(k)}\mathbf{y}^{(k)T} + \frac{1}{\mathbf{g}^{(k)T}\mathbf{p}^{(k)}}\mathbf{g}^{(k)}\mathbf{g}^{(k)T};$$

(c) *the rank-one formula*

$$\mathbf{B}^{(k+1)} = \mathbf{B}^{(k)} + \frac{1}{\alpha^{(k)}\mathbf{w}^{(k)T}\mathbf{p}^{(k)}}\mathbf{w}^{(k)}\mathbf{w}^{(k)T},$$

where $\mathbf{w}^{(k)} = \mathbf{y}^{(k)} + \alpha^{(k)}\mathbf{g}^{(k)}$. Note that unlike (3.1.2), (3.1.4) and (3.1.5) *these formulae do not involve any matrix-vector products.*

In a recent paper (Gill and Murray, 1973c) it has been demonstrated how this algorithm can be generalized directly to the linearly constrained case by recurring an approximation to the projected Hessian matrix $\mathbf{G}_A{}^{(k)} = \mathbf{Z}^T\mathbf{G}^{(k)}\mathbf{Z}$ of Method I, Chapter II. (We recall that $\mathbf{Z}^{(k)}$ is the matrix orthogonal to the set of active constraints $\hat{\mathbf{A}}^{(k)}$, and it is recommended that $\mathbf{Z}^{(k)}$ be obtained from the last $n - t$ columns of the orthogonal matrix $\mathbf{Q}^{(k)}$ associated with the LQ factorization of $\hat{\mathbf{A}}^{(k)T}$,

$$\begin{aligned}\hat{\mathbf{A}}^{(k)T} &= [\hat{\mathbf{L}}^{(k)} \quad \mathbf{0}]\,\mathbf{Q}^{(k)} \\ &= [\hat{\mathbf{L}}^{(k)} \quad \mathbf{0}]\begin{bmatrix}\mathbf{Q}_1{}^{(k)} \\ \mathbf{Z}^{(k)T}\end{bmatrix}.) \qquad (3.3.1)\end{aligned}$$

If we denote the quasi-Newton approximation to $\mathbf{G}_A^{(k)}$ as $\mathbf{B}_A^{(k)}$ we obtain, as in (2.5.1) of Chapter II, the direction of search by solving the equations

$$\mathbf{B}_A^{(k)}\mathbf{p}_A^{(k)} = -\mathbf{g}_A^{(k)},$$

and setting $\mathbf{p}^{(k)} = \mathbf{Z}^{(k)}\mathbf{p}_A^{(k)}$. As in the unconstrained algorithm the Cholesky factors of $\mathbf{B}_A^{(k)} = \mathbf{L}_A^{(k)}\mathbf{D}_A^{(k)}\mathbf{L}_A^{(k)T}$ can be used to compute $\mathbf{p}_A^{(k)}$ and methods given by Gill and Murray (1973c) are available for modifying the factors during the updating of the second-derivative information (rank-two corrections to $\mathbf{B}_A^{(k)}$) and constraint information (corrections to the matrix $\mathbf{Z}$). The overall method has several important features.

(a) If the notation $\mathbf{p}_A$ is used for all vectors $\mathbf{Z}^T\mathbf{p}$ then all the well-known revised quasi-Newton formulae can be applied to the linearly constrained case by adding the suffix A to all the quantities $\mathbf{B}^{(k)}$, $\mathbf{y}^{(k)}$, $\mathbf{p}^{(k)}$ and $\mathbf{g}^{(k)}$. For example, the complementary DFP formula becomes

$$\mathbf{B}_A^{(k+1)} = \mathbf{B}_A^{(k)} + \frac{1}{\alpha^{(k)}\mathbf{y}_A^{(k)T}\mathbf{p}_A^{(k)}}\mathbf{y}_A^{(k)}\mathbf{y}_A^{(k)T} + \frac{1}{\mathbf{g}_A^{(k)T}\mathbf{p}_A^{(k)}}\mathbf{g}_A^{(k)}\mathbf{g}_A^{(k)T}.$$

In fact, from the considerable wealth of experimental evidence available (see for example Gill, Murray and Pitfield, 1972) this is the most effective of the three formulae given.

(b) The difficulties experienced with the Goldfarb and Murtagh–Sargent methods when a constraint is dropped from the basis are not present with the revised algorithm. When a constraint is dropped and the *LQ* factorization of the matrix of active constraints is updated, the matrix orthogonal to the new active basis is given by $[\mathbf{z} \quad \mathbf{Z}^{(k)}]$ where $\mathbf{Z}^{(k)T}\mathbf{z} = \mathbf{0}$ and $\mathbf{z}^T\mathbf{z} = 1$. Consider the matrix

$$\mathbf{\Theta} = \begin{bmatrix} \mathbf{v}^T\mathbf{z} & \mathbf{v}^T\mathbf{Z}^{(k)} \\ \mathbf{Z}^{(k)T}\mathbf{v} & \mathbf{Z}^{(k)T}\mathbf{G}^{(k)}\mathbf{Z}^{(k)} \end{bmatrix},$$

where $\mathbf{v} = \big(\mathbf{g}(\mathbf{x}^{(k)} + h\mathbf{z}) - \mathbf{g}(\mathbf{x}^{(k)})\big)/h$, $\|\mathbf{v}\| = \|\mathbf{G}^{(k)}\mathbf{z}\| + O(h)$ and $\mathbf{G}^{(k)}$ is the exact Hessian matrix at $\mathbf{x}^{(k)}$. We have

$$\mathbf{\Theta} = \begin{bmatrix} \mathbf{z}^T\mathbf{G}^{(k)}\mathbf{z} & \mathbf{z}^T\mathbf{G}^{(k)}\mathbf{Z}^{(k)} \\ \mathbf{Z}^{(k)T}\mathbf{G}^{(k)}\mathbf{z} & \mathbf{G}_A^{(k)} \end{bmatrix} + \mathbf{R}(h),$$

where $\|\mathbf{R}(h)\| = O(h)$. Consequently we have

$$\mathbf{\Theta} = \begin{bmatrix} \mathbf{z}^T \\ \mathbf{Z}^{(k)T} \end{bmatrix} \mathbf{G}^{(k)}\,[\mathbf{z} \quad \mathbf{Z}^{(k)}] + \mathbf{R}(h) = \mathbf{G}_A^{(k+1)} + \mathbf{R}(h)$$

and we have obtained an $O(h)$ approximation to the projected Hessian on the new set of active constraints at the cost of a single gradient evaluation. Thus in the quasi-Newton case we can form the approximation

$$\begin{bmatrix} \mathbf{v}^T\mathbf{z} & \mathbf{v}^T\mathbf{Z}^{(k)} \\ \mathbf{Z}^{(k)T}\mathbf{v} & \mathbf{B}_A^{(k)} \end{bmatrix},$$

which will have all the information we need to compute the direction of search during the next iteration.

(c) The degree of orthogonality of $\mathbf{p}^{(k)}$ with respect to the constraint normals $\hat{\mathbf{A}}^{(k)}$ is unchanged for all iterations for which $\hat{\mathbf{A}}^{(k+1)} = \hat{\mathbf{A}}^{(k)}$, that is during the rank-two updating of the curvature information in $\mathbf{B}_A^{(k)}$. When the basis of active constraints is altered the remarks of Section 2.8, Chapter II, apply.

(d) As in the unconstrained case, the condition number of $\mathbf{L}_A^{(k)}\mathbf{D}_A^{(k)}\mathbf{L}_A^{T(k)}$ can be altered to give an acceptable $\mathbf{p}^{(k)}$; however much $\mathbf{B}_A^{(k)}$ is altered, $\mathbf{p}^{(k)}$ is still orthogonal to $\hat{\mathbf{A}}^{(k)T}$. It is important that this modification is not done unnecessarily, since otherwise the rate of convergence will be affected; for the reasons given in Section 2.8, Chapter II, $\mathbf{B}_A^{(k)}$ has the smallest condition number over all the possible choices of the matrix $\mathbf{Z}^{(k)}$, and this ensures that unnecessary modifications are avoided.

(e) It can be shown that if we define $\mathbf{B}_A^{(k)} = \mathbf{Z}^{(k)T}\mathbf{B}^{(k)}\mathbf{Z}^{(k)}$, the operations of projection and rank-one modification are commutative. This implies that the resulting approximate projected Hessian is identical to that which would have been obtained by updating $\mathbf{B}^{(k)}$ and then projecting.

(f) The first-order estimates of the Lagrange multipliers are computed as in the modified Newton algorithm in Section 2.8 of Chapter II, that is from the equations

$$\hat{\mathbf{L}}^{(k)T}\boldsymbol{\lambda} = \mathbf{Q}_1^{(k)}\mathbf{g}^{(k)}.$$

An advantage of using this quasi-Newton method as part of a mathematical programming library package is that the algorithm shares basic subroutines with methods for the unconstrained problem and linearly constrained problem for which second derivatives are available.

3.4. Factorized Forms of the Standard Algorithms

Numerical methods using matrix factorizations similar to those suggested in the last section can be applied to the Goldfarb and Murtagh–Sargent algorithms. Consider first the Goldfarb algorithm, where we can recur the factorization

$$\mathbf{H}_G^{(k)} = \mathbf{L}_G^{(k)}\mathbf{D}_G^{(k)}\mathbf{L}_G^{(k)T}$$

in place of $\mathbf{H}_G^{(k)}$. It is not possible to recur the Cholesky factors of the inverse of $\mathbf{H}_G^{(k)}$ since it is singular, and as a result we are obliged to use rank-one updates formed by matrix–vector products. This introduces rounding error dependent upon the condition number of the matrix involved. Due to the rank deficiency of $\mathbf{H}_G^{(k)}$ the number of columns of $\mathbf{L}^{(k)}$ that require updating will only equal the rank of $\mathbf{H}_G^{(k)}$; although this gives some numerical and computational advantages, it can be shown that it does not automatically guarantee the orthogonality of $\mathbf{H}_G^{(k)}$ to the constraint normals. The Lagrange multipliers can be determined using the same methods discussed in the previous section.

Modification of the Murtagh–Sargent algorithm is slightly more satisfactory since the matrix $\mathbf{H}^{(k)}$ is non-singular and we can recur the factors $\mathbf{L}^{(k)}$ and $\mathbf{D}^{(k)}$ where

$$\mathbf{B}^{(k)} = \mathbf{H}^{(k)-1} = \mathbf{L}^{(k)}\mathbf{D}^{(k)}\mathbf{L}^{(k)T}.$$

To ensure the numerical stability of the updating process, the matrix $\mathbf{B}^{(k)}$ must be restricted to be positive definite. This restriction is less satisfactory than that of the last section where only the matrix $\mathbf{B}_A^{(k)}$ need be positive definite. The Lagrange multipliers could be determined by recurring either the Cholesky factors of $\hat{\mathbf{A}}^{(k)T}\mathbf{H}^{(k)}\hat{\mathbf{A}}^{(k)}$ or the orthogonal factorization of $\mathbf{D}^{(k)-\frac{1}{2}}\mathbf{L}^{(k)-1}\hat{\mathbf{A}}^{(k)}$. In the latter case the multipliers are determined by finding the least-squares solution of

$$\mathbf{D}^{(k)-\frac{1}{2}}\mathbf{L}^{(k)-1}\hat{\mathbf{A}}^{(k)}\boldsymbol{\omega}^{(k)} = \mathbf{D}^{(k)-\frac{1}{2}}\mathbf{L}^{(k)-1}\mathbf{g}^{(k)}. \tag{3.4.1}$$

One of the disadvantages of the dual form of the search direction defined by (3.2.4) and (3.2.5) is the worsening of the condition of the method due to the product of several matrices appearing as the coefficient matrix in the set of equations (3.2.4). We now define an alternative form of this algorithm which avoids this problem.

Let $\mathbf{M}$ be a $t \times t$ non-singular matrix and let $\hat{\mathbf{Q}}$ be a $t \times n$ matrix of rank t such that

$$\hat{\mathbf{A}}^{(k)T} = \mathbf{M}\hat{\mathbf{Q}}. \tag{3.4.2}$$

If we substitute for $\hat{\mathbf{A}}^{(k)}$ in (3.2.4) we obtain

$$\begin{aligned}\mathbf{p}^{(k)} &= \mathbf{H}^{(k)}\,(\hat{\mathbf{Q}}^T\mathbf{M}^T(\mathbf{M}\hat{\mathbf{Q}}\mathbf{H}^{(k)}\hat{\mathbf{Q}}^T\mathbf{M}^T)^{-1}\mathbf{M}\hat{\mathbf{Q}}\mathbf{H}^{(k)} - \mathbf{I})\,\mathbf{g}^{(k)}\\ &= \mathbf{H}^{(k)}\,(\hat{\mathbf{Q}}^T\boldsymbol{\theta}^{(k)} - \mathbf{g}^{(k)}),\end{aligned} \tag{3.4.3}$$

where

$$\boldsymbol{\theta}^{(k)} = (\hat{\mathbf{Q}}\mathbf{H}^{(k)}\hat{\mathbf{Q}}^T)^{-1}\hat{\mathbf{Q}}\mathbf{H}^{(k)}\mathbf{g}^{(k)}. \tag{3.4.4}$$

We note that $\boldsymbol{\omega}^{(k)} = \mathbf{M}^{-T}\boldsymbol{\theta}^{(k)}$ and the columns of $\hat{\mathbf{Q}}^T$ must lie in the range of $\hat{\mathbf{A}}^{(k)}$. The objective now is to choose the factorization (3.4.2) such that $\hat{\mathbf{Q}}\mathbf{H}^{(k)}\hat{\mathbf{Q}}^T$ has a minimum condition number. This can be done if we set $\mathbf{M} = \hat{\mathbf{L}}^{(k)}$ and $\hat{\mathbf{Q}} = \mathbf{Q}_1{}^{(k)}$ where $\hat{\mathbf{L}}^{(k)}$ and $\mathbf{Q}_1{}^{(k)}$ are the matrices associated with the *LQ* factorization given in equation (3.3.1). The Lagrange multipliers $\boldsymbol{\omega}^{(k)}$, which now do not play an explicit role in the definition of $\mathbf{p}^{(k)}$, can be determined from the set of equations $\hat{\mathbf{L}}^{(k)T}\boldsymbol{\omega}^{(k)} = \boldsymbol{\theta}^{(k)}$ and we note that $\boldsymbol{\omega}^{(k)}$ is no longer found as the least-squares solution of the set of over-determined equations (3.4.1). The matrices recurred in the factorized form of the Murtagh–Sargent algorithm are as follows

(i) the Cholesky factors of $\mathbf{B}^{(k)}$,

(ii) the Cholesky factors of $\mathbf{Q}_1{}^{(k)}\mathbf{B}^{(k)-1}\mathbf{Q}_1{}^{(k)T}$,

and (iii) the orthogonal factors of $\hat{\mathbf{A}}^{(k)T}$.

The matrix $\mathbf{Z}^{(k)}$ is not required during the computation and consequently at the cost of some increase in the complexity of the implementation only the matrices $\hat{\mathbf{L}}^{(k)}$ and $\mathbf{Q}_1{}^{(k)}$ need be stored.

Although the vector $\boldsymbol{\theta}^{(k)}$ of equation (3.4.4) is now computed as accurately as possible there is still the possibility of cancellation in $\mathbf{p}^{(k)}$ near the solution. As we converge to a stationary point we have $\mathbf{p}^{(k)} \doteqdot \mathbf{0}$ and, since $\mathbf{H}^{(k)}$ is of full rank the smallness of $\mathbf{p}^{(k)}$ occurs as a result of cancellation between $\mathbf{Q}_1{}^{(k)T}\boldsymbol{\theta}^{(k)}$ and $\mathbf{g}^{(k)}$. As we shall now show, this problem can be avoided if we recur the matrix $\mathbf{Z}^{(k)}$. Since $\mathbf{Q}^{(k)}$ in (3.3.1) is orthogonal, the vector $\mathbf{g}^{(k)} \in E^n$ can be written in the form

$$\mathbf{g}^{(k)} = \mathbf{Q}_1{}^{(k)T}\mathbf{v} + \mathbf{Z}^{(k)}\mathbf{u},$$

where $\mathbf{v}$ and $\mathbf{u}$ are t- and $(n-t)$-vectors respectively. Multiplying this last equation successively by $\mathbf{Q}_1{}^{(k)}$ and $\mathbf{Z}^T$ we obtain $\mathbf{v} = \mathbf{Q}_1{}^{(k)}\mathbf{g}^{(k)}$ and $\mathbf{u} = \mathbf{Z}^{(k)T}\mathbf{g}^{(k)} = \mathbf{g}_A{}^{(k)}$.

Substituting for $\mathbf{g}^{(k)}$ in equation (3.4.4) we have

$$\begin{aligned}\boldsymbol{\theta}^{(k)} &= (\mathbf{Q}_1{}^{(k)}\mathbf{H}^{(k)}\mathbf{Q}_1{}^{(k)T})^{-1}\mathbf{Q}_1{}^{(k)}\mathbf{H}^{(k)}(\mathbf{Q}_1{}^{(k)T}\mathbf{v} + \mathbf{Z}^{(k)}\mathbf{g}_A{}^{(k)})\\ &= \mathbf{v} + (\mathbf{Q}_1{}^{(k)}\mathbf{H}^{(k)}\mathbf{Q}_1{}^{(k)T})^{-1}\mathbf{Q}_1{}^{(k)}\mathbf{H}^{(k)}\mathbf{Z}^{(k)}\mathbf{g}_A{}^{(k)}\\ &= \mathbf{v} + \bar{\mathbf{v}}, \text{ say.}\end{aligned}$$

Substituting for $\boldsymbol{\theta}^{(k)}$ and $\mathbf{g}^{(k)}$ in the equation (3.4.3) defining $\mathbf{p}^{(k)}$ gives

$$\mathbf{p}^{(k)} = \mathbf{H}^{(k)}(\mathbf{Q}_1{}^{(k)T}\bar{\mathbf{v}} - \mathbf{Z}^{(k)}\mathbf{g}_A{}^{(k)}).$$

Both vectors in the parentheses converge to zero with $\mathbf{p}^{(k)}$ but there is no cancellation error since they are orthogonal. We note that the direction of search can be written as

$$\mathbf{p}^{(k)} = \mathbf{H}^{(k)}[\mathbf{Q}_1{}^{(k)T}(\mathbf{Q}_1{}^{(k)}\mathbf{H}^{(k)}\,\mathbf{Q}_1{}^{(k)T})^{-1}\mathbf{Q}_1{}^{(k)}\mathbf{H}^{(k)} - \mathbf{I}]\,\mathbf{Z}^{(k)}\mathbf{g}_A{}^{(k)}.$$

3.5. The Choice of Active Set

In Chapter II, Section 2.6, we considered various methods for determining the set of active constraints. In this section we shall extend the discussion by considering in detail rules which depend upon some derivatives of $F(\mathbf{x})$ that may be available. We shall only be concerned with criteria for *deleting* constraints from the active basis—the reader will recall that the strategy for *adding* constraints is fixed by the relative magnitude of the steplength $\alpha^{(k)}$ and the step to the nearest constraint. These criteria attempt to determine whether or not it is worthwhile to delete a constraint by comparing the estimated reduction of $F(\mathbf{x})$ obtained by remaining on a constraint with the reduction that might be obtained by deleting it. Since these quantities are not known in

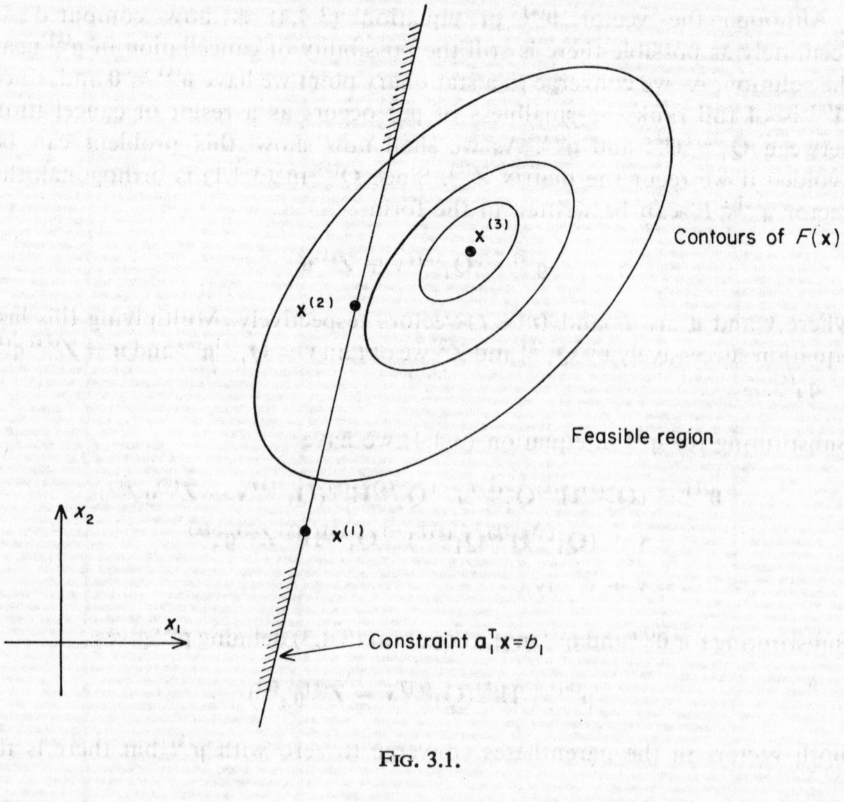

FIG. 3.1.

advance some *a priori* estimates must be made; because these estimates may be substantially in error, the general rule is to err on the side of conservatism and drop a constraint only if the improvement will be significant.

To give insight into how we may furnish estimates of the required quantities, we shall consider the minimization of a *positive-definite quadratic form* using Newton's method. Let $\mathbf{x}^{(1)}$ be a current approximation to the solution and assume that $\mathbf{x}^{(1)}$ satisfies the t constraints $\hat{\mathbf{A}}^{(1)T}\mathbf{x}^{(1)} = \mathbf{b}^{(1)}$. Assume that the minimum of $F(\mathbf{x})$ on the manifold $\hat{\mathbf{A}}^{(1)T}\mathbf{x} = \mathbf{b}^{(1)}$ is at the point $\mathbf{x}^{(2)}$ and that $\mathbf{x}^{(3)}$ is the minimum on the set of constraints $\hat{\mathbf{A}}^{(2)T}\mathbf{x} = \mathbf{b}^{(2)}$ made up of all the rows of $\hat{\mathbf{A}}^{(1)T}$ save the last—there is no loss of generality in assuming that the constraints have been so arranged so that the last constraint is deleted. If the respective function values are $F^{(1)}$, $F^{(2)}$ and $F^{(3)}$, we are interested in the quantities $F^{(1)} - F^{(2)}$ and $F^{(2)} - F^{(3)}$. The latter being the *additional* gain obtained by moving off the constraint. Figure 3.1 depicts a two-dimensional example with a single constraint $\mathbf{a}_1{}^T\mathbf{x} = b_1$. We can compute the direction of search $\mathbf{p}^{(1)}$ using either the primal form, (2.4.5)

$$\mathbf{p}^{(1)} = -\mathbf{Z}^{(1)}(\mathbf{Z}^{(1)T}\mathbf{G}\mathbf{Z}^{(1)})^{-1}\mathbf{Z}^T\mathbf{g}^{(1)}, \tag{3.5.1}$$

or the dual form (2.4.9 and 2.4.10)

$$\mathbf{p}^{(1)} = \mathbf{G}^{-1}(\hat{\mathbf{A}}^{(1)}\boldsymbol{\omega}^{(1)} - \mathbf{g}^{(1)}), \tag{3.5.2}$$

where

$$\boldsymbol{\omega}^{(1)} = (\hat{\mathbf{A}}^{(1)T}\mathbf{G}^{-1}\hat{\mathbf{A}}^{(1)})^{-1}\hat{\mathbf{A}}^{(1)T}\mathbf{G}^{-1}\mathbf{g}^{(1)}. \tag{3.5.3}$$

We note that since the function is convex these directions are identical (see Chapter II, Theorem 2.2) and give the exact step to the point $\mathbf{x}^{(2)}$.

LEMMA 3.1. *Let $\boldsymbol{\omega}^{(1)}$ and $\boldsymbol{\omega}^{(2)}$ be the second-order estimates of the Lagrange multipliers at the points $\mathbf{x}^{(1)}$ and $\mathbf{x}^{(2)}$ respectively—they are the exact Lagrange multipliers since $F(\mathbf{x})$ is quadratic. If $\mathbf{u}$ is the t-th column of $(\hat{\mathbf{A}}^{(1)T}\mathbf{G}^{-1}\hat{\mathbf{A}}^{(1)})^{-1}$, then*

$$\begin{bmatrix}\boldsymbol{\omega}^{(2)}\\ \mathbf{0}\end{bmatrix} - \boldsymbol{\omega}^{(1)} = -\frac{\omega_t{}^{(1)}}{u_t}\mathbf{u}.$$

Proof. The equations for the vector $\boldsymbol{\omega}^{(2)}$ are given by

$$(\hat{\mathbf{A}}^{(2)T}\mathbf{G}^{-1}\hat{\mathbf{A}}^{(2)})\,\boldsymbol{\omega}^{(2)} = \hat{\mathbf{A}}^{(2)T}\mathbf{G}^{-1}\mathbf{g}^{(2)},$$

or equivalently

$$\left(\begin{bmatrix}\hat{\mathbf{A}}^{(2)T}\\ \mathbf{0}\end{bmatrix}\mathbf{G}^{-1}[\hat{\mathbf{A}}^{(2)}\quad \mathbf{0}]\right)^{-1}\begin{bmatrix}\boldsymbol{\omega}^{(2)}\\ \mathbf{0}\end{bmatrix} = \begin{bmatrix}\hat{\mathbf{A}}^{(2)T}\\ \mathbf{0}\end{bmatrix}\mathbf{G}^{-1}\mathbf{g}^{(2)}.$$

Substituting the identity

$$[\hat{\mathbf{A}}^{(2)} \quad \mathbf{0}] = \hat{\mathbf{A}}^{(1)} - \mathbf{a}_t\mathbf{e}_t^T$$

and noting that

$$\mathbf{g}^{(2)} = \mathbf{G}\mathbf{p}^{(1)} + \mathbf{g}^{(1)}, \quad \hat{\mathbf{A}}^{(1)T}\mathbf{p}^{(1)} = \mathbf{0} \quad \text{and} \quad \mathbf{e}_t^T \begin{bmatrix} \boldsymbol{\omega}^{(2)} \\ 0 \end{bmatrix} = 0,$$

we obtain, after some algebraic manipulation

$$(\hat{\mathbf{A}}^{(1)T}\mathbf{G}^{-1}\hat{\mathbf{A}}^{(1)}) \begin{bmatrix} \boldsymbol{\omega}^{(2)} \\ 0 \end{bmatrix} - \mathbf{e}_t\mathbf{a}_t^T\mathbf{G}^{-1}\hat{\mathbf{A}}^{(1)} \begin{bmatrix} \boldsymbol{\omega}^{(2)} \\ 0 \end{bmatrix}$$

$$= \hat{\mathbf{A}}^{(1)T}\mathbf{G}^{-1}\mathbf{g}^{(1)} - \mathbf{e}_t\mathbf{a}_t^T\mathbf{G}^{-1}\mathbf{g}^{(1)}.$$

Pre-multiplying these equations by $(\hat{\mathbf{A}}^{(1)T}\mathbf{G}^{-1}\hat{\mathbf{A}}^{(1)})^{-1}$ and substituting for $\boldsymbol{\omega}^{(1)}$ from (3.5.2) gives

$$\begin{bmatrix} \boldsymbol{\omega}^{(2)} \\ 0 \end{bmatrix} - (\hat{\mathbf{A}}^{(1)T}\mathbf{G}^{-1}\hat{\mathbf{A}}^{(1)})^{-1}\mathbf{e}_t\mathbf{a}_t^T\mathbf{G}^{-1}\hat{\mathbf{A}}^{(1)} \begin{bmatrix} \boldsymbol{\omega}^{(2)} \\ 0 \end{bmatrix}$$

$$= \boldsymbol{\omega}^{(1)} - (\hat{\mathbf{A}}^{(1)T}\mathbf{G}^{-1}\hat{\mathbf{A}}^{(1)})^{-1}\mathbf{e}_t\mathbf{a}_t^T\mathbf{G}^{-1}\mathbf{g}^{(1)}.$$

It is clear from this last expression that

$$\begin{bmatrix} \boldsymbol{\omega}^{(2)} \\ 0 \end{bmatrix} - \boldsymbol{\omega}^{(k)} = \gamma\,(\hat{\mathbf{A}}^{(1)T}\mathbf{G}^{-1}\hat{\mathbf{A}}^{(1)})^{-1}\mathbf{e}_t$$

$$= \gamma\mathbf{u}, \text{ by definition,}$$

where γ is a scalar. Pre-multiplying this equation by $\mathbf{e}_t^T$ gives $\gamma = -\omega_t^{(1)}/u_t$ and the lemma is proved. ∎

THEOREM 3.1. *If the direction* $\mathbf{p}^{(1)}$ *is defined by equations* (3.5.1) *or* (3.5.2), *and* $\mathbf{p}^{(2)}$ *is the direction* $\mathbf{p}^{(2)} = \mathbf{x}^{(3)} - \mathbf{x}^{(2)} = \mathbf{G}^{-1}(\hat{\mathbf{A}}^{(2)}\boldsymbol{\omega}^{(2)} - \mathbf{g}^{(2)})$ *then*

$$F^{(1)} - F^{(2)} = \tfrac{1}{2}\mathbf{p}^{(1)T}\mathbf{G}\mathbf{p}^{(1)} \quad \textit{and} \quad F^{(2)} - F^{(3)} = \tfrac{1}{2}\,\omega_t^{(1)2}/u_t,$$

where $\mathbf{u}^T$ *is the t-th row of* $(\hat{\mathbf{A}}^{(1)T}\mathbf{G}^{-1}\hat{\mathbf{A}}^{(1)})^{-1}$.

Proof. Since $F(\mathbf{x})$ is quadratic we have

$$F^{(2)} = F^{(1)} + \mathbf{g}^{(1)T}\mathbf{p}^{(1)} + \tfrac{1}{2}\mathbf{p}^{(1)T}\mathbf{G}\mathbf{p}^{(1)}.$$

Substituting for $\mathbf{p}^{(1)}$ from (3.5.1) gives

$$F^{(1)} - F^{(2)} = -\tfrac{1}{2}\mathbf{g}^{(1)T}\mathbf{p}^{(1)} = \tfrac{1}{2}\mathbf{p}^{(1)T}\mathbf{G}\mathbf{p}^{(1)}. \tag{3.5.4}$$

Similarly

$$F^{(2)} - F^{(3)} = -\tfrac{1}{2}\mathbf{g}^{(2)T}\mathbf{p}^{(2)} = \tfrac{1}{2}\mathbf{p}^{(2)T}\mathbf{G}\mathbf{p}^{(2)}. \tag{3.5.5}$$

From the definition of $\mathbf{p}^{(2)}$ we have

$$\begin{aligned}\mathbf{p}^{(2)} &= \mathbf{G}^{-1}(\hat{\mathbf{A}}^{(2)}\boldsymbol{\omega}^{(2)} - \mathbf{g}^{(2)})\\ &= \mathbf{G}^{-1}\left(\hat{\mathbf{A}}^{(1)}\begin{bmatrix}\boldsymbol{\omega}^{(2)}\\ \mathbf{0}\end{bmatrix} - \mathbf{g}^{(2)}\right).\end{aligned}$$

Substituting the value of $\begin{bmatrix}\boldsymbol{\omega}^{(2)}\\ \mathbf{0}\end{bmatrix}$ defined by Lemma 3.1, we obtain

$$\begin{aligned}\mathbf{p}^{(2)} &= \mathbf{G}^{-1}\left(-\frac{\omega_t^{(1)}}{u_t}\hat{\mathbf{A}}^{(1)}\mathbf{u} + \hat{\mathbf{A}}^{(1)}\boldsymbol{\omega}^{(1)} - \mathbf{g}^{(2)}\right)\\ &= \mathbf{G}^{-1}\left(-\frac{\omega_t^{(1)}}{u_t}\hat{\mathbf{A}}^{(1)}\mathbf{u} + \hat{\mathbf{A}}^{(1)}\boldsymbol{\omega}^{(1)} - \mathbf{G}\mathbf{p}^{(1)} - \mathbf{g}^{(1)}\right)\\ &= -\frac{\omega_t^{(1)}}{u_t}\mathbf{G}^{-1}\hat{\mathbf{A}}^{(1)}\mathbf{u}, \text{ from the definition of } \mathbf{p}^{(1)}.\end{aligned}$$

Substituting this value of $\mathbf{p}^{(2)}$ in (3.5.5) gives

$$F^{(2)} - F^{(3)} = \tfrac{1}{2}\omega_t^{(1)2}/u_t,$$

which proves the theorem. ▮

A suitable strategy for selecting which constraint (if any) to delete, would be to find the constraint for which $\Delta F_{\max}$, the maximum value of $\Delta F = F^{(2)} - F^{(3)}$ over all constraints with a negative Lagrange multiplier, and delete the corresponding constraint if

$$\Delta F_{\max} \geqslant F^{(1)} - F^{(2)}. \tag{3.5.6}$$

This would ensure that $F^{(1)} - F^{(3)} \geqslant 2(F^{(1)} - F^{(2)})$. From equation (3.5.4) the value of $F^{(1)} - F^{(2)}$ can be either $-\tfrac{1}{2}\mathbf{g}^{(1)T}\mathbf{p}^{(1)}$ or $\tfrac{1}{2}\mathbf{p}^{(1)T}\mathbf{G}\mathbf{p}^{(1)}$ depending upon which value is more easily obtained. The inequality (3.5.6) constitutes an *ideal* test in that it assumes the knowlege of $F^{(2)} - F^{(3)}$ for each constraint. In most algorithms the exact second-order estimates of the Lagrange multipliers are not known since the second derivatives are not available. However, similar tests have been devised which approximate the quantities of (3.5.6) and these are defined as *substitute* tests. The first of these, which was used by Rosen (1960), has the form

$$-\mathbf{g}^{(k)T}\mathbf{p}^{(k)} = \mathbf{p}^{(k)T}\mathbf{p}^{(k)} = \|\mathbf{p}^{(k)}\|_2^2 \leqslant \tfrac{1}{4}\lambda_s^{(k)2}/\beta_s, \tag{3.5.7}$$

where $\lambda^{(k)}$ are first order estimates of the Lagrange multipliers which satisfy the equations $(\hat{\mathbf{A}}^{(k)T}\hat{\mathbf{A}}^{(k)})\,\lambda^{(k)} = \hat{\mathbf{A}}^{(k)T}\mathbf{g}^{(k)}$ and β_s is the sth diagonal element of $(\hat{\mathbf{A}}^{(k)T}\hat{\mathbf{A}}^{(k)})^{-1}$. Rosen has used the value $\mathbf{G} = \mathbf{I}$ and has included the factor $\frac{1}{4}$—this is valid since the introduction of any constant γ causes a move to be made off a constraint if the *additional* reduction in $F(\mathbf{x})$ exceeds γ times the reduction obtained by remaining on the constraint.

Unfortunately, methods appearing recently in the literature have attempted to apply Rosen's test directly rather than use the original form (3.5.6). For example, Goldfarb uses (3.5.7) despite the fact that

$$\|\mathbf{p}^{(k)}\|_2^2 = \|\mathbf{H}_G{}^{(k)}\mathbf{g}^{(k)}\|_2^2 \neq -\,\mathbf{g}^{(k)T}\mathbf{p}^{(k)};$$

similarly Murtagh and Sargent use (3.5.7) with β_s the sth diagonal element of $(\hat{\mathbf{A}}^{(k)T}\mathbf{H}^{(k)}\hat{\mathbf{A}}^{(k)})^{-1}$. In both these applications the values of $-\,\mathbf{g}^{(k)T}\mathbf{p}^{(k)}$ should be used on the left-hand side of (3.5.6), and we emphasize that the test (3.5.6) is valid only in the case where $\mathbf{p}^{(k)T}\mathbf{p}^{(k)} = -\,\mathbf{g}^{(k)T}\mathbf{p}^{(k)}$, that is, when

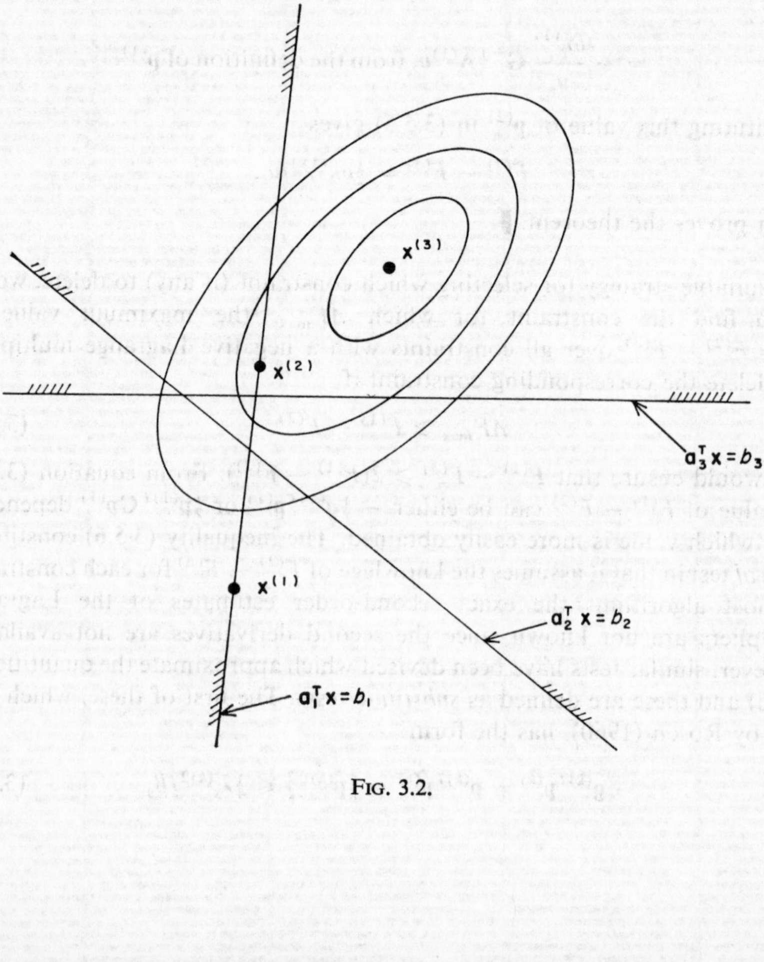

FIG. 3.2.

$\mathbf{G} = \mathbf{I}$ in the relation (3.5.4). (We note that the tests given by Fletcher (1972b) and Murtagh and Sargent (1969) contain misprints.)

For any of the tests to be meaningful, three conditions should hold.

(i) The ideal test must hold on the quadratic problem.

(ii) The ideal test must be meaningful on the non-quadratic problem.

(iii) The substitute test must be a reasonable approximation to the ideal test.

For a Newton-type algorithm (iii) obviously applies. It might appear that (i) also holds but unfortunately the test does not take into account the possibility of another constraint lying between $\mathbf{x}^{(1)}$ and $\mathbf{x}^{(2)}$ or $\mathbf{x}^{(3)}$. In this event it is not possible to achieve the predicted reductions—even for a quadratic function. A test for which (i) holds must take into account the size of the residuals of the inactive constraints. Consider the situation depicted in Fig. 3.2; if $\mathbf{a}_3{}^T\mathbf{x} = b_3$ is the only inactive constraint, a move off

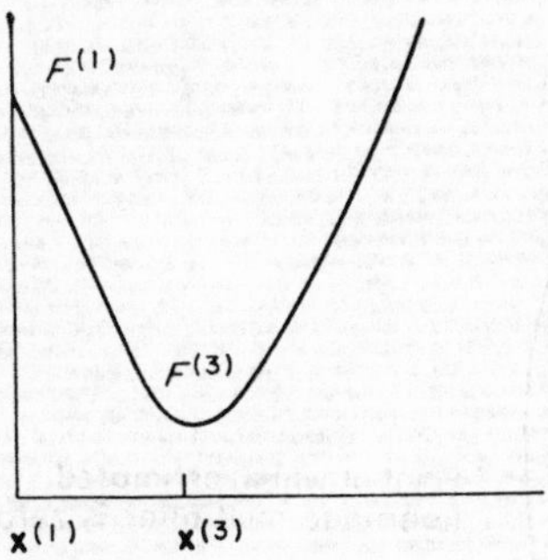

FIG. 3.3.

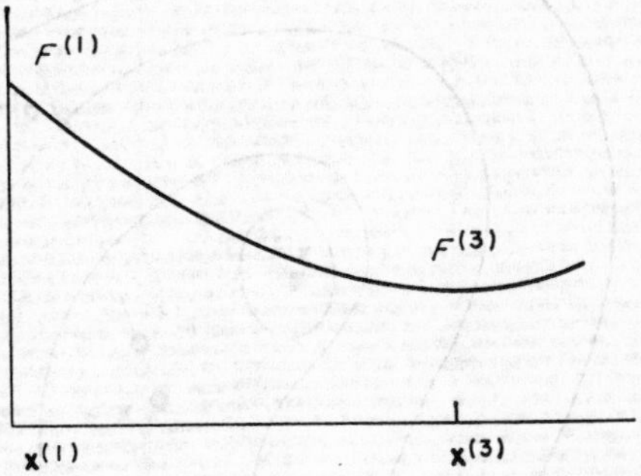

FIG. 3.4.

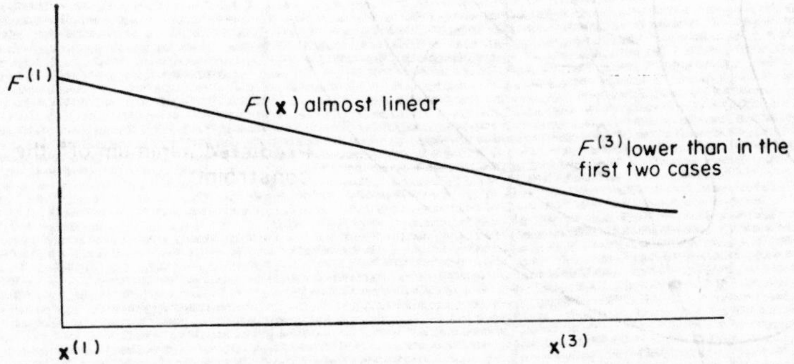

FIG. 3.5.

the active constraint $\mathbf{a}_1^T\mathbf{x} = b_1$ is beneficial, but this will not be the case if the constraint $\mathbf{a}_2^T\mathbf{x} = b_2$ is present.

The magnitude of the direction of search depends upon which constraint is deleted. The tests take no account of the magnitude of $\|\mathbf{p}^{(k)}\|$, however, the probability of violating an inactive constraint increases with the magnitudes of $\|\mathbf{x}^{(2)} - \mathbf{x}^{(1)}\|$ and $\|\mathbf{x}^{(3)} - \mathbf{x}^{(1)}\|$, therefore the expected decrease is more likely to be achieved by deleting some constraints than by deleting others. To illustrate this point consider Figs 3.3, 3.4 and 3.5.

The figures demonstrate how $F(\mathbf{x})$ could vary along alternative directions $\mathbf{x}^{(1)} - \mathbf{x}^{(3)}$ obtained by deleting three alternative active constraints. The largest negative Lagrange multiplier occurs in the first case but the test (3.5.6) is such that the last constraint given in Fig. 3.5 will be deleted because the near linearity of $F(\mathbf{x})$ produces a very small value of β_s. In general the quantity $\|\mathbf{x}^{(3)} - \mathbf{x}^{(1)}\|$ is not known but the deletion of the constraint with the largest negative Lagrange multiplier will generally lead to a smaller step.

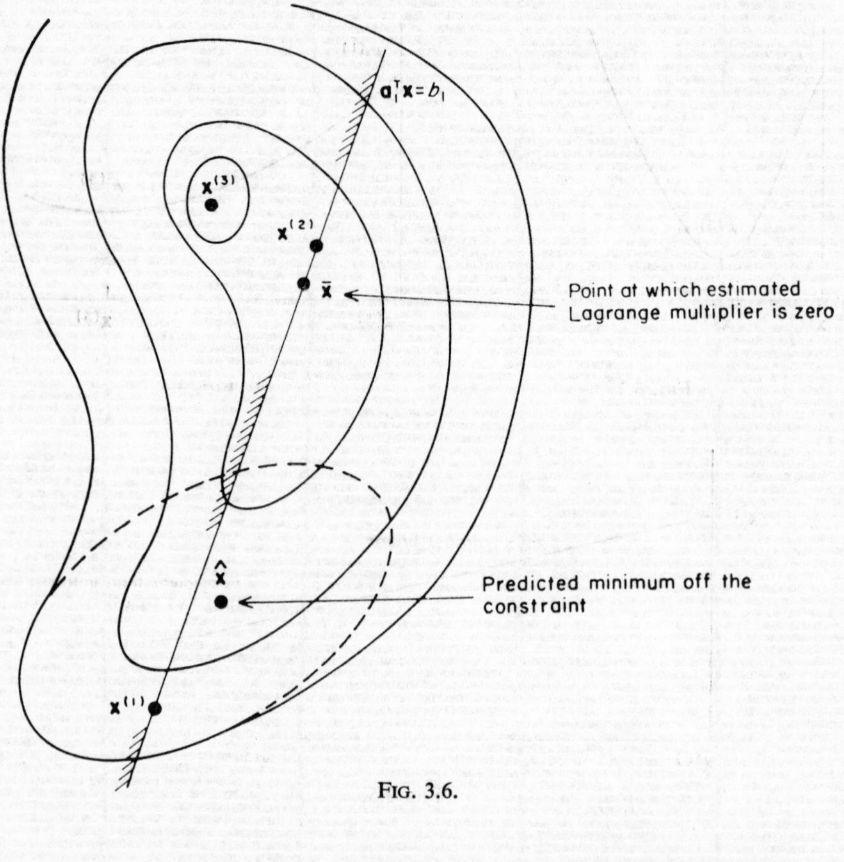

FIG. 3.6.

If the matrix $\hat{\mathbf{A}}^{(k)T}\mathbf{G}^{(k)-1}\hat{\mathbf{A}}^{(k)}$ is indefinite, and there is no reason to suppose that it will not be even in the neighbourhood of the minimum, then the quantities u_t could be negative or even zero. In this event the assumptions underlying the test are violated even when $F(\mathbf{x})$ is a quadratic function. The same applies on the occasions when $\mathbf{Z}^{(k)T}\mathbf{G}^{(k)}\mathbf{Z}^{(k)}$ is indefinite—although this occurs less frequently.

Clearly if condition (i) does not apply then neither will (ii), but unfortunately there are additional complications caused by the non-quadratic behaviour of $F(\mathbf{x})$. Consider the situation depicted in Fig. 3.6; in this case the sign of the estimate of the Lagrange multiplier changes sign, being negative on the line segment $[\mathbf{x}^{(1)}, \bar{\mathbf{x}})$ and positive on the line segment $(\bar{\mathbf{x}}, \mathbf{x}^{(2)}]$. This implies that we erroneously perform a test at $\mathbf{x}^{(1)}$ and we may drop the constraint from the basis when it should be retained. The converse situation applied in Fig. 3.7 where the constraint would be retained although the minimum lies interior to the constraint. These examples indicate that the consistency of

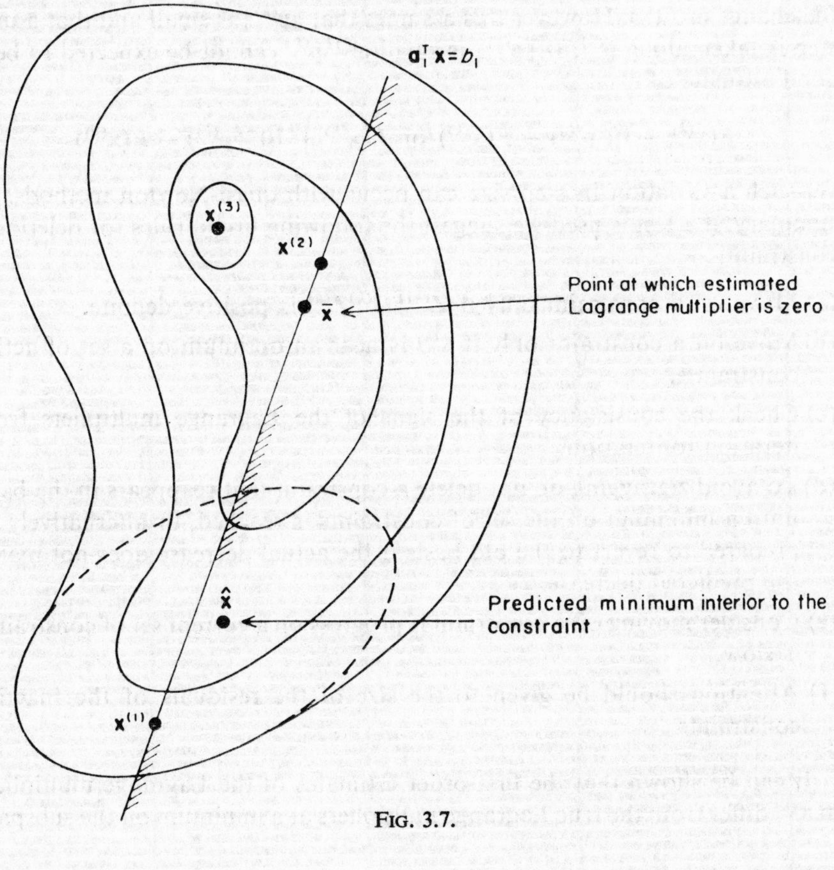

FIG. 3.7.

the signs of the Lagrange multipliers should be checked from one iteration to the next and that the test is always more reliable at points closer to $\mathbf{x}^{(2)}$—which agrees with our requirement that $\|\mathbf{x}^{(2)} - \mathbf{x}^{(1)}\|$ be small.

When the Hessian matrix is unavailable a substitute test must be used and as we have seen there are two general types of method. Firstly, if the Hessian is approximated by finite differences as described in Chapter II then the merits of the resulting substitute test are almost identical to those of the ideal test. Secondly, for quasi-Newton methods, we only have a matrix $\mathbf{B}^{(k)}$ which *approximates* $\mathbf{G}^{(k)}$. It is our experience that the magnitude of $\|\mathbf{G}^{(k)}\|$ and $\|\mathbf{B}^{(k)}\|$ can differ widely. Moreover the magnitude of $\|\mathbf{B}^{(k)}\|$ can vary widely for different update formulae generating the same sequence of estimates. One way in which this affects the algorithm concerns the ratio of $\|\mathbf{p}^{(k)}\|$ to $\|\bar{\mathbf{p}}\|$, where $\bar{\mathbf{p}}$ is the actual step to the minimum. In Newton-type methods this ratio is rarely outside the limits 0.1–10 whereas for quasi-Newton methods the ratio can vary between 10^{-4} and 10^4 (see Murray, 1972c). It could be argued that whatever the step, $\mathbf{g}^{(k)T}\mathbf{p}^{(k)}$ will be a good estimate of the change in $F(\mathbf{x})$. However this assumes that $\|\mathbf{p}^{(k)}\|$ is small and that a unit step is taken along $\mathbf{p}^{(k)}$. If $\|\mathbf{p}^{(k)}\|$ is small $\mathbf{g}^{(k)T}\mathbf{p}^{(k)}$ cannot be expected to be a good estimate of

$$F(\mathbf{x}^{(k)} + 10^4\mathbf{p}^{(k)}) - F(\mathbf{x}^{(k)}) \text{ or } F(\mathbf{x}^{(k)} + 10^{-4}\mathbf{p}^{(k)}) - F(\mathbf{x}^{(k)}),$$

yet such a variation in step size can occur with quasi-Newton methods. In summary, if a test is used we suggest the following broad rules for deleting a constraint.

(a) Move off a constraint only if $\mathbf{Z}^{(k)T}\mathbf{G}^{(k)}\mathbf{Z}^{(k)}$ is positive definite.

(b) Move off a constraint only if $\mathbf{x}^{(k)}$ is near an optimum on a set of active constraints.

(c) Check the consistency of the signs of the Lagrange multipliers from iteration to iteration.

(d) To avoid zigzagging do not delete a constraint that reappears in the basis until a minimum on the set of constraints is reached, or alternatively be prepared to revert to the old basis if the actual decrease does not match the predicted decrease.

(e) Consider moving off a constraint if progress on a current set of constraints is slow.

(f) Attention should be given to the size of the residuals of the inactive constraints.

It can be shown that the first-order estimates of the Lagrange multipliers at $\mathbf{x}^{(k)}$ differ from the true Lagrange multipliers at a minimum on the subspace by $O(\|\mathbf{g}_A^{(k)}\|)$. It follows that if $\|\mathbf{g}_A^{(k)}\|$ is small compared with $\lambda_i^{(k)}$, $i = 1, 2, \ldots, t$, then we can be reasonably confident that the sign of each $\lambda_i^{(k)}$ is correct. This property is utilized in the test used in the current NPL procedures. The test requires $\|\mathbf{g}_A^{(k)}\|_2$ to fall below a weak tolerance ε_1 before any constraints are considered eligible for deletion. (If a Newton-type method is used we impose the additional requirement that the matrix $\mathbf{G}_A^{(k)}$, or its finite-difference approximation, be positive definite.) If these conditions hold, a constraint with the most negative Lagrange multiplier $\lambda_s^{(k)}$ is deleted if

$$\lambda_s^{(k)} \leqslant -\gamma\varepsilon_1 \tag{3.5.8}$$

where γ is a preassigned positive scalar. If there is no $\lambda_j^{(k)}$ satisfying this criterion, $\|\mathbf{g}_A\|_2$ is reduced further until $\|\mathbf{g}_A^{(k)}\| \leqslant \varepsilon_2$ and (3.5.8) is reapplied with ε_2 replacing ε_1. If the smallest Lagrange multiplier estimate is still close to zero, the techniques described in Chapter II, Section 2.6, to deal with small Lagrange multipliers are applied. It is hoped that in the future more of the rules (a)–(f) can be incorporated in the tests.

3.6. Linearly Constrained Algorithms which do not Require Derivatives

Quasi-Newton methods can be applied to unconstrained problems for which analytical derivatives are unavailable by using either of the finite-difference approximations

$$\bar{g}_j^{(k)} = (F(\mathbf{x}^{(k)} + h\mathbf{e}_j) - F(\mathbf{x}^{(k)}))/h, \qquad j = 1, 2, \ldots, n, \tag{3.6.1}$$

$$\bar{g}_j^{(k)} = (F(\mathbf{x}^{(k)} + h\mathbf{e}_j) - F(\mathbf{x}^{(k)} - h\mathbf{e}_j))/2h, \qquad j = 1, 2, \ldots, n, \tag{3.6.2}$$

in place of $\mathbf{g}^{(k)}$ in the basic iteration. Formula (3.6.1) is known as the *forward-difference* approximation to $\mathbf{g}^{(k)}$ and has an associated truncation error

$$R_F(h) = \|\bar{\mathbf{g}}^{(k)} - \mathbf{g}^{(k)}\| = O(h).$$

Similarly (3.6.2) is the *central-difference* approximation and has truncation error $R_c(h)$ for which $R_c(h) = O(h^2)$. We note that the accuracy advantage of the central-difference approximation is reduced by the requirement of an additional n function evaluations. Unfortunately there is a limit to the amount that the finite-difference interval h can be reduced due to the significant cancellation which occurs when quantities of similar magnitude are subtracted. Cancellation error is particularly evident in the neighbourhood of a stationary point where $\|\mathbf{g}^{(k)}\|$ is very small. It is now generally recognized (Gill and Murray 1972a, Fletcher 1972c) that the scalar h should have a *fixed* value which approximately balances the truncation error against the cancellation error. With this value of h the cheaper forward-difference formula is used until $\mathbf{x}^{(k)}$ is in a neighbourhood where $\|\mathbf{g}\|$ is small, in which event a switch to central differences is made. At present, quasi-Newton methods using these techniques are generally more effective than any other method which utilize only function values.

The same basic technique of replacing $\mathbf{g}^{(k)}$ by $\bar{\mathbf{g}}^{(k)}$ can be applied in the methods of Goldfarb and Murtagh–Sargent for the linearly constrained problem. The disadvantage of such an implementation is that essentially an $n - t$ variable problem is being solved on the manifold $\hat{\mathbf{A}}^{(k)}$ yet full n function evaluations are required to compute an approximation to the gradient. This disadvantage is not present if finite-difference versions of the Gill–Murray or revised dual (Section 3.4) algorithms are used, since we can approximate the projected gradient $\mathbf{g}_A{}^{(k)}$ directly, using

$$(\bar{\mathbf{g}}_A{}^{(k)})_j = (F(\mathbf{x}^{(k)} + h\mathbf{z}_j) - F(\mathbf{x}^{(k)}))/h, \qquad j = 1, \ldots, n - t,$$

where $\mathbf{z}_j$ is the jth column of the matrix $\mathbf{Z}^{(k)}$. The central-difference formula can be generalized similarly, and the choice of h is identical to the unconstrained case (Gill and Murray, 1972a). (Since the gradient $\mathbf{g}^{(k)}$ is usually non-zero at a constrained stationary point, it might appear that the Goldfarb and Murtagh–Sargent methods will never require central differences, however this is not the case since, in formulae (3.1.1) and (3.2.3) respectively for $\mathbf{p}^{(k)}$, the operators $\mathbf{H}_G{}^{(k)}$ and $\mathbf{V}^{(k)}\mathbf{H}^{(k)}$ almost annihilate $\mathbf{g}^{(k)}$ in the neighbourhood of a stationary point and any errors in $\bar{\mathbf{g}}^{(k)}$ are emphasized.)

3.7. Methods Based upon Solving a Quadratic and Linear Program at Each Iteration

The methods discussed so far have chosen the search direction as the solution of the quadratic problem

$$\underset{\mathbf{p}}{\text{minimize}}\ \{\tfrac{1}{2}\mathbf{p}^T\mathbf{B}^{(k)}\mathbf{p} + \mathbf{g}^{(k)T}\mathbf{p}\}$$

subject to the constraints $\hat{\mathbf{A}}^{(k)T}\mathbf{p} = \gamma\mathbf{e}_s$, where γ is a scalar such that $\gamma \geqslant 0$. If γ is non-zero then this implies that a decision has been made to delete the sth constraint from the active set. It is possible to generalize this method so that the search direction is the solution of the inequality constraint quadratic problem with constraints $\hat{\mathbf{A}}^{(k)T}\mathbf{p} \geqslant \mathbf{0}$. It is advisable to add further conditions to prevent $\mathbf{p}^{(k)}$ from violating constraints which are currently inactive, and so the final *QP* for the direction becomes

$$\left.\begin{aligned}&\underset{\mathbf{p}}{\text{minimize}}\ \{\tfrac{1}{2}\mathbf{p}^T\mathbf{B}^{(k)}\mathbf{p} + \mathbf{g}^{(k)T}\mathbf{p}\},\\ &\text{subject to the constraints}\\ &\qquad\hat{\mathbf{A}}^{(k)T}\mathbf{p} \geqslant \mathbf{0},\\ &\qquad\bar{\mathbf{A}}^{(k)T}\mathbf{p} \geqslant \bar{\mathbf{b}}^{(k)} - \bar{\mathbf{A}}^{(k)T}\mathbf{x}^{(k)},\end{aligned}\right\} \qquad (3.7.1)$$

where $\bar{\mathbf{A}}^{(k)T}$ is the matrix of inactive constraints. (From the remarks of Chapter II, Section 2.4, the solution $\mathbf{p}^{(k)}$ will be bounded if $\mathbf{B}^{(k)}$ is positive definite, and this is usually the case with quasi-Newton methods.) It is possible to move off a large number of constraints at each iteration since we do not force any of the current active constraints to be active at the commencement of the next iteration. This does not necessarily imply that on average fewer constraints are active than with other methods since we are just as likely to add a large number of new constraints. The Lagrange multipliers of the quadratic problem (3.7.1) must be positive at the solution and they can be viewed as estimates of the Lagrange multipliers of the original problem. Unfortunately these estimates are very poor away from the solution of *LCP* since they are computed using the matrix $\mathbf{B}^{(k)}$ which may bear no relation to $\mathbf{G}^{(k)}$ during early iterations.

The strategy of solving (3.7.1) is very susceptible to zigzagging, but this can be overcome by changing some of the inequalities to equalities or restricting the size of the solution. Solving (3.7.1) does not completely eliminate the problem of determining the active set since the *QP* problem itself requires an underlying strategy for determining the active set. The latter problem should be less difficult since we are in the "ideal" situation of knowing the exact matrix of second derivatives of (3.7.1). (However, the reader will recall from Section 3.5 that knowing the Hessian matrix does not eliminate all the problems.) Another disadvantage is that the amount of computation is significantly increased and it is no longer possible to give a realistic bound on the number of operations necessary to solve (3.7.1).

A number of methods have been suggested in the literature for solving the general constrained problem by solving a *linear program* at each iteration. A straightforward linearization of the nonlinear function does not in general lead to a bounded solution since the number of constraints may be less than the dimension of the problem. Griffith and Stewart (1961) proposed adding constraints of the form

$$|p_i| \leqslant h, \tag{3.7.2}$$

where h is some preassigned scalar. An effect of introducing these constraints is that only a unit step along $\mathbf{p}^{(k)}$ is required and the steplength algorithm can be dispensed with. Griffith and Stewart also regard these additional constraints as restricting $\mathbf{p}^{(k)}$ to ensure that the problem is solved over a region in which the linear approximation is valid.

Wilson (1963) constructed a quadratic program by making a quadratic approximation to $F(\mathbf{x})$ using the Hessian matrix and adding constraints in the same way as Griffith and Stewart. Wilson was particularly concerned with the nonlinearly constrained problem but clearly the algorithm is valid for the simpler case. Curiously the computational results reported for

Wilson's algorithm have been poor. In the cases where the Hessian is unavailable a quasi-Newton approximation to the Hessian can be made (see Fletcher, 1972a).

With all the methods based upon adding constraints of the form (3.7.2), h may be increased or decreased at the next iteration depending on the result of evaluating $F(\mathbf{x}^{(k)} + \mathbf{p}^{(k)})$. If the value of $F^{(k)} - F(\mathbf{x}^{(k)} + \mathbf{p}^{(k)})$ is not sufficiently close to the predicted decrease in the function, the iteration is repeated with a smaller value of h. Clearly h should be as large as possible and none of the constraints (3.7.2) should be active at the solution. The reader is referred to Fletcher for details on rules for the manipulation of h. Apart from the forementioned disadvantages of solving the inequality constrained problem (3.7.1) every iteration, the value of $\mathbf{p}^{(k)}$ depends critically on the choice of the parameter h. Certainly if some of the constraints (3.7.2) are active, the Lagrange multipliers of the constrained problem are not good estimates of the Lagrange multipliers of the original problem, even in the neighbourhood of the solution.

An attractive means of limiting the stepsize is to alter the Hessian approximation by adding to it a positive semi-definite matrix. The objective function is then

$$\tfrac{1}{2}\mathbf{p}^T(\mathbf{B}^{(k)} + \mathbf{E}^{(k)})\,\mathbf{p} + \mathbf{g}^{(k)T}\mathbf{p},$$

where $\mathbf{E}^{(k)}$ is a positive semi-definite matrix. Again the adjustment of the modification is made on similar lines to that for the adjustment of the parameter h (see Chapter II, Section 2.3).

Once the *QP* problem (3.7.1) has been formulated we still need a method to solve it. We would naturally prefer to use a method based upon recurring matrix factorizations, and slightly modified versions of the quasi-Newton and modified Newton methods given in Sections 3.3, 3.4 and 2.5 can be used. (Whichever method is used some saving in computational effort can be made by preserving information used in solving one *QP* for the solution of the next.)

It is our opinion that quasi-Newton methods based upon active set strategies are likely to be more effective on the general linearly constrained problem than the methods discussed in this section. This is because the quadratic approximation is often inaccurate due to the violation of the quasi–Newton condition as the sequence $\{\mathbf{x}^{(k)}\}$ moves off and on a large number of constraints. Under these circumstances it seems unreasonable to invest considerable computational effort in determining $\mathbf{p}^{(k)}$.

Chapter IV

Methods for Large-scale Linearly Constrained Problems

PHILIP E. GILL AND WALTER MURRAY

Division of Numerical Analysis and Computing,
National Physical Laboratory

4.1. Introduction

When considering the methods discussed in Chapters II and III for use on very large problems, it is advisable to examine how the amount of resources required (computation and storage) depends on the number of variables and constraints. All the methods given involve the solution of many sets of linear algebraic equations; the dimensions of these systems, and therefore the amount of work required to solve them, depends upon the number of variables, n, and on the number of constraints, m. The storage used is also related to n and m, since it is necessary to have access to the $m \times n$ matrix of constraints, $\mathbf{A}^T$, to the $m \times n$ Hessian matrix $\mathbf{G}$ (or some approximation to it) and to various factorizations of these and related matrices. When the methods are implemented as given, the number of arithmetic operations per iteration is of the order $n^3 + nm$ and $n^2 + nm$ for Newton-type and quasi-Newton methods, respectively, and the storage required is of the order of $n^2 + nm$ locations for both techniques.

When n or m becomes very large, it is clear that two difficulties can occur: the computation time required may become too long to justify solving the problem; and, more critical, there may not be enough storage locations, either in core or on auxiliary storage, to contain the matrices and factorizations required. If essentially all of the elements of the matrices $\mathbf{A}^T$ and $\mathbf{G}$ are non-zero then it is impossible in a practical sense to solve very large problems.

Fortunately, however, the matrices that accompany most very large problems have a very high proportion of zero elements. The ratio of non-zero elements to the total number of elements in a matrix is termed its *density*. A matrix with an insignificant number of zero elements is called *dense*; a matrix with a high proportion of zero entries is called *sparse*. In practice, density tends to decrease as the size of the problem (number of variables or constraints) increases, and the number of non-zero elements often increases only linearly with n or m.

Besides having a low density, the matrices that occur in large problems nearly always have a structure or pattern. In a structured matrix the non-zero and zero elements are not scattered at random, but are known to occur in certain positions due to the nature of the problem and the relationships among the variables. Structured problems arise in many applications, including the scheduling of production, inventory and distribution activities, dynamic economic systems, decentralized production systems and some stochastic programming problems.

Two important examples that illustrate the kinds of structure encountered are the following. An industrial process may have some constraints applying to individual time intervals and some constraints relating to the whole time period. This gives a constraint matrix of the form

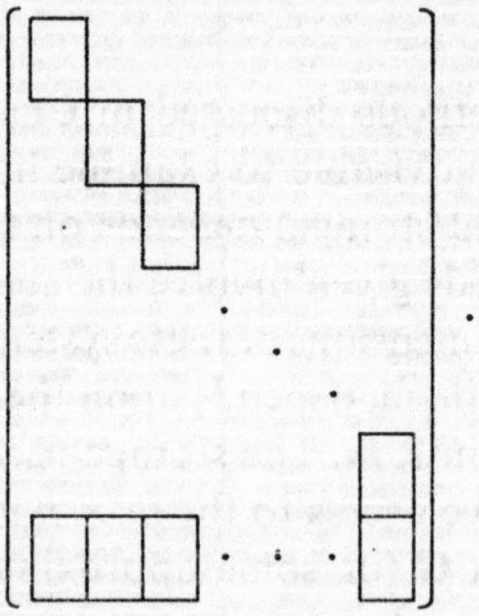

(4.1.1)

Alternatively there may be particular activities or variables which apply to every sector of an economic model, giving constraints of the form

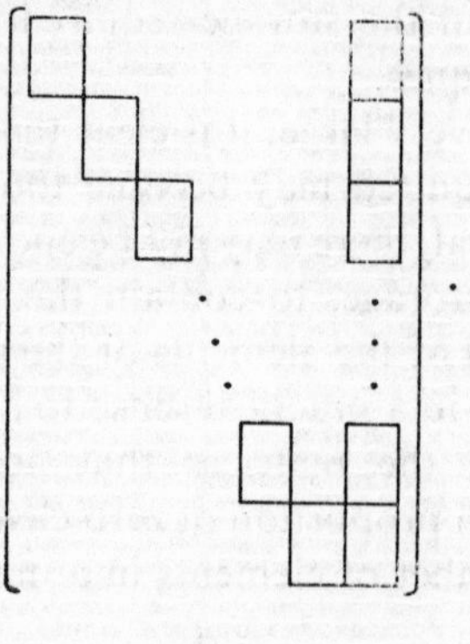

(4.1.2)

The structures (4.1.1) and (4.1.2) are known as block-diagonal constraints with coupling constraints and coupling variables respectively.

Given that very large problems will generally have sparsity and structure, it is possible to re-consider how such problems might be solved by taking advantage of this knowledge to reduce the amount of computation and storage required to an acceptable level. For example, a multiplication involving a zero element need not be executed, and a large block of zeros in a structured matrix need not be stored.

A further consideration in developing methods for large problems might be that the computation could be organized in connection with the transfer of data from auxiliary storage. Based on this criterion, a useful classification of large sparse problems is the following: a *medium-scale* problem can be solved entirely in-core by taking advantage of sparsity, while a *large-scale* problem can be solved only with the aid of auxiliary storage. It should be noted that the distinction between medium- and large-scale problems is entirely a question of whether the relevant matrices and factorizations can fit into core memory; thus this definition of the scale of a problem is related to its solution on a particular computer. Nonetheless, the distinction is important because some of the methods to be discussed take specific account of the use of auxiliary storage.

Our approach to finding methods for solving large problems will be two-fold.

(a) We shall consider how to implement the methods already discussed in a way which exploits sparsity in **A** or **G**. This approach is based upon the use of sparse matrix techniques to minimize the storage and the number of arithmetic operations required. It is essential when handling sparse matrices to store only the non-zero elements of a matrix and to use some logical operation to decide when arithmetic operations are necessary. If the matrix is stored in a haphazard manner, elements can be accessed only by the lengthy process of completely searching all of the data. However, so-called *indexing techniques* have been devised for storing the data in a form which facilitates the efficient retrieval of non-zero elements. We shall be more concerned here with the actual mathematical manipulation of sparse problems and we shall not consider indexing techniques in detail—the reader is referred to the paper by Pooch and Nieder (1973) for a complete survey of indexing techniques for sparse matrices. In summary, the first approach is to make methods suitable for the dense case efficient when applied to sparse problems.

(b) In order to take full advantage of sparsity it may prove worthwhile to deviate from the basic strategy of the methods recommended in Chapters II and III, and to devise new methods specifically designed for sparse problems.

Previously we have not been too concerned with the number of arithmetic operations per iteration provided that the methods were not inordinately inefficient. It was considered that the minimization of the number of iterations or number of function and gradient evaluations was of prime importance. However, for medium- or large-scale problems, gaining access to the appropriate elements of a matrix may require the traversal of a complicated data structure in core, or a transfer from auxiliary storage, and hence the overhead associated with each operation can become very expensive. Our second class of methods consists of those for which the computation is organized to take advantage of such considerations—usually by reducing an optimization problem to a related sequence of simpler optimization problems. The methods devised by the second approach may not be efficient for dense problems, as contrasted with the first approach. However, the second approach may lead to algorithms that are more efficient for many sparse problems in terms of storage and computation time. Each of these approaches (a) and (b) is related to a particular class of methods for the solution of large sets of linear algebraic equations and the first part of this chapter is devoted to reviewing such methods. Part II is concerned with the solution of unconstrained minimization problems and Part III with linearly constrained problems.

Part I
Numerical Methods for the Solution of Large Sparse Sets of Linear Equations

4.2. Classification of Methods

Methods for the solution of the linear equations

$$\mathbf{Ax} = \mathbf{b} \tag{4.2.1}$$

can be divided into two classes: *direct methods*, in which **A** is transformed into a matrix which is easily invertible, and *iterative methods*, in which the matrix **A** is used directly to generate a sequence of vectors which tend to the solution of (4.2.1). We shall describe briefly the most effective methods in each of these classes and consider their implementation in the case where **A** is a large sparse matrix.

4.3. Direct Methods based upon Matrix Factorizations

(a) The method of Gauss–Jordan elimination is based upon the idea of reducing **A** to diagonal form by a sequence of transformations. An elementary matrix can be constructed which is the identity matrix except for its jth column, viz,

$$\mathbf{T}_j = \begin{pmatrix} 1 & & & t_{1j} & & & \\ & \cdot & & \cdot & & & \\ & & \cdot & \cdot & & & \\ & & 1 & t_{j-1,j} & & & \\ & & & t_{jj} & & & \\ & & & t_{j+1,j} & 1 & & \\ & & & \cdot & & \cdot & \\ & & & \cdot & & & \cdot \\ & & & t_{nj} & & & 1 \end{pmatrix}. \tag{4.3.1}$$

The jth column of $\mathbf{T}_j$ can be defined so that when the partial product

$$\mathbf{A}_j = \mathbf{T}_{j-1}\,\mathbf{T}_{j-2}\ldots\mathbf{T}_1\mathbf{A}$$

is pre-multiplied by $\mathbf{T}_j$, the resulting matrix $\mathbf{A}_{j+1}$ has its jth column equal to the jth column of the identity matrix. The elements of $\mathbf{T}_j$ are computed according to the rule

$$t_{ij} = \begin{cases} -\,a_{ij}{}^{(j)}/a_{jj}{}^{(j)}, & i = 1, 2, \ldots, j-1, j+1, \ldots, n, \\ 1/a_{jj}{}^{(j)}, & i = j, \end{cases}$$

where $a_{ij}{}^{(j)}$ is the ijth element of $\mathbf{A}_j$. The element $a_{jj}{}^{(j)}$ is called the *pivot*. By definition, the matrix

$$\mathbf{A}_{n+1} = \mathbf{T}_n\mathbf{T}_{n-1}\ldots\mathbf{T}_1\mathbf{A}$$

is equal to the identity matrix and consequently

$$\mathbf{A}^{-1} = \mathbf{T}_n\mathbf{T}_{n-1}\ldots\mathbf{T}_1. \tag{4.3.2}$$

If the computation is carried out exactly as described, the elements of $\mathbf{T}_j$ can become arbitrarily large, since there is no *a priori* control on the size of $a_{jj}{}^{(j)}$, leading to a deterioration in the accuracy of the solution. In practice it is usual to slightly modify the algorithm so that an alternative pivot is chosen which guarantees that the sub-diagonal elements of $\mathbf{T}_j$ are bounded in magnitude by unity. This modification gives a matrix $\mathbf{A}_{n+1}$ which is a permutation of the identity matrix (see Fox, 1964, pp. 73–75).

For practical computation Gauss–Jordan elimination has been superseded by methods which we shall describe later in this section. However, the method illustrates very well a technique which is of fundamental importance in large-scale numerical analysis, namely, the idea of a *product form* of an algorithm. Since the elements of $\mathbf{A}_{j+1}$ are linear combinations of the rows of $\mathbf{A}_j$, new non-zero elements may be created in columns $j+1$ through n of $\mathbf{A}_{j+1}$, and the amount of storage required generally increases as the elimination proceeds. This phenomenon is called *fill-in* (we assume in all the following discussion that the matrix is sufficiently sparse to ensure that the storage of the problem is still possible after fill-in has occured). Since $\mathbf{A}_{j+1}$ will generally contain more non-zero elements than $\mathbf{A}_j$, an efficient method of storing these additional elements is required. Since the large and sparse matrix $\mathbf{A}$ must be stored in compact form (that is, just the non-zero elements) it is clearly inefficient to insert new elements in $\mathbf{A}_j$. This problem can be overcome by storing the separate factors $\mathbf{T}_j$ rather than obtaining $\mathbf{A}^{-1}$ explicitly by multiplying out the matrix product (4.3.2). This representation is the so-called *product form of the inverse* (PFI). Only the jth column of $\mathbf{A}_j$ is required for the definition of $\mathbf{T}_j$, and this column can be computed using

$$\mathbf{A}_j\mathbf{e}_j = \mathbf{T}_{j-1}\,\mathbf{T}_{j-2}\ldots\mathbf{T}_1\,\mathbf{A}\mathbf{e}_j. \tag{4.3.3}$$

The matrix $\mathbf{A}$ and products $\mathbf{T}_j$ can be stored in-core or on some auxiliary storage device, depending upon the amount of internal storage available. In the latter case the use of (4.3.2) requires the sequential transfer of the matrices $\mathbf{T}_j$ into the fast store. In practice only the non-zero elements of the jth column of $\mathbf{T}_j$ are stored for each j and in general this requires less storage than $\mathbf{A}^{-1}$.

Research in numerical analysis has indicated that in general it is inadvisable (and unnecessary) in respect of stability and sparsity to compute $\mathbf{A}^{-1}$; equation (4.2.1) is usually far better solved using some *factorization* of $\mathbf{A}$. The following methods are based upon those factorizations most commonly appearing in the literature.

(b) The matrix $\mathbf{A}$ can be factorized into the product of a lower-triangular matrix $\mathbf{L}$ and an upper-triangular matrix $\mathbf{U}$ using Gaussian elimination with interchanges. This factorization is performed by reducing $\mathbf{A}$ to upper-triangular form using matrices of the form

$$\mathbf{M}_j = \begin{pmatrix} 1 & & & & & & \\ & \cdot & & & & & \\ & & \cdot & & & & \\ & & & 1 & & & \\ & & & & 1 & & \\ & & & & m_{j+1,j} & 1 & \\ & & & & \vdots & & \cdot \\ & & & & \vdots & & & \cdot \\ & & & & m_{n,j} & & & & 1 \end{pmatrix}. \tag{4.3.4}$$

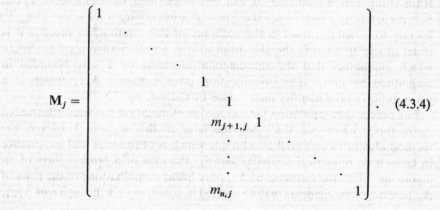

This matrix reduces to zero the sub-diagonal elements of the jth column of the partial product

$$\mathbf{A}_j = \mathbf{M}_{j-1}\mathbf{M}_{j-2}\ldots\mathbf{M}_1\mathbf{A},$$

the elements of $\mathbf{M}_j$ being computed according to the rule

$$m_{ij} = -a_{ij}^{(j)}/a_{jj}^{(j)}, \qquad i = j+1, j+2, \ldots, n,$$

where $a_{ij}^{(j)}$ denotes the ijth element of $\mathbf{A}_j$. Clearly the upper-triangular matrix $\mathbf{U}$ is given by

$$\begin{aligned}\mathbf{U} &= \mathbf{M}_{n-1}\mathbf{M}_{n-2}\ldots\mathbf{M}_1\mathbf{A},\\ &= \mathbf{L}^{-1}\mathbf{A}, \quad \text{say,}\end{aligned} \tag{4.3.5}$$

and it follows that

$$\mathbf{L} = \mathbf{M}_1^{-1}\mathbf{M}_2^{-1}\ldots\mathbf{M}_{n-1}^{-1}.$$

It is easily verified that

$$\mathbf{M}_j^{-1} = \begin{pmatrix} 1 & & & & & & \\ & \cdot & & & & & \\ & & \cdot & & & & \\ & & & 1 & & & \\ & & & & 1 & & \\ & & & & -m_{j+1,j} & 1 & \\ & & & & \cdot & & \cdot \\ & & & & \cdot & & & \cdot \\ & & & & \cdot & & & & \cdot \\ & & & & -m_{n,j} & & & & & 1 \end{pmatrix} \tag{4.3.6}$$

and if $\mathbf{L}$ is formed explicitly, its jth column is the jth column of $\mathbf{M}_j^{-1}$.

In large-scale applications it is common practice to hold $\mathbf{L}^{-1}$ by storing the separate factors $\mathbf{M}_j$ explicitly. The product form (4.3.5) is referred to as the *elimination form of the inverse* (EFI).

In the interest of numerical stability a row interchange must be made at each stage to ensure that $a_{jj}^{(j)}$ is the largest in modulus of the diagonal and sub-diagonal elements of the jth column of $\mathbf{A}_j$, and so we have

$$|m_{ij}| \leqslant 1, \qquad i = j+1, j+2, \ldots, n. \tag{4.3.7}$$

This strategy for choosing the pivot element is called *partial pivoting* and it can be shown that the final factorization is of the form

$$\mathbf{L}^{-1}\mathbf{PA} = \mathbf{U},$$

where **P** is a permutation matrix (see Wilkinson 1965, 206–207). For notational convenience, however, we shall continue to refer to (4.3.5) as the EFI.

Like the Gauss–Jordan elimination method, fill-in occurs. Reid (1971a) has suggested how the fill-in can be reduced by allowing a wider choice of pivotal element. The modified algorithm is based on the following observation. The error in a solution found by *LU* factorization is determined by the growth of elements in the matrix **U**, and the function of interchanges in partial pivoting is to limit this growth. This effect can often be achieved by requiring

$$|m_{ij}| \leqslant 1/\beta \tag{4.3.8}$$

instead of (4.3.7) where the scalar β is the *relative pivot tolerance*. During the reduction there may be several candidates for the pivotal row which give multipliers satisfying the relation (4.3.8). From these, a pivot can be chosen to give (in some sense) the least build-up of non-zero elements in the sub-matrix which must be subsequently reduced. An obvious choice is the row with the least number of non-zero elements.

The method of storing **U** depends upon the amount of in-core storage available, but the method used must allow for the fact that during the factorization new non-zero elements are created in $\mathbf{A}_j$. If the problem is small enough to fit in the fast store, **U** can be stored explicitly in linked-list form (sometimes known as threaded-list form) which enables elements to be efficiently inserted into **U**. Alternatively if an auxiliary storage device must be used, we can take advantage of the fact that

$$\mathbf{U} = \mathbf{U}_n \ldots \mathbf{U}_1,$$

where

$$\mathbf{U}_k = \begin{pmatrix} 1 & & & u_{1k} & & & \\ & \cdot & & \vdots & & & \\ & & \cdot & \vdots & & & \\ & & & 1 \quad u_{k-1,k} & & & \\ & & & u_{kk} & & & \\ & & & & 1 & & \\ & & & & & \cdot & \\ & & & & & & \cdot \\ & & & & & & & 1 \end{pmatrix}. \tag{4.3.9}$$

Then

$$\mathbf{U}^{-1} = \mathbf{U}_1^{-1} \ldots \mathbf{U}_n^{-1}$$

where

$$\mathbf{U}_k^{-1} = \begin{pmatrix} 1 & & & -u_{1k}/u_{kk} & & & \\ & \cdot & & \cdot & & & \\ & & \cdot & \cdot & & & \\ & & 1 & -u_{k-1,k}/u_{kk} & & & \\ & & & 1/u_{kk} & & & \\ & & & & 1 & & \\ & & & & & \cdot & \\ & & & & & & \cdot \\ & & & & & & & 1 \end{pmatrix}.$$

At the jth stage of the reduction the elements u_{kj}, $k = 1, \ldots, j$, and m_{kj}, $k = j + 1, \ldots, n$ are computed using the jth column of $\mathbf{A}_j$. This column can be computed as

$$\mathbf{A}_j\mathbf{e}_j = \mathbf{M}_{j-1}\mathbf{M}_{j-2} \ldots \mathbf{M}_1\mathbf{A}\mathbf{e}_j.$$

(c) We have shown that Gaussian elimination produces matrices $\mathbf{L}$ and $\mathbf{U}$ such that $\mathbf{A} = \mathbf{LU}$. This relation can be used directly to obtain the factorization since if we equate corresponding elements we have

$$\sum_{k=1}^{i-1} l_{ik}u_{kj} + u_{ij} = a_{ij}, \qquad j \geqslant i,$$

$$\sum_{k=1}^{j} l_{ik}u_{kj} = a_{ij}, \; i > j.$$

Rewriting these equations in the form

$$u_{ij} = a_{ij} - \sum_{k=1}^{i-1} l_{ik}u_{kj}, \qquad j \geqslant i,$$

$$l_{ij} = \left(a_{ij} - \sum_{k=1}^{j-1} l_{ik}u_{kj}\right)\bigg/ u_{jj}, \qquad i > j,$$

we see that the rows of $\mathbf{U}$ and $\mathbf{L}$ can be alternately determined in their natural order. This method is particularly useful when $\mathbf{A}$ is symmetric and positive definite. In this case interchanges are not required and storage can be halved by defining the diagonal elements of $\mathbf{L}$ to be such that $\mathbf{U}$ is $\mathbf{L}^T$.

(d) We have shown that the first stage of computing the EFI involves computing the elementary matrix $\mathbf{M}_1$ for which

$$\mathbf{M}_1\mathbf{a} = a_1\mathbf{e}_1, \tag{4.3.10}$$

where $\mathbf{a}$ is the first column of $\mathbf{A}$ and a_1 is the first element of $\mathbf{a}$. At the jth step we repeat this reduction on the first column of the sub-matrix formed by the last $(n - j + 1)$ rows and columns of $\mathbf{A}_j$. However, a reduction very similar to (4.3.10) can also be performed using a so-called Householder matrix, which is of the form

$$\left.\begin{aligned} &\mathbf{Q} = \mathbf{I} + \frac{1}{\tau}\mathbf{w}\mathbf{w}^T, \\ \text{where}\quad &\mathbf{w} = \begin{Bmatrix} a_1 + \rho \\ a_2 \\ \vdots \\ a_n \end{Bmatrix}, \\ &\tau = -\rho w_1 \quad \text{and} \quad \rho = \text{sign}(a_1)\left(\sum_{i=1}^{n} a_i^2\right)^{\frac{1}{2}}. \end{aligned}\right\} \tag{4.3.11}$$

With the Householder reduction the expression (4.3.10) is of the form

$$\mathbf{Q}\mathbf{a} = -\rho\mathbf{e}_1. \tag{4.3.12}$$

The matrix $\mathbf{Q}$ is symmetric and orthogonal and can be stored as ρ and the elements of $\mathbf{a}$. The matrix $\mathbf{A}$ can be reduced to upper-triangular form $\mathbf{R}$ using a sequence of Householder matrices $\mathbf{Q}_j$, $j = 1, 2, \ldots, n - 1$, where

$$\mathbf{Q}_j = \begin{bmatrix} \mathbf{I} & \mathbf{0} \\ \mathbf{0} & \overline{\mathbf{Q}}_j \end{bmatrix} \tag{4.3.13}$$

and $\overline{\mathbf{Q}}_j$ is an $(n - j + 1) \times (n - j + 1)$ matrix of the form (4.3.11). This finally gives

$$\mathbf{A}_n = \mathbf{R} = \mathbf{Q}_{n-1} \ldots \mathbf{Q}_1\mathbf{A}.$$

If we denote the matrix $\mathbf{Q}_{n-1} \ldots \mathbf{Q}_1$ as $\mathbf{Q}$ we have

$$\mathbf{Q}\mathbf{A} = \mathbf{R}, \tag{4.3.14}$$

where, from the orthogonality of each $\mathbf{Q}_j$ we have $\mathbf{Q}\mathbf{Q}^T = \mathbf{Q}^T\mathbf{Q} = \mathbf{I}$. (4.3.14) is known as the *QR* factorization of $\mathbf{A}$ and as with the EFI the factorization is essentially stored using the columns $\mathbf{A}_j\mathbf{e}_j$ for $j = 1, \ldots, n$.

(e) The reduction of $\mathbf{A}$ to upper-triangular form can be effected in an alternative manner in which elements of a *row* of the matrix $\mathbf{A}$ are reduced to zero rather than elements of a column. We shall show later in Section 4.4

that this has some advantages when a pre-processing technique is used in order to minimize the fill-in. Consider the sequence

$$\mathbf{A}_1 = \mathbf{A}, \qquad \mathbf{A}_{j+1} = \mathbf{P}_{j+1}\mathbf{A}_j, \qquad j = 1, \ldots, n-1,$$

where $\mathbf{A}_j$ is of the form

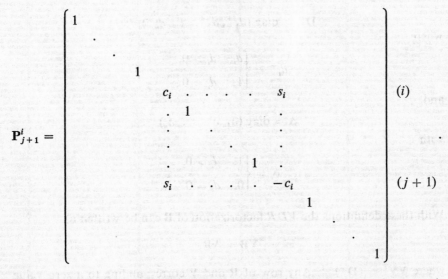

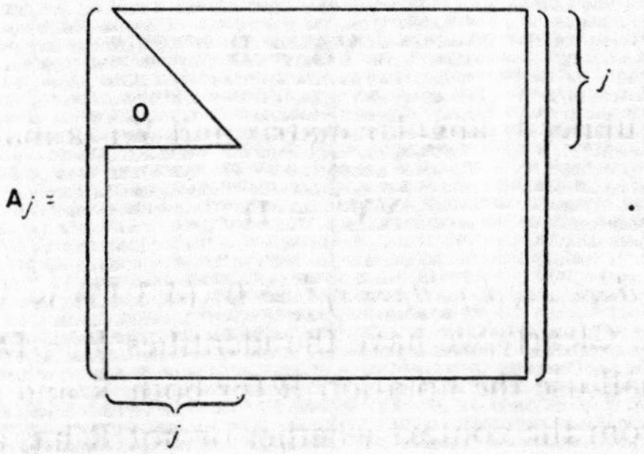

The matrix $\mathbf{P}_{j+1}$ is a product of plane rotations of the form

$$\mathbf{P}_{j+1} = \mathbf{P}^{j}_{j+1}\,\mathbf{P}^{j-1}_{j+1}\ldots\mathbf{P}^{1}_{j+1},$$

where each $\mathbf{P}^{i}_{j+1}$ is a symmetric orthogonal matrix of the form

$$\mathbf{P}^{i}_{j+1} = \begin{pmatrix} 1 & & & & & & & & \\ & \ddots & & & & & & & \\ & & 1 & & & & & & \\ & & & c_i & \cdots & s_i & & & \\ & & & \vdots & 1 & \vdots & & & \\ & & & \vdots & \ddots & \vdots & & & \\ & & & \vdots & 1 & \vdots & & & \\ & & & s_i & \cdots & -c_i & & & \\ & & & & & & 1 & & \\ & & & & & & & \ddots & \\ & & & & & & & & 1 \end{pmatrix} \begin{matrix} \\ \\ \\ (i) \\ \\ \\ \\ (j+1) \\ \\ \\ \\ \end{matrix}$$

The elements c_i and s_i are chosen such that the $(j+1)$th diagonal submatrix of $\mathbf{A}_{j+1}$ is upper triangular. The method is not satisfactory in this form because $n(n-1)/2$ square roots are required and it is difficult to implement efficiently in product form.

(f) In the following we shall describe a method which can be viewed as a means of computing the QR factorization (4.3.14) of $\mathbf{A}$ without the use of square roots. The method is easily implemented in product form. At the final stage, when $\mathbf{A}$ is non-singular, we have $\mathbf{A}$ in the form

$$\mathbf{VA} = \hat{\mathbf{R}} \tag{4.3.15}$$

where $\hat{\mathbf{R}}$ is a unit upper-triangular matrix and $\mathbf{V}$ is a matrix such that

$$\mathbf{VV}^T = \mathbf{D}^{-1},$$

$\mathbf{D}$ being $\text{diag}(d_1, d_2, \ldots, d_n)$, $d_i = r_{ii}{}^2 \neq 0$. (4.3.15) is known as the *VDR factorization* of $\mathbf{A}$. Clearly we have the identities $\mathbf{V} = \mathbf{D}^{-\frac{1}{2}}\mathbf{Q}$ and $\mathbf{R} = \mathbf{D}^{\frac{1}{2}}\hat{\mathbf{R}}$. Henceforth we shall use the notation $\mathbf{R}$ for both $\mathbf{R}$ and $\hat{\mathbf{R}}$ above since it will always be clear from the context whether or not $\mathbf{R}$ has a unit diagonal.

In order to define the method for computing the *VDR* factorization of $\mathbf{A}$ we shall be utilizing the *VDR* factorization of intermediate matrices which are not of full rank and consequently the definition (4.3.15) must be extended as follows. If $\mathbf{B}$ is an $n \times n$ matrix of rank $j\,(j < n)$ then $n - j$ diagonal elements r_{ii} are zero. The columns of $\mathbf{V}$ and rows of $\mathbf{R}$ corresponding to non-zero values of r_{ii} are unique. We now define diagonal matrices

$$\mathbf{D}^+ = \text{diag}\,(d_1{}^+, d_2{}^+, \ldots, d_n{}^+),$$

where

$$d_i{}^+ = \begin{cases} d_i, & d_i > 0, \\ 1, & d_i = 0, \end{cases}$$

and

$$\mathbf{\Delta} = \text{diag}\,(\delta_1, \delta_2, \ldots, \delta_n)$$

with

$$\delta_i = \begin{cases} 1, & d_i > 0, \\ 0, & d_i = 0. \end{cases}$$

With these definitions the *VDR* factorization of $\mathbf{B}$ can be written as

$$\mathbf{VB} = \mathbf{\Delta R},$$

where $\mathbf{VV}^T = (\mathbf{D}^+)^{-1}$. Any row of $\mathbf{R}$ and $\mathbf{V}$ corresponding to a zero value of $\mathbf{D}$ is not unique, but the j rows of $\mathbf{R}$ corresponding to $d_i > 0$ are unique and have unit diagonal elements. In practice the non-unique rows of $\mathbf{R}$ and $\mathbf{V}$ are chosen as rows of the identity matrix. If the sth row of $\mathbf{V}$ is chosen as $\mathbf{e}_s{}^T$ then the sth column of $\mathbf{V}$ must be equal to $\mathbf{e}_s$. This can be verified if the identity $\mathbf{V}\mathbf{V}^T = (\mathbf{D}^+)^{-1}$ is post-multiplied by $\mathbf{e}_s$ giving

$$\mathbf{V}\mathbf{V}^T\mathbf{e}_s = \mathbf{e}_s.$$

Since $\mathbf{V}^T\mathbf{e}_s = \mathbf{e}_s$ we have $\mathbf{V}\mathbf{e}_s = \mathbf{e}_s$ as required.

Let $\mathbf{B}$ be the matrix made up of j rows of $\mathbf{A}$ and $n - j$ rows of the zero matrix—we shall not specify any particular ordering of the rows of $\mathbf{B}$—and assume that the *VDR* factorization of $\mathbf{B}$, denoted by $\mathbf{VB} = \mathbf{\Delta R}$, is known. We shall describe a method of computing the *VDR* factors of the matrix $\mathbf{\bar{B}}$ obtained by replacing a zero row of $\mathbf{B}$ by a new row $\mathbf{a}^T$. This technique leads naturally to a method for computing the *VDR* factorization of $\mathbf{A}$ since if $\mathbf{A}_0$ denotes the zero matrix with factorization

$$\mathbf{V}_0\mathbf{A}_0 = \mathbf{\Delta}_0\mathbf{R}_0$$

where $\mathbf{R}_0 = \mathbf{I}, \mathbf{\Delta}_0 = \mathbf{D}_0 = \mathbf{0}$ and $\mathbf{V}_0 = \mathbf{I}$, the rows of $\mathbf{A}$ can be added one by one to $\mathbf{A}_0$.

From our earlier remarks the diagonal matrix $\mathbf{D}$ associated with the factorization $\mathbf{VB} = \mathbf{\Delta R}$ has $n - j$ zero elements and $\mathbf{V}$ has j unique columns and $n - j$ columns of the identity matrix. Let $\mathbf{p}$ be the vector such that

$$\mathbf{R}^T\mathbf{p} = \mathbf{a}$$

and p_s the first element of $\mathbf{p}$ such that $p_s \neq 0$ (the recurrence relations are invalid if $p_s = 0$) and $d_s = 0$. Define

$$\mathbf{\bar{B}} = \mathbf{B} + \mathbf{e}_s\mathbf{a}^T,$$

(that is, the row $\mathbf{a}^T$ is added into the sth position). Pre-multiplying by $\mathbf{V}$ and using the *VDR* factorization of $\mathbf{B}$ we have

$$\mathbf{V\bar{B}} = \mathbf{\Delta R} + \mathbf{V}\mathbf{e}_s\mathbf{a}^T.$$

By definition, the sth column of $\mathbf{V}$ is $\mathbf{e}_s$, giving

$$\begin{aligned} \mathbf{V\bar{B}} &= \mathbf{\Delta R} + \mathbf{e}_s\mathbf{a}^T \\ &= \mathbf{\Delta R} + \mathbf{e}_s\mathbf{p}^T\mathbf{R} \\ &= (\mathbf{\Delta} + \mathbf{e}_s\mathbf{p}^T)\,\mathbf{R} \\ &= (\mathbf{D}^+)^{-1}(\mathbf{D}^+)(\mathbf{\Delta} + \mathbf{e}_s\mathbf{p}^T)\,\mathbf{R} \\ &= (\mathbf{D}^+)^{-1}(\mathbf{D} + \mathbf{e}_s\mathbf{p}^T)\,\mathbf{R} \end{aligned} \qquad (4.3.16)$$

by virtue of the fact that $\mathbf{D}^+\mathbf{\Delta} = \mathbf{D}$ and $\mathbf{D}^+\mathbf{e}_s = \mathbf{e}_s$. It has been shown by Gill, Murray and Saunders (1974) that

$$\mathbf{D} + \mathbf{e}_s\mathbf{p}^T = \mathbf{\tilde{V}}^T\mathbf{\tilde{D}}\mathbf{\tilde{R}}, \qquad (4.3.17)$$

where

$$\tilde{\mathbf{R}} = \begin{bmatrix} 1 & \beta_1 p_2 & \beta_1 p_3 & \cdot & \cdot & \beta_1 p_s & \beta_1 p_{s+1} & \beta_1 p_{s+2} & \cdot & \cdot & \cdot & \beta_1 p_n \\ & 1 & \beta_2 p_3 & \cdot & \cdot & \beta_2 p_s & \beta_2 p_{s+1} & \beta_2 p_{s+2} & \cdot & \cdot & \cdot & \beta_2 p_n \\ & & 1 & \cdot & \cdot & \cdot & \cdot & \cdot & \cdot & \cdot & \cdot & \cdot \\ & & & \cdot & \cdot & \cdot & \cdot & \cdot & \cdot & \cdot & \cdot & \cdot \\ & & & & & 1 & \beta_s p_{s+1} & \beta_s p_{s+2} & \cdot & \cdot & \cdot & \beta_s p_n \\ & & & & & & 1 & 0 & & & & 0 \\ & & & & & & & 1 & & & & \cdot \\ & & & & & & & & & & & 1 \end{bmatrix}, \tag{4.3.18}$$

$$\tilde{\mathbf{V}}^T = \begin{bmatrix} 1 - p_1\beta_1 & -p_1\beta_2 & -p_1\beta_3 & \cdot & \cdot & -p_1\beta_s & 0 & \cdot & \cdot & \cdot \\ 0 & 1 - p_2\beta_2 & -p_2\beta_3 & \cdot & \cdot & -p_2\beta_s & 0 & \cdot & \cdot & \cdot \\ 0 & 0 & 1 - p_3\beta_3 & \cdot & \cdot & -p_3\beta_s & 0 & \cdot & \cdot & \cdot \\ \cdot & 0 & \cdot & & & \cdot & \cdot & & & \cdot \\ \cdot & \cdot & \cdot & & & \cdot & \cdot & & & \cdot \\ \beta_1 & \beta_2 & \beta_3 & \cdot & \cdot & \beta_s & 0 & \cdot & \cdot & \cdot \\ 0 & 0 & 0 & & & 0 & 1 & \cdot & & \cdot \\ & & & & & & & & \cdot & \cdot \\ & & & & & & & & & 1 \end{bmatrix}, \tag{4.3.19}$$

$$\begin{aligned} \tilde{\mathbf{D}} &= \operatorname{diag}(\tilde{d}_1, \tilde{d}_2, \ldots, \tilde{d}_n) \\ &= \operatorname{diag}(\hat{d}_1, \ldots \hat{d}_{s-1}, \hat{d}_s, d_{s+1}, \ldots, d_n), \end{aligned}$$

and the matrix $(\tilde{\mathbf{D}}^+)^{\frac{1}{2}}\tilde{\mathbf{V}}(\mathbf{D}^+)^{-\frac{1}{2}}$ is orthogonal. The vectors $\hat{\mathbf{d}}$ and $\boldsymbol{\beta}$ are generated by the following recurrence relations:

(i) define $t_0 = 1$;

(ii) for $k = 1, 2, \ldots, s-1$ compute the following

if $d_k = 0$ then set $v_k = 0$ otherwise set $v_k = p_k/d_k$,

$t_k = t_{k-1} + v_k p_k$,

$\hat{d}_k = d_k t_k / t_{k-1}$,

$\beta_k = v_k / t_k$;

(iii) define $\hat{d}_s = p_s^2/t_{s-1}$, and $\beta_s = 1/p_s$.

Substituting (4.3.17) in (4.3.16) gives

$$\mathbf{V\bar{B}} = (\mathbf{D}^+)^{-1}\tilde{\mathbf{V}}^T\tilde{\mathbf{D}}\tilde{\mathbf{R}}\mathbf{R}. \tag{4.3.20}$$

From the orthogonality of $(\tilde{\mathbf{D}}^+)^{\frac{1}{2}}\,\tilde{\mathbf{V}}(\mathbf{D}^+)^{-\frac{1}{2}}$ we have

$$\tilde{\mathbf{V}}(\mathbf{D}^+)^{-1}\tilde{\mathbf{V}}^T = (\tilde{\mathbf{D}}^+)^{-1}, \tag{4.3.21}$$

and consequently multiplying (4.3.20) by $\tilde{\mathbf{V}}$ and substituting from (4.3.21) gives

$$\tilde{\mathbf{V}}\mathbf{V}\mathbf{B} = (\tilde{\mathbf{D}}^+)^{-1}\tilde{\mathbf{D}}\tilde{\mathbf{R}}\mathbf{R}.$$

Now $(\tilde{\mathbf{D}}^+)^{-1}\tilde{\mathbf{D}} = \tilde{\mathbf{\Delta}}$, where $\tilde{\mathbf{\Delta}} = \operatorname{diag}(\tilde{\delta}_1, \tilde{\delta}_2, \tilde{\delta}_3, \ldots, \tilde{\delta}_n)$ with

$$\tilde{\delta}_i = \begin{cases} 1, & \tilde{d}_i > 0, \\ 0, & \tilde{d}_i = 0. \end{cases}$$

Hence

$$\tilde{\mathbf{V}}\mathbf{V}\bar{\mathbf{B}} = \tilde{\mathbf{\Delta}}\tilde{\mathbf{R}}\mathbf{R}.$$

Now

$$\begin{aligned}(\tilde{\mathbf{V}}\mathbf{V})(\tilde{\mathbf{V}}\mathbf{V})^T &= \tilde{\mathbf{V}}\mathbf{V}\mathbf{V}^T\tilde{\mathbf{V}}^T \\ &= \tilde{\mathbf{V}}(\mathbf{D}^+)^{-1}\tilde{\mathbf{V}}^T \\ &= (\tilde{\mathbf{D}}^+)^{-1}, \text{ from (4.3.21).}\end{aligned}$$

Consequently, if we write $\tilde{\mathbf{V}}\mathbf{V} = \bar{\mathbf{V}}$, $\tilde{\mathbf{D}} = \bar{\mathbf{D}}$, $\tilde{\mathbf{R}}\mathbf{R} = \bar{\mathbf{R}}$ and $\tilde{\mathbf{\Delta}} = \bar{\mathbf{\Delta}}$ then we have a factorization of $\bar{\mathbf{B}}$ of the form required.

By adding each row of **A** in turn and using the results just obtained, we can generate a product form of the factorization (4.3.15). As the factorization proceeds a new element of the diagonal matrix **D** becomes non-zero and a new row of **R** and column of **V** are defined. Let $\mathbf{D}_j$, $\mathbf{V}_j$ and $\mathbf{R}_j$ denote the matrices $\tilde{\mathbf{D}}$, $\tilde{\mathbf{V}}$ and $\tilde{\mathbf{R}}$ defined at (4.3.17) which are associated with the matrix made up of j rows of **A**. Then we have

$$\mathbf{V}_n\mathbf{V}_{n-1}\cdots\mathbf{V}_0\mathbf{A} = \mathbf{\Delta}_n\mathbf{R}_n\cdots\mathbf{R}_1\mathbf{R}_0$$

or

$$\mathbf{VA} = \mathbf{\Delta R}$$

if we write $\mathbf{R} = \mathbf{R}_n \ldots \mathbf{R}_1\mathbf{R}_0$, $\mathbf{V} = \mathbf{V}_n\mathbf{V}_{n-1}\ldots\mathbf{V}_0$, $\mathbf{\Delta} = \mathbf{\Delta}_n$ and $\mathbf{D} = \mathbf{D}_n$. Since **A** is non-singular $\mathbf{\Delta} = \mathbf{I}$ and we have (4.3.15).

The matrices (4.3.18) and (4.3.19) are particular types of so-called *special matrices* (see Gill, Golub, Murray and Saunders, 1974) and we shall come across them again in Section 4.5. We shall use the notation $\tilde{\mathbf{R}} = \tilde{\mathbf{R}}(\boldsymbol{\beta}, \mathbf{p}, \boldsymbol{\gamma})$ to denote a *special upper-triangular matrix* constructed from the vectors $\mathbf{p}$, $\boldsymbol{\beta}$ and $\boldsymbol{\gamma}$ according to

$$[\tilde{\mathbf{R}}]_{ij} = \begin{cases} \beta_i p_j, & i < j, \\ \gamma_i, & i = j, \\ 0, & i > j. \end{cases}$$

If the diagonal elements of $\tilde{\mathbf{R}}$ form the vector $\mathbf{e} = (1, 1, \ldots, 1)^T$ we shall write either $\tilde{\mathbf{R}} = \tilde{\mathbf{R}}(\boldsymbol{\beta}, \mathbf{p}, \mathbf{e})$ or just $\tilde{\mathbf{R}} = \tilde{\mathbf{R}}(\boldsymbol{\beta}, \mathbf{p})$. Similarly we shall define $\tilde{\mathbf{M}} = \tilde{\mathbf{M}}(\mathbf{p}, \boldsymbol{\beta}, \boldsymbol{\gamma}) = [\tilde{\mathbf{R}}(\boldsymbol{\beta}, \mathbf{p}, \boldsymbol{\gamma})]^T$ as a *special lower-triangular matrix*.

The important feature of the matrices $\mathbf{R}_j$ and $\mathbf{V}_j$ is that they *both* can be constructed from the pair of vectors $[\mathbf{p}, \boldsymbol{\beta}]$, which can be stored in packed form on an auxiliary file. Their special form can be exploited to obtain the solution of (4.2.1) or more strictly,

$$\mathbf{R}_n \ldots \mathbf{R}_1 \mathbf{x} = \mathbf{V}_n \mathbf{V}_{n-1} \ldots \mathbf{V}_1 \mathbf{b},$$

in an efficient manner.

All the methods given so far have been "row" methods, in that the factorization of $\mathbf{A}$ is obtained by forming linear combinations of its rows. We can define a complete set of *column methods* in which the matrix $\mathbf{A}^T$ is factorized using any of the techniques (*a*)–(*f*). The *QR* and *VDR* factorizations of $\mathbf{A}^T$ are known as the *LQ* and *LDV* factorizations of $\mathbf{A}$ respectively. The *LQ* and *LDV* factorizations will figure prominently in later applications—the reader will recall the earlier use of the *LQ* factorization in Chapter II.

The *LQ* or *LDV* factorization can be used to solve equation (4.2.1) in an alternative manner suggested by Gill and Murray (1973a). This technique does not require the storage of an orthogonal matrix but computes the solution $\mathbf{x}$ by solving the equations

$$\mathbf{A}\mathbf{A}^T\mathbf{u} = \mathbf{b}, \tag{4.3.22}$$

and setting

$$\mathbf{x} = \mathbf{A}^T\mathbf{u}. \tag{4.3.23}$$

If $\mathbf{A} = \mathbf{LQ}$ then equation (4.3.22) becomes

$$\mathbf{LL}^T\mathbf{u} = \mathbf{b}, \tag{4.3.24}$$

which can be solved using a forward and backward substitution. If the *LDV* factorization is used, the coefficient matrix for (4.3.22) becomes $\mathbf{R}^T\mathbf{DR}$. This method is particularly effective on medium-scale problems where $\mathbf{R}$ is stored in linked-list form (see Saunders, 1972a) and Paige (1973) has shown that the method is numerically stable.

4.4. Pre-processing Techniques

If the initial row and column ordering of a sparse matrix $\mathbf{A}$ are altered, the amount of fill-in occurring with any of the methods described in the last section will vary. It is often useful to rearrange the rows and columns of an arbitrarily sparse matrix before the factorization commences in order to reduce the subsequent storage requirements. In mathematical terms we seek permutation matrices $\mathbf{P}_1$ and $\mathbf{P}_2$ such that the fill-in during the solution of the equations

$$\mathbf{P}_1\mathbf{AP}_2\mathbf{y} = \mathbf{P}_1\mathbf{b},$$

is less than that during the solution of (4.2.1). The solution $\mathbf{x}$ can be obtained from $\mathbf{y}$ using $\mathbf{x} = \mathbf{P}_2\mathbf{y}$. The best ordering of a matrix depends upon the factorization used, as the following example demonstrates.

Consider the factorization of a square unsymmetric matrix with the structure (4.1.2) using any of the row methods described in the last section. Since linear combinations of rows of $\mathbf{A}$ are being formed, fill-in will occur only within each of the blocks, whereas if a column method is used, fill-in will occur throughout the matrix. Matrices of the type (4.1.2) are known as *dual-angular* matrices. A matrix of the form (4.1.1) is known as a *block-angular* matrix and clearly column methods have less fill-in when applied to such matrices. If a matrix naturally occurs in either dual- or block-angular form then a row or column method, respectively, should be used to perform the factorization. Weil and Kettler (1971) have suggested an algorithm for arranging an arbitrarily sparse rectangular matrix into block-angular form. It is still possible that the resulting blocks will have a significant number of zero elements and Saunders (1972a) has suggested that the Weil–Kettler algorithm be applied recursively to each of the succeeding blocks until the matrix is no longer reducible. This gives the matrix $\mathbf{P}_1\mathbf{AP}_2$ in so-called *nested* block-angular form. The same algorithm can be used to produce nested dual-angular matrices if applied to the transpose of $\mathbf{A}$.

There are other pre-processing techniques available. One useful re-arrangement of **A** in view of the factorizations being considered is to choose $\mathbf{P}_1$ and $\mathbf{P}_2$ such that $\mathbf{P}_1\mathbf{A}\mathbf{P}_2$ is of the form

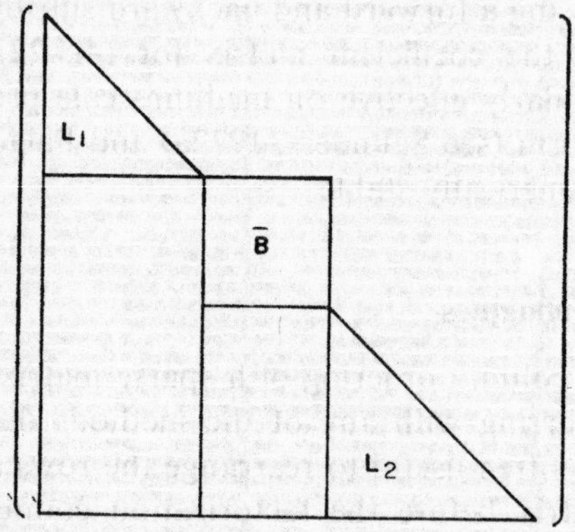

. (4.4.1)

This matrix is lower triangular except for the matrix $\bar{\mathbf{B}}$, defined as a *bump*. The lower-triangular matrices $\mathbf{L}_1$ and $\mathbf{L}_2$ are known as the forward triangle and backward triangle respectively. It is now necessary to factorize only the matrix $\bar{\mathbf{B}}$ and fill-in will occur only in the columns below $\bar{\mathbf{B}}$. Hellerman and Rarick (1971, 1972) have given two algorithms for determining a further re-ordering of the matrix $\bar{\mathbf{B}}$. These algorithms give a matrix $\mathbf{P}_1\mathbf{A}\mathbf{P}_2$ as in (4.4.1), together with a matrix $\bar{\mathbf{B}}$ which is itself lower triangular save for further bumps $\mathbf{B}_1, \mathbf{B}_2, \ldots, \mathbf{B}_j$ (there may be any number), each of which is lower triangular save for columns of non-zero elements called *spikes*. For example, a bump $\mathbf{B}_j$ could be of the form

$$\mathbf{B}_j = \begin{bmatrix} \times & \cdot & \cdot & \cdot & \cdot & \times \\ \cdot & \times & \cdot & \cdot & \cdot & \times \\ \times & \cdot & \times & \times & \cdot & \times \\ \cdot & \cdot & \times & \times & \cdot & \cdot \\ \cdot & \times & \times & \times & \times & \times \\ \times & \times & \cdot & \times & \times & \cdot \end{bmatrix} \tag{4.4.2}$$

with × denoting the non-zero elements. Our example has spikes in the fourth and last columns. The recurrence relations defining the *LU* factorization of $\mathbf{P}_1\mathbf{A}\mathbf{P}_2$ imply that fill-in occurs only in the columns beneath a bump, or more specifically in columns which are below spikes. For example, the *LU* factorization of (4.4.2) is of the form

$$\begin{bmatrix} \times & \cdot & \cdot & \cdot & \cdot & \cdot \\ \cdot & \times & \cdot & \cdot & \cdot & \cdot \\ \times & \cdot & \times & \cdot & \cdot & \cdot \\ \cdot & \cdot & \times & \times & \cdot & \cdot \\ \cdot & \times & \times & \times & \times & \cdot \\ \times & \times & \cdot & \times & \times & \times \end{bmatrix} \begin{bmatrix} \times & \cdot & \cdot & \cdot & \cdot & \times \\ \cdot & \times & \cdot & \cdot & \cdot & \times \\ \cdot & \cdot & \times & \times & \cdot & \times \\ \cdot & \cdot & \cdot & \times & \cdot & \times \\ \cdot & \cdot & \cdot & \cdot & \times & \times \\ \cdot & \cdot & \cdot & \cdot & \cdot & \times \end{bmatrix}.$$

If we apply the *VDR* factorization to a matrix which has been obtained by applying the Hellerman and Rarick scheme to $\mathbf{A}^T$ then similar savings in fill-in are achieved. In this case the $\mathbf{V}_j$ and $\mathbf{R}_j$ corresponding to non-spike rows are equal to the identity matrix with the unit element v_{jj} replaced by $1/\beta_j$ and an elementary matrix of the form (4.3.4) respectively, the number of non-trivial $\mathbf{V}_j$'s being equal to the number of spike rows. Our earlier discussion of row and column methods implies that (4.4.1) is also a useful form for the *LQ* and *LDV* methods.

We can also use pre-processing techniques to minimize fill-in when $\mathbf{A}$ is symmetric. In particular, if $\mathbf{A}$ can be permuted to be of the form.

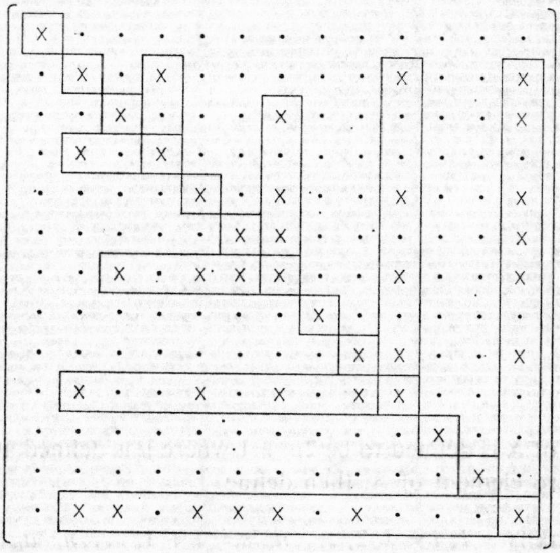

, (4.4.3)

then the unit lower-triangular matrix **L** associated with the Cholesky factorization $\mathbf{A} = \mathbf{LDL}^T$ is of the form

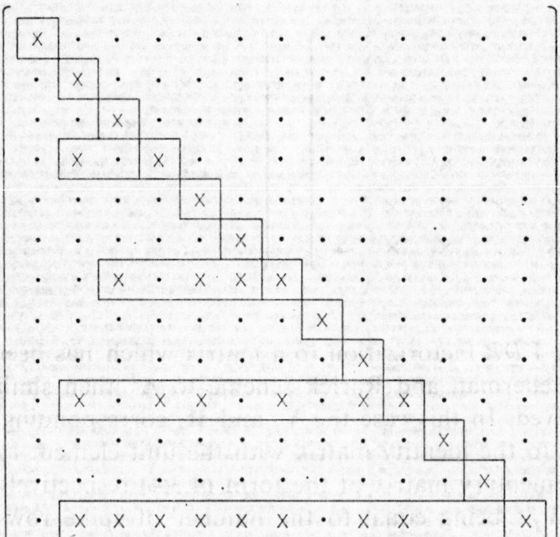

with fill-in occurring only in the spikes (see George, 1971).

Suppose **A** is a band matrix, for example,

$$\mathbf{A} = \begin{bmatrix}
\times & \times & \times & \times & \cdot & \cdot & \cdot & \cdot & \cdot & \cdot & \cdot & \cdot & \cdot \\
\times & \times & \times & \times & \times & \cdot & \cdot & \cdot & \cdot & \cdot & \cdot & \cdot & \cdot \\
\times & \times & \times & \times & \times & \times & \cdot & \cdot & \cdot & \cdot & \cdot & \cdot & \cdot \\
\times & \times & \times & \times & \times & \times & \times & \cdot & \cdot & \cdot & \cdot & \cdot & \cdot \\
\cdot & \times & \times & \times & \times & \times & \times & \times & \cdot & \cdot & \cdot & \cdot & \cdot \\
\cdot & \cdot & \times & \times & \times & \times & \times & \times & \times & \cdot & \cdot & \cdot & \cdot \\
\cdot & \cdot & \cdot & \times & \times & \times & \times & \times & \times & \times & \cdot & \cdot & \cdot \\
\cdot & \cdot & \cdot & \cdot & \times & \times & \times & \times & \times & \times & \times & \cdot & \cdot \\
\cdot & \cdot & \cdot & \cdot & \cdot & \times & \times & \times & \times & \times & \times & \times & \cdot \\
\cdot & \cdot & \cdot & \cdot & \cdot & \cdot & \times & \times & \times & \times & \times & \times & \times \\
\cdot & \cdot & \cdot & \cdot & \cdot & \cdot & \cdot & \times & \times & \times & \times & \times & \times \\
\cdot & \cdot & \cdot & \cdot & \cdot & \cdot & \cdot & \cdot & \times & \times & \times & \times & \times \\
\cdot & \cdot & \cdot & \cdot & \cdot & \cdot & \cdot & \cdot & \cdot & \times & \times & \times & \times
\end{bmatrix}.$$

The *bandwidth* of **A** is defined to be $2\mu + 1$ where μ is defined as follows. Let a_{is} be a non-zero element of **A**, then define

$$\mu = \max\{s - i;\ i = 1, 2, \ldots, n,\ \ s = i + 1, \ldots, n,\ \ a_{is} \neq 0\}.$$

(If **A** is unsymmetric we can define the bandwidth as $\mu + \bar{\mu} + 1$ where

$$\bar{\mu} = \max\{i - s;\ i = 1, 2, \ldots, n,\quad s = 1, \ldots i - 1,\ a_{si} \neq 0\}.)$$

It can easily be shown that the bandwidth of the Cholesky factor, **L**, for a matrix with bandwidth $2\mu + 1$ is $\mu + 1$. The number of multiplications required to compute the elements of **L** and **D** is

$$\frac{n}{2}(\mu + 1)(\mu + 2),$$

which compares favourably with $\frac{1}{6}n^3 + O(n^2)$ multiplications for computing the factorization of a dense matrix. The additional operations required to do the backward and forward substitutions for the solution **x** are given by

$$2n(\mu + 1).$$

Alway and Martin (1965) have given an algorithm for permuting the rows and columns of a sparse matrix in order to minimize the bandwidth. However, the minimization is difficult and expensive to determine and in practice it may often be possible merely to reduce the bandwidth.

4.5. Updating the Factorizations

The reader will recall that the minimization methods presented in Chapters II and III require the solution of many sets of equations which differ from each other by only a single row or column. It is useful, therefore, to be able to modify the factors of the matrix and thereby obtain a new solution more efficiently. This is especially important in the solution of linear-programming problems where a large number of modifications are often necessary. In this section we shall demonstrate how to modify the factorizations (a)–(f) when rows or columns of the matrix are added or deleted, paying particular attention to the method of storing and accessing any additional information.

The majority of methods appearing in the literature have been concerned with the modification of factorizations when *columns* of a matrix are added or deleted. There are historical reasons for this; updating a matrix when columns are exchanged occurs in the solution of linear-programming problems posed in a so-called *Canonical Form* (see Section 4.12). However, column-updating methods can be effectively applied when *rows* are being added or deleted if the transpose of the matrix is factorized and updated. (This is not always satisfactory and wherever possible we shall define row-updating methods.)

(i) As in our discussion of inversion methods, the technique of updating the inverse of **A** directly gives us a clue as to how we must efficiently update a factorization. Assume that an $n \times n$ non-singular matrix $\bar{\mathbf{A}}$ is formed from **A** by replacing the rth column $\mathbf{a}_r$ by $\mathbf{a}_s$. The following identity must hold:

$$\bar{\mathbf{A}} = \mathbf{A} + (\mathbf{a}_s - \mathbf{a}_r)\,\mathbf{e}_r^T. \qquad (4.5.1)$$

Using the Householder modification rule we can write down $\bar{\mathbf{A}}^{-1}$ directly as

$$\bar{\mathbf{A}}^{-1} = \mathbf{A}^{-1} - \alpha^{-1}\mathbf{A}^{-1}(\mathbf{a}_s - \mathbf{a}_r)\,\mathbf{e}_r^T\mathbf{A}^{-1},$$

where

$$\alpha = 1 + \mathbf{e}_r^T\mathbf{A}^{-1}(\mathbf{a}_s - \mathbf{a}_r).$$

Thus

$$\bar{\mathbf{A}}^{-1} = (\mathbf{I} - \alpha^{-1}\mathbf{A}^{-1}(\mathbf{a}_s - \mathbf{a}_r)\mathbf{e}_r^T)\,\mathbf{A}^{-1}$$
$$= \mathbf{T}_r\mathbf{A}^{-1}, \text{ say,}$$

where $\mathbf{T}_r$ is an elementary matrix of the form (4.3.1). The updating of $\mathbf{A}^{-1}$ to give $\bar{\mathbf{A}}^{-1}$ involves finding a new elementary matrix which becomes part of the product form already available for **A**.

(ii) In 1969 Bartels and Golub suggested a numerically stable method for updating the EFI during column exchanges based upon Gaussian elimination with row interchanges. The analogue of (4.3.5), which results from dropping the column $\mathbf{a}_r$ and inserting the column $\mathbf{a}_s$ in the last position can be written as

$$\mathbf{L}^{-1}\bar{\mathbf{A}} = \mathbf{H},$$

where $\bar{\mathbf{A}}$ is the required matrix, and **H** is an upper–Hessenberg matrix of the form

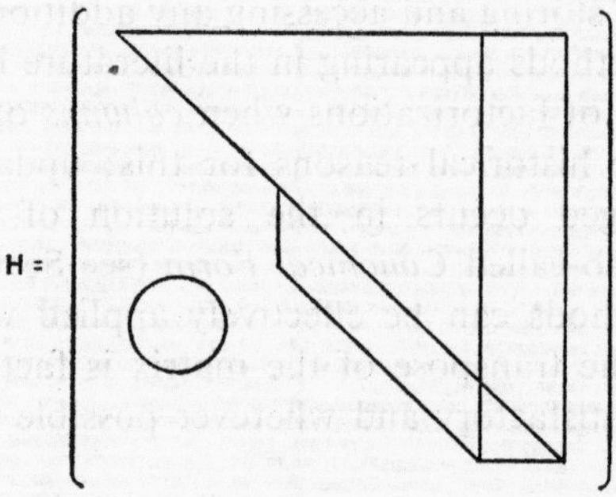

with last column $\mathbf{L}^{-1}\mathbf{a}_s$. We now require to reduce the matrix $\mathbf{H}$ to upper-triangular form. This can be achieved using Gaussian elimination with row interchanges by means of a sequence of elementary matrices of the form

$$\begin{pmatrix} 1 & & & & & & \\ & \ddots & & & & & \\ & & 1 & & & & \\ & & & 1 & & & \\ & & & -m_{j+1,j} & 1 & & \\ & & & & & \ddots & \\ & & & & & & 1 \end{pmatrix}, \qquad \text{with } |m_{ij}| \leqslant 1. \tag{4.5.2}$$

The matrices (4.5.2) are called *updates* and they are stored individually, i.e. the factors $\mathbf{L}^{-1}$ are stored in product form as before. As in the initial LU factorization, a relative pivot tolerance can be used to limit the error growth except that in this case there are only two choices for the pivotal row (since $\mathbf{H}$ is in upper-Hessenberg form).

This algorithm has been implemented by Reid (1973) for medium-scale problems, the factor $\mathbf{U}$ being stored in linked-list form. Unfortunately, for large-scale problems the Bartels–Golub algorithm is difficult to implement since individual elements of the matrix $\mathbf{U}$ must be accessed during the updating process and this inhibits the sequential storage of the factors in an auxiliary file.

(iii) Another method of updating the LU factorization, described below, is related to a method described by Forrest and Tomlin (1972); it has fill-in properties similar to those of the Bartels–Golub algorithm but its numerical stability cannot be guaranteed. From (4.3.5) and (4.5.1) we have

$$\begin{aligned} \mathbf{L}^{-1}\overline{\mathbf{A}} &= \mathbf{U} + \mathbf{L}^{-1}(\mathbf{a}_s - \mathbf{a}_r)\,\mathbf{e}_r^T \\ &= (\mathbf{I} + \mathbf{w}\mathbf{v}^T)\,\mathbf{U}, \end{aligned} \tag{4.5.3}$$

where $\mathbf{w}$ and $\mathbf{v}$ are such that $\mathbf{U}^T\mathbf{v} = \mathbf{e}_r$ and $\mathbf{w} = \mathbf{L}^{-1}(\mathbf{a}_s - \mathbf{a}_r)$. We note that $v_j = 0$ for $j = 1, 2, \ldots, r-1$.

Let $\mathbf{N}_1$ be a matrix of the form (4.3.4) such that

$$\mathbf{N}_1^T\mathbf{v} = v_r\mathbf{e}_r.$$

This implies that the sub-diagonal elements of the rth column of $\mathbf{N}_1$ are given by $-v_j/v_r$, $j = r+1, \ldots, n$. We can rewrite equation (4.5.3) as

$$\mathbf{L}^{-1}\overline{\mathbf{A}} = (\mathbf{I} + \mathbf{w}\mathbf{v}^T)\,\mathbf{N}_1\mathbf{N}_1^{-1}\mathbf{U}$$
$$= \mathbf{N}_1(\mathbf{I} + \overline{\mathbf{w}}\mathbf{e}_r^{\,T})\,\mathbf{N}_1^{-1}\mathbf{U},$$

where $\overline{\mathbf{w}} = v_r\mathbf{N}_1^{-1}\mathbf{w}$. The matrix $\mathbf{N}_1^{-1}$ is upper triangular and we shall denote it as $\mathbf{U}_1$. Thus

$$\mathbf{N}_1^{-1}\mathbf{L}^{-1}\overline{\mathbf{A}} = (\mathbf{I} + \mathbf{w}\mathbf{e}_r^{\,T})\,\mathbf{U}_1\mathbf{U}.$$

The matrix $\mathbf{I} + \overline{\mathbf{w}}\mathbf{e}_r^{\,T}$ is an elementary matrix with factorization

$$\mathbf{I} + \overline{\mathbf{w}}\mathbf{e}_r^{\,T} = \mathbf{N}_2\mathbf{U}_2,$$

where $\mathbf{U}_2$ is of the form (4.3.9) with diagonal and super-diagonal elements of the rth column given by $\overline{w}_j$, $j = 1, 2, \ldots, r$, and $\mathbf{N}_2$ is of the form (4.3.4) with sub-diagonal elements of the rth column given by $\overline{w}_j/(1 + \overline{w}_r)$, $j = r+1, \ldots, n$. This implies that the updated factorization is of the form

$$\overline{\mathbf{L}}^{-1}\overline{\mathbf{A}} = \overline{\mathbf{U}}, \tag{4.5.4}$$

where $\overline{\mathbf{L}}^{-1} = \mathbf{N}_2^{-1}\mathbf{N}_1^{-1}\mathbf{L}^{-1}$ and $\overline{\mathbf{U}} = \mathbf{U}_2\mathbf{U}_1\mathbf{U}$. We note that, as with the Bartels–Golub method, $\mathbf{L}^{-1}$ is no longer a lower-triangular matrix, but a product of elementary matrices. It is the use of the diagonal pivots v_r and $1 + \overline{w}_r$ when they do not satisfy a relative pivot tolerance criterion of the form (4.3.8) which could lead to loss of accuracy. Although this algorithm can be implemented in product form, there is no known efficient method based upon EFI which can be guaranteed to be numerically stable on large-scale problems. However, either methods (ii) or (iii) can be used for medium-scale problems and we assert that the Bartels–Golub algorithm is superior with respect to both stability and fill-in. This implies that if a method based upon the EFI is preferred for medium-scale problems, there is no reason why the Bartels–Golub algorithm should not be used.

(iv) Gill, Murray and Saunders (1973, 1974) have suggested a numerically stable scheme for updating the *LQ* and *LDV* factorizations of a large sparse matrix when columns are exchanged (or equivalently methods for modifying the *QR* and *VDR* factorizations when rows are exchanged). A complete derivation of the recurrence relations involved is beyond the scope of this text but we shall give a brief outline of the method in the *LDV* case. The reader is referred to the original paper for further details.

Let $\mathbf{A}$ be an $n \times n$ non-singular matrix and let the $n \times (n+1)$ matrix $[\mathbf{A}\ \ \mathbf{0}]$ have an *LDV* factorization

$$[\mathbf{A}\ \mathbf{0}] = [\mathbf{L}\ \mathbf{0}]\,\mathbf{DV},$$

where $\mathbf{L}$ is a unit lower-triangular matrix, $\mathbf{D} = \operatorname{diag}(d_1, d_2, \ldots, d_n, 1)$ and $\mathbf{VV}^T = \mathbf{D}^{-1}$. Let a column $\mathbf{a}_s$ be added to $[\mathbf{A}\ \ \mathbf{0}]$ to give the matrix $\hat{\mathbf{A}}$. Then

$$\begin{aligned}\hat{\mathbf{A}} &= [\mathbf{A}\ \mathbf{a}_s]\\ &= [\mathbf{A}\ \mathbf{0}] + \mathbf{a}_s\mathbf{e}_{n+1}^T\\ &= [\mathbf{L}\ \mathbf{0}]\,\mathbf{DV} + \mathbf{Lpe}_{n+1}^T\\ &= [\mathbf{L}\ \mathbf{0}]\left(\mathbf{DV} + \begin{bmatrix}\mathbf{p}\\ \mathbf{0}\end{bmatrix}\mathbf{e}_{n+1}^T\right),\end{aligned} \tag{4.5.5}$$

where $\mathbf{p}$ is the solution of $\mathbf{Lp} = \mathbf{a}_s$. Now $\mathbf{D}^{\frac{1}{2}}\mathbf{V}$ is orthogonal and the last column of $[\mathbf{A}\ \ \mathbf{0}]$ is zero; hence $\mathbf{D}^{\frac{1}{2}}\mathbf{V}$ is really of the form

$$\mathbf{D}^{\frac{1}{2}}\mathbf{V} = \begin{bmatrix}\mathbf{Q} & \mathbf{0}\\ \mathbf{0} & 1\end{bmatrix},$$

where $\mathbf{Q}$ is the orthogonal matrix in the *LQ* factorization of $\mathbf{A}$ itself. Since $d_{n+1}^{\frac{1}{2}} = 1$ this means that $\mathbf{e}_{n+1}^T\mathbf{V} = \mathbf{e}_{n+1}^T$. Substituting in (4.5.5) gives

$$\bar{\mathbf{A}} = [\mathbf{L}\ \mathbf{0}]\left(\mathbf{D} + \begin{bmatrix}\mathbf{p}\\ \mathbf{0}\end{bmatrix}\mathbf{e}_{n+1}^T\right)\mathbf{V}.$$

The matrix

$$\mathbf{D} + \begin{bmatrix}\mathbf{p}\\ \mathbf{0}\end{bmatrix}\mathbf{e}_{n+1}^T$$

has an *LDV* factorization $\mathbf{L}_1\mathbf{D}_1\mathbf{V}_1$ where

$$\mathbf{L}_1 = \begin{bmatrix}\tilde{\mathbf{M}}_1 & \mathbf{0}\\ \boldsymbol{\beta}^T & 1\end{bmatrix},$$

$$\mathbf{D}_1 = \operatorname{diag}(\tilde{d}_1, \tilde{d}_2, \tilde{d}_3, \ldots, \tilde{d}_n, \alpha_1{}^2),$$

$$\mathbf{V}_1 = \left[\begin{array}{c|c}\tilde{\mathbf{N}}_1 & \boldsymbol{\beta}\\ -\mathbf{p}^T & 1\end{array}\right],$$

and the matrix $\hat{\mathbf{D}}^{\frac{1}{2}}\hat{\mathbf{V}}\mathbf{D}^{-\frac{1}{2}}$ is orthogonal. Both $\tilde{\mathbf{M}}_1$ and $\tilde{\mathbf{N}}_1$ are special lower-triangular matrices defined by

$$\begin{aligned}\tilde{\mathbf{M}}_1 &= \tilde{\mathbf{M}}_1(\mathbf{p}, \boldsymbol{\beta}),\\ \tilde{\mathbf{N}}_1 &= \tilde{\mathbf{N}}_1(\boldsymbol{\beta}, -\mathbf{p}, \boldsymbol{\theta})\\ &= \tilde{\mathbf{M}}_1{}^T - \boldsymbol{\beta}\mathbf{p}^T,\end{aligned}$$

where the vectors $\bar{\mathbf{d}}, \boldsymbol{\beta}, \boldsymbol{\theta}$ and the scalar $\alpha_1{}^2$ are generated by the following recurrence relations:

$$\left.\begin{aligned}&\text{(i) define } t_0 = 1;\\ &\text{(ii) for } j = 1, 2, \ldots, n \text{ set}\\ &\quad t_j = t_{j-1} + p_j{}^2/d_j,\\ &\quad \tilde{d}_j = d_j t_j/t_{j-1},\\ &\quad \beta_j = p_j/(d_j t_j),\\ &\quad \theta_j = 1 - p_j\beta_j;\\ &\text{(iii) define } \alpha_1{}^2 = 1/t_n.\end{aligned}\right\} \tag{4.5.6}$$

If $\hat{\mathbf{A}} = [\hat{\mathbf{L}}\ \ \mathbf{0}]\,\hat{\mathbf{D}}\hat{\mathbf{V}}$ then $\hat{\mathbf{L}} = \mathbf{L}\tilde{\mathbf{M}}_1$, $\hat{\mathbf{D}} = \mathbf{D}_1$ and $\hat{\mathbf{V}} = \mathbf{V}_1\mathbf{V}$.

If $\bar{\mathbf{A}}$ is the matrix obtained from $\mathbf{A}$ by replacing the rth column $\mathbf{a}_r$ by $\mathbf{a}_s$ then we have the identity

$$[\bar{\mathbf{A}}\ \ \mathbf{0}] = (\hat{\mathbf{A}} - \mathbf{a}_r\mathbf{e}_r{}^T)\,\boldsymbol{\Pi}, \tag{4.5.7}$$

where $\boldsymbol{\Pi}$ is a permutation matrix which interchanges the rth and sth columns of an $(n+1) \times (n+1)$ matrix. If we compute the rth column of $\hat{\mathbf{D}}\hat{\mathbf{V}}$ as

$$\begin{bmatrix}\mathbf{q}\\ \alpha_2\end{bmatrix} = \hat{\mathbf{D}}\hat{\mathbf{V}}\mathbf{e}_r,$$

we have

$$\begin{aligned}\mathbf{a}_r &= \hat{\mathbf{A}}\mathbf{e}_r\\ &= [\hat{\mathbf{L}}\ \ \mathbf{0}]\,\hat{\mathbf{D}}\hat{\mathbf{V}}\mathbf{e}_r\\ &= [\hat{\mathbf{L}}\ \ \mathbf{0}]\begin{bmatrix}\mathbf{q}\\ \alpha_2\end{bmatrix}\end{aligned}$$

and

$$\mathbf{e}_r = \hat{\mathbf{V}}^T\begin{bmatrix}\mathbf{q}\\ \alpha_2\end{bmatrix},$$

since $(\hat{\mathbf{D}}^{\frac{1}{2}}\hat{\mathbf{V}})^T(\hat{\mathbf{D}}^{\frac{1}{2}}\hat{\mathbf{V}}) = \mathbf{I}$. Substituting for $\mathbf{a}_r$ and $\mathbf{e}_r$ in (4.5.7) gives

$$[\bar{\mathbf{A}}\ \mathbf{0}] = [\hat{\mathbf{L}}\ \mathbf{0}]\left(\hat{\mathbf{D}} - \begin{bmatrix}\mathbf{q}\\ \alpha_2\end{bmatrix}[\mathbf{q}^T\ \alpha_2]\right)\hat{\mathbf{V}}\mathbf{\Pi}. \tag{4.5.8}$$

Gill, Murray and Saunders (1974) have shown that

$$\mathbf{D} - \begin{bmatrix}\mathbf{q}\\ \alpha_2\end{bmatrix}[\mathbf{q}^T\ \alpha_2] = \mathbf{L}_2\mathbf{D}_2\mathbf{V}_2,$$

where

$$\mathbf{L}_2 = \begin{bmatrix}\tilde{\mathbf{M}}_2 & \mathbf{0}\\ \alpha_2\boldsymbol{\sigma}^T & 0\end{bmatrix}$$

$$\mathbf{D}_2 = \mathrm{diag}\,(\bar{d}_1, \ldots, \bar{d}_n, 1),$$

$$\mathbf{V}_2 = \begin{bmatrix}\tilde{\mathbf{M}}_2{}^T & \alpha_2\boldsymbol{\sigma}\\ \mathbf{q}^T & \alpha_2\end{bmatrix}$$

and the matrix $\mathbf{D}_2^{\frac{1}{2}}\mathbf{V}_2\hat{\mathbf{D}}^{-\frac{1}{2}}$ is orthogonal. The matrix $\tilde{\mathbf{M}}_2 = \tilde{\mathbf{M}}_2(\mathbf{q}, \boldsymbol{\sigma})$ is a special lower-triangular matrix and the vectors $\bar{\mathbf{d}}$ and $\boldsymbol{\sigma}$ are generated by the following recurrence relations:

$$\left.\begin{aligned}
&\text{(i) define } t_{n+1} = \alpha_2{}^2/\alpha_1{}^2;\\
&\text{(ii) for } j = n, n-1, \ldots, 1 \text{ set}\\
&\qquad t_j = t_{j+1} + q_j{}^2/\hat{d}_j,\\
&\qquad \bar{d}_j = \hat{d}_j t_{j+1}/t_j,\\
&\qquad \sigma_j = -\,q_j/(\hat{d}_j t_{j+1}).
\end{aligned}\right\} \tag{4.5.9}$$

Using the factors $\mathbf{L}_2$, $\mathbf{D}_2$ and $\mathbf{V}_2$ in (4.5.8) gives

$$\begin{aligned}[\bar{\mathbf{A}}\ \mathbf{0}] &= [\hat{\mathbf{L}}\ \mathbf{0}]\,\mathbf{L}_2\mathbf{D}_2\mathbf{V}_2\mathbf{V}\mathbf{\Pi}\\ &= [\bar{\mathbf{L}}\ \mathbf{0}]\,\bar{\mathbf{D}}\bar{\mathbf{V}},\end{aligned}$$

where

$$\bar{\mathbf{L}} = \mathbf{L}\tilde{\mathbf{M}}_1\tilde{\mathbf{M}}_2,$$

$$\bar{\mathbf{D}} = \mathbf{D}_2,$$

and

$$\bar{\mathbf{V}} = \mathbf{V}_2\mathbf{V}_1\mathbf{V}\mathbf{\Pi}.$$

The methods (i), (ii), (iii) and (iv) are all designed to update factorizations when columns of $\mathbf{A}$ are added or deleted. Methods (i) and (ii) can also be used when *rows* of $\mathbf{A}$ are being exchanged if we define

$$\overline{\mathbf{A}} = \mathbf{A} + \mathbf{e}_r(\mathbf{a}_s - \mathbf{a}_r)^T$$

instead of (4.5.1). If the numerically stable Bartels–Golub or Gill–Murray–Saunders schemes are used, then the "$U^T L^T$" and VDR factorizations must be used respectively.

(v) Saunders (1972b) has suggested a product form of the LDV algorithm in which $\mathbf{V}$ is not stored. This algorithm is based on the computation of $\mathbf{x}$ using equations (4.3.22) and (4.3.23) and enables either row or column changes to be made. Consider an arbitrary rank-one modification

$$\overline{\mathbf{A}} = \mathbf{A} + \mathbf{x}\mathbf{y}^T.$$

(If columns are being exchanged then $\mathbf{x} = (\mathbf{a}_s - \mathbf{a}_r)$ and $\mathbf{y} = \mathbf{e}_r$; if rows are exchanged then the roles of $\mathbf{x}$ and $\mathbf{y}$ are reversed.) Now

$$\overline{\mathbf{A}\mathbf{A}^T} = \mathbf{A}\mathbf{A}^T + \mathbf{x}\mathbf{y}^T\mathbf{A}^T + \mathbf{A}\mathbf{y}\mathbf{x}^T + (\mathbf{y}^T\mathbf{y})\,\mathbf{x}\mathbf{x}^T.$$

It is easily verified that this expression can be written as a rank-two symmetric formula

$$\overline{\mathbf{A}\mathbf{A}^T} = \mathbf{A}\mathbf{A}^T + \left(\rho\mathbf{x} + \frac{1}{\rho}\mathbf{A}\mathbf{y}\right)\left(\rho\mathbf{x} + \frac{1}{\rho}\mathbf{A}\mathbf{y}\right)^T - \frac{1}{\rho^2}\mathbf{A}\mathbf{y}\mathbf{y}^T\mathbf{A}^T, \qquad (4.5.10)$$

where $\rho = (\mathbf{y}^T\mathbf{y})^{\frac{1}{2}}$. If we substitute the LDV factorization of $\mathbf{A}$ we obtain

$$\overline{\mathbf{A}\mathbf{A}^T} = \mathbf{L}(\mathbf{D} + \mathbf{p}\mathbf{p}^T)\,\mathbf{L}^T - \frac{1}{\rho^2}\mathbf{A}\mathbf{y}\mathbf{y}^T\mathbf{A}^T, \qquad (4.5.11)$$

where

$$\mathbf{L}\mathbf{p} = \mathbf{x} + \frac{1}{\rho}\mathbf{A}\mathbf{y}.$$

The Cholesky factors of $\mathbf{D} + \mathbf{p}\mathbf{p}^T$ are of the form

$$\mathbf{D} + \mathbf{p}\mathbf{p}^T = \mathbf{L}_1\mathbf{D}_1\mathbf{L}_1{}^T$$

with $\mathbf{D}_1 = \operatorname{diag}(\tilde{d}_1, \tilde{d}_2, \ldots, \tilde{d}_n)$ and $\mathbf{L}_1 = \mathbf{L}_1(\mathbf{p}, \boldsymbol{\beta})$ a special lower-triangular matrix with vectors $\boldsymbol{\beta}$ and $\tilde{\mathbf{d}}$ defined by the recurrence relations (4.5.6). Equation (4.5.11) can be further extended to be of the form

$$\overline{\mathbf{A}\mathbf{A}^T} = \mathbf{L}\mathbf{L}_1(\mathbf{D}_1 - \mathbf{q}\mathbf{q}^T)\,\mathbf{L}_1{}^T\mathbf{L}^T,$$

where

$$\mathbf{L}\mathbf{L}_1\mathbf{q} = \frac{1}{\rho}\mathbf{A}\mathbf{y}.$$

Now

$$\mathbf{D}_1 - \mathbf{q}\mathbf{q}^T = \mathbf{L}_2\mathbf{D}_2\mathbf{L}_2{}^T,$$

where $\mathbf{D}_1 = \operatorname{diag}(\bar{d}_1, \bar{d}_2, \ldots, \bar{d}_n)$, $\mathbf{L}_2 = \mathbf{L}_2(\mathbf{q}, \boldsymbol{\sigma})$ and the vectors $\boldsymbol{\sigma}$ and $\bar{\mathbf{d}}$ are defined by the recurrence relations (4.5.9) with $t_{n+1} = 1 - \mathbf{q}^T\mathbf{D}_1{}^{-1}\mathbf{q}$. Thus we can write $\overline{\mathbf{A}\mathbf{A}^T} = \overline{\mathbf{L}\mathbf{D}\mathbf{L}}^T, \overline{\mathbf{D}} = \mathbf{D}$ and $\overline{\mathbf{L}} = \mathbf{L}\mathbf{L}_1\mathbf{L}_2$. The factors of $\overline{\mathbf{A}\mathbf{A}^T}$ are a product of special lower-triangular matrices which can be stored as a sequence of updates on an auxiliary storage device (see Saunders, 1972b, for more details).

In summary, associated with each of the factorizations (a)–(f) of Section 4.3 are methods for isolating special structures by pre-processing, computing the initial factorization of a matrix and for modifying the factorization as rows or columns enter or leave the matrix, i.e. for generating the factors of subsequent matrices without recourse to refactorization. Refactorization fulfils two different functions in large-scale optimization. The first is to recompute an accurate solution after an accumulation of rounding error or a catastrophic breakdown of the updating process. The second is to limit the storage required, particularly on large-scale problems. (In the course of iterations following a refactorization the storage required usually increases, due either to fill-in within the factors or to the accumulation of information concerning the updating in a list or sequential file.) When the storage increases, the computation time for each solution of a set of equations increases also. A point is ultimately reached when refactorization, although costly in itself, will result in a saving in the total computational time. Suppose t_j is the time taken to compute the jth solution $t_{j+1} > t_j$ and T is the time for a refactorization. (It is assumed that the refactorization times are approximately equal, which is usually the case in large-scale problems since the majority of rows or columns remain in the matrix during several refactorizations.) If a refactorization is performed at the $(k+1)$th step, the average time per solution for the first k steps is

$$\left.\begin{aligned} t_k{}^* &= \left(T + \sum_{j=1}^{k} t_j\right)\Big/ k, \qquad k > 0, \\ t_0{}^* &= T. \end{aligned}\right\}$$

It is usually found that as k increases, $t_k{}^*$ behaves as in Fig. 4.1, with a minimum occurring at $\bar{k}$: a refactorization should be performed at this point.

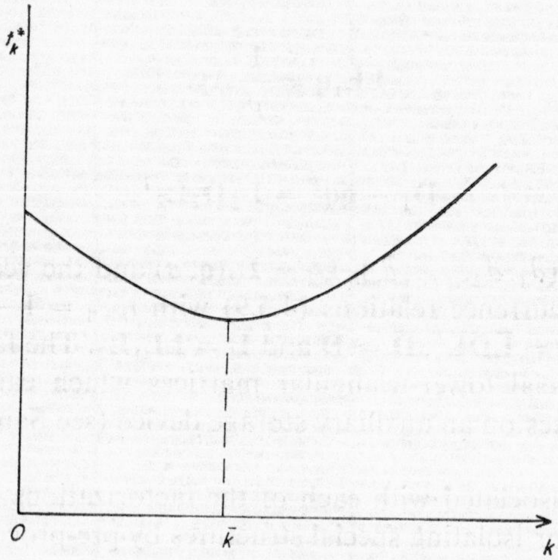

FIG. 4.1.

For large-and medium-scale problems this strategy can be automated in the program simply by computing $t_k{}^*$ and refactorizing when $t_{k+1}^* > t_k{}^*$.

4.6. Conjugate-gradient Methods

In this section we describe a method for solving $\mathbf{Ax} = \mathbf{b}$ with $\mathbf{A}$ symmetric and positive definite, which requires the storage of only the original matrix. The vector $\mathbf{x}$ can be viewed as the unique solution of the problem

$$\underset{\mathbf{x}}{\text{minimize}} \; \{\tfrac{1}{2}\mathbf{x}^T\mathbf{Ax} - \mathbf{b}^T\mathbf{x}\}. \qquad (4.6.1)$$

Suppose a non-singular matrix $\mathbf{P}$ is known, such that

$$\mathbf{P}^T\mathbf{AP} = \mathbf{D}, \qquad (4.6.2)$$

where $\mathbf{D}$ is a diagonal matrix. The columns of $\mathbf{P}$ are said to be *A-conjugate*. If we define $\mathbf{y}$ such that $\mathbf{x} = \mathbf{Py}$ then $\mathbf{y}$ can be determined as the solution of the problem

$$\underset{\mathbf{y}}{\text{minimize}} \; \{\tfrac{1}{2}\mathbf{y}^T\mathbf{Dy} - \mathbf{b}^T\mathbf{Py}\}.$$

The objective function of this modified problem is a sum of squares and thus the solution can be found by minimizing along each of the n co-ordinate directions in turn. For reasons which will become evident later we shall define

$$\mathbf{P} = [\mathbf{p}^{(0)}, \mathbf{p}^{(1)}, \ldots, \mathbf{p}^{(n-1)}] \quad \text{and} \quad \mathbf{y} = (y_0, y_1, \ldots, y_{n-1})^T.$$

In general the matrix $\mathbf{P}$ is not known *a priori* but it is possible to compute the columns of $\mathbf{P}$ sequentially. Once $\mathbf{p}^{(0)}$ is known then y_0 can be determined. The point of significance is that to compute $\mathbf{p}^{(k)}$ only $\mathbf{p}^{(k-1)}$ is required since the partial sums of

$$\mathbf{x} = \sum_{k=0}^{n-1} y_k \mathbf{p}^{(k)}$$

can be stored and the earlier columns of $\mathbf{P}$ discarded. The steps of one of the best-known algorithms, suggested by Hestenes and Stiefel (1952) are as follows.

(i) define $\mathbf{r}^{(0)} = \mathbf{b} - \mathbf{A}\mathbf{x}^{(0)}$ (usually $\mathbf{x}^{(0)} = \mathbf{0}$) and $\mathbf{p}^{(0)} = \mathbf{r}^{(0)}$;

(ii) for $k = 0, 1, 2, \ldots, n-1$ define

$$\left.\begin{aligned}
y_k &= \|\mathbf{r}^{(k)}\|_2^2/\mathbf{p}^{(k)T}\mathbf{A}\mathbf{p}^{(k)},\\
\mathbf{x}^{(k+1)} &= \mathbf{x}^{(k)} + y_k\mathbf{p}^{(k)},\\
\mathbf{r}^{(k+1)} &= \mathbf{r}^{(k)} - y_k\mathbf{A}\mathbf{p}^{(k)},\\
&\quad (\text{if } \|\mathbf{r}^{(k+1)}\|_2 = 0 \quad \text{then} \quad \mathbf{x}^{(k+1)} \text{ is the solution})\\
\beta_k &= \|\mathbf{r}^{(k+1)}\|_2^2/\|\mathbf{r}^{(k)}\|_2^2,\\
\mathbf{p}^{(k+1)} &= \mathbf{r}^{(k+1)} + \beta_k\mathbf{p}^{(k)}.
\end{aligned}\right\} \tag{4.6.3}$$

The vector $\mathbf{r}^{(0)}$ can be overwritten on $\mathbf{b}$, and $\mathbf{r}^{(k+1)}$, $\mathbf{p}^{(k+1)}$ and $\mathbf{x}^{(k+1)}$ on $\mathbf{r}^{(k)}$, $\mathbf{p}^{(k)}$ and $\mathbf{x}^{(k)}$ respectively; so that only an additional $2n$ locations are required.

If exact arithmetic is used the solution is found in m steps, where $m \leqslant n$. Unfortunately in the presence of rounding error the solution may not be obtained in even n steps. In this event the iteration can be continued with $k = n, n+1, \ldots$ and consequently, for the purposes of practical computation, this method should be regarded as an iterative technique. The precise reasons for the non-convergent behaviour are not yet fully understood.

The vector $\mathbf{r}^{(k)}$ is equal to

$$\mathbf{r}^{(k)} = \mathbf{b} - \mathbf{A}\mathbf{x}^{(k)},$$

and is thus the negative gradient of the objective function (4.6.1) and the residual of the linear equations at the point $\mathbf{x}^{(k)}$. The vectors $\mathbf{r}^{(k)}$ are $\mathbf{A}$-conjugate like the vectors $\mathbf{p}^{(k)}$, and consequently the method is known as the conjugate-gradient method. The reader is referred to Reid (1971b) for a survey of conjugate-gradient methods for linear equations.

The success of the conjugate-gradient method can be assured only if the matrix **A** is positive definite. Recently Paige and Saunders (1973) have overcome this restriction by noting the similarity between the Lanczos algorithm for tri-diagonalizing a matrix and the method of conjugate gradients. Briefly the Lanczos method (Lanczos, 1950) determines a matrix **V** such that

$$\mathbf{V}^T\mathbf{A}\mathbf{V} = \mathbf{T} \quad \text{and} \quad \mathbf{V}^T\mathbf{V} = \mathbf{I},$$

where **T** is a tri-diagonal matrix. If we wish to solve (4.2.1) when **A** is positive definite then this can be achieved by first finding the Cholesky factors $\mathbf{T} = \mathbf{L}\mathbf{D}\mathbf{L}^T$, solving

$$\mathbf{L}\mathbf{D}\mathbf{L}^T\mathbf{y} = \mathbf{V}^T\mathbf{b},$$

and setting $\mathbf{x} = \mathbf{V}\mathbf{y}$. Since **T** is tri-diagonal, **L** is bi-diagonal and it is possible to arrange the computation so that it is unnecessary to store the columns of **V**. If **A** is indefinite then so is **T** and the formal equivalence of this algorithm with (4.6.3) implies that it is the implicit use of the Cholesky factorization (which is unstable when applied to indefinite matrices) which causes the breakdown of the conjugate-gradient method when **A** is indefinite. Paige and Saunders suggest that in place of finding the Cholesky factors of **T** we determine the *LQ* factors and solve

$$\mathbf{L}\mathbf{Q}\mathbf{y} = \mathbf{V}^T\mathbf{b}.$$

Again the computation can be arranged so that no matrices need be stored. This method is still "iterative" but does not break down when **A** is indefinite.

4.7. Iterative Methods for the Solution of Large Sparse Sets of Linear Equations

In many practical problems involving large sparse systems of linear equations (for example, in solving partial differential equations by finite-element or finite-difference methods) iterative methods are more effective than direct methods. This section reviews the salient features of some common iterative methods.

A "splitting" of the matrix **A** into complementary parts **B** and **C**, such that $\mathbf{A} = \mathbf{B} - \mathbf{C}$, defines the iterative process

$$\mathbf{B}\mathbf{x}^{(k+1)} = \mathbf{C}\mathbf{x}^{(k)} + \mathbf{b}, \tag{4.7.1}$$

where $\mathbf{x}^{(k)}$ is the estimate of the solution at the kth stage. Particular splittings are often defined in terms of the diagonal, sub-diagonal and super-diagonal constituents of **A**:

$$\mathbf{A} \equiv \mathbf{D} - \mathbf{L} - \mathbf{U},$$

where **D** is a diagonal matrix, and **L** and **U** are respectively lower- and upper-triangular matrices with zero diagonal elements. For example, if all the diagonal elements of **A** are non-zero the Gauss–Seidel method involves solving cyclicly for a single variable using the latest estimates of the remainder:

$$\begin{aligned} x_1^{(k+1)} &= (b_1 - a_{12}x_2^{(k)} - a_{13}x_3^{(k)} - \dots - a_{1n}x_n^{(k)})/a_{11}, \\ x_2^{(k+1)} &= (b_2 - a_{21}x_1^{(k+1)} - a_{23}x_3^{(k)} - \dots - a_{2n}x_n^{(k)})/a_{22}, \\ &\cdot \quad \cdot \quad \cdot \quad \cdot \quad \cdot \quad \cdot \quad \cdot \quad \cdot \\ x_n^{(k+1)} &= (b_n - a_{n1}x_1^{(k+1)} - a_{n2}x_2^{(k+1)} - \dots - a_{n,n-1}x_{n-1}^{(k+1)})/a_{nn}. \end{aligned} \tag{4.7.2}$$

This iteration corresponds to the splitting

$$\mathbf{B} = \mathbf{D} - \mathbf{L}, \qquad \mathbf{C} = \mathbf{U}. \tag{4.7.3}$$

Similarly, the Jacobi iteration, which involves the elements of $\mathbf{x}^{(k)}$ everywhere on the right-hand side of (4.7.2) is defined by

$$\mathbf{B} = \mathbf{D}, \qquad \mathbf{C} = \mathbf{L} + \mathbf{U}. \tag{4.7.4}$$

The element $x_j^{(k+1)}$ defined by the Gauss–Seidel iteration is given by $x_j^{(k+1)} = x_j^{(k)} + p_j^{(k)}$ where

$$p_j^{(k)} = (b_j - a_{j1}x_1^{(k+1)} - \dots - a_{jj}x_j^{(k)} - \dots - a_{jn}x_n^{(k)})/a_{jj}.$$

An important generalization of (4.7.2), the method of *successive over-relaxation*, (SOR), is defined by using $x_j^{(k+1)} = x_j^{(k)} + \omega p_j^{(k)}$, where ω is a fixed positive scalar called the relaxation parameter. It can be shown that this corresponds to the splitting

$$\mathbf{B} = \omega^{-1}(\mathbf{D} - \omega\mathbf{L}), \qquad \mathbf{C} = \omega^{-1}[(1-\omega)\mathbf{D} + \omega\mathbf{U}].$$

By permitting **D** to denote a block-diagonal matrix and forming the matrices **B** and **C** accordingly we can include the *block-iterative* methods in our considerations.

If $\mathbf{e}^{(k)}$ denotes $\mathbf{x} - \mathbf{x}^{(k)}$, the error after the kth cycle has been completed, we have from (4.7.1)

$$\mathbf{e}^{(k+1)} = \mathbf{B}^{-1}\mathbf{C}\mathbf{e}^{(k)}$$

$$= (\mathbf{I} - \mathbf{B}^{-1}\mathbf{A})\,\mathbf{e}^{(k)}, \tag{4.7.5}$$

and it follows that the rate of convergence is determined by the eigenvalues of $\mathbf{B}^{-1}\mathbf{C}$. Clearly, the nearer the eigenvalues of $\mathbf{B}^{-1}\mathbf{A}$ are to unity, the more rapid the convergence. Classes of matrices for which convergence can be guaranteed include matrices which are symmetric and positive definite, and matrices which are diagonally dominant (i.e. $|a_{ii}| > \sum_{j \neq i} |a_{ij}|$). We are particularly interested in the positive-definite symmetric case, and under these circumstances iterative techniques can be regarded as methods for the minimization of the quadratic function (4.6.1). Equation (4.7.1) can be rearranged to be of the form

$$\mathbf{x}^{(k+1)} = \mathbf{x}^{(k)} + \mathbf{B}^{-1}\mathbf{r}^{(k)}, \tag{4.7.6}$$

and since $\mathbf{r}^{(k)}$ is the negative gradient of (4.6.1), the iteration (4.7.6) can be regarded as a Newton-type method for the minimization of (4.6.1) in which $\mathbf{A}^{-1}$ is replaced by a fixed easily-invertible matrix $\mathbf{B}^{-1}$. From our experience in unconstrained minimization we expect this to be an effective algorithm only if $\mathbf{B}$ is a good approximation of $\mathbf{A}$ (cf. (4.7.5)). This is the case for some problems arising in the solution of partial differential equations but not so for general optimization problems.

Part II
Unconstrained Optimization

4.8. Newton-type Methods with Second Derivatives Available

It has been shown in Section 2.3 of Chapter II that when $\mathbf{G}^{(k)}$ is positive definite the direction of search can be obtained by solving the equations

$$\mathbf{G}^{(k)}\mathbf{p}^{(k)} = -\,\mathbf{g}^{(k)}. \tag{4.8.1}$$

When the matrix $\mathbf{G}^{(k)}$ is large and sparse the equations can be solved by any of the methods discussed in Part I of this Chapter, the particular method chosen depending upon the source of the problem and type of structure (if any) of $\mathbf{G}^{(k)}$.

(a) The method of Cholesky factorization can be used if the amount of fill-in is expected to be acceptable. This method is particularly effective for the following objective function which often occurs when a collection of inter-related "sub-systems" are to be optimized. Let $F(\mathbf{x})$ be the function

$$F(\mathbf{x}) = \sum_{j=1}^{q-1} f_j(\mathbf{x}_j, \mathbf{y}) + f_0(\mathbf{y}), \tag{4.8.2}$$

where $\mathbf{x} = (\mathbf{x}_1{}^T, \mathbf{x}_2{}^T, \ldots, \mathbf{x}_{q-1}^T, \mathbf{y}^T)^T$ with $\mathbf{x}_j$ an n_j-vector, $j = 1, 2, \ldots, q-1$, $\mathbf{y}$ an n_q-vector and

$$n = \sum_{j=1}^{q} n_j.$$

It is easily verified that the Hessian matrix of the function (4.8.2) is of the form

$$\mathbf{G} = \begin{bmatrix} \mathbf{G}_{11} & & & & & & \mathbf{G}_{1q} \\ & \mathbf{G}_{22} & & & & & \mathbf{G}_{2q} \\ & & \mathbf{G}_{33} & & & & \mathbf{G}_{3q} \\ & & & \cdot & & & \cdot \\ & & & & \cdot & & \cdot \\ & & & & & \cdot & \cdot \\ & & & & & \mathbf{G}_{q-1,q-1} & \mathbf{G}_{q-1,q} \\ \mathbf{G}_{q1} & \mathbf{G}_{q2} & \mathbf{G}_{q3} & \cdot & \cdot & \mathbf{G}_{q,q-1} & \mathbf{G}_{qq} \end{bmatrix} \tag{4.8.3}$$

where $\mathbf{G}_{jj}$ and $\mathbf{G}_{qj}$ are $n_j \times n_j$ and $n_q \times n_j$ matrices respectively with $\mathbf{G}_{jj}$ symmetric and $\mathbf{G}_{qj} = \mathbf{G}_{jq}{}^T$. From our remarks of Section 4.4 we know that factorization of this matrix into $\mathbf{G} = \mathbf{LDL}^T$, induces fill-in only in the blocks already containing some non-zero elements. Clearly, if we apply a pre-processing strategy to an arbitrary matrix in order to isolate any structure similar to (4.8.3), we are implicitly rewriting the objective function to be of the form (4.8.2). The elements of $\mathbf{G}^{(k)}$ are nonlinear functions of $\mathbf{x}$ but the sparsity pattern is independent of $\mathbf{x}$. Since systems of equations with the same sparsity pattern are repeatedly being solved it is worthwhile putting considerable effort into pre-processing the matrix $\mathbf{G}$—should this be necessary.

If $\mathbf{G}(\mathbf{x})$ cannot be guaranteed to be positive definite then a modified Newton method must be used, with $\mathbf{G}^{(k)}$ being replaced by $\overline{\mathbf{G}}^{(k)}$ if it is not sufficiently positive definite. Clearly we require $\mathbf{G}^{(k)}$ and $\overline{\mathbf{G}}^{(k)}$ to have the same sparsity pattern and two methods having this property are those of Gill and Murray (Chapter II, method (b)) and Hebden's implementation of the Levenberg–

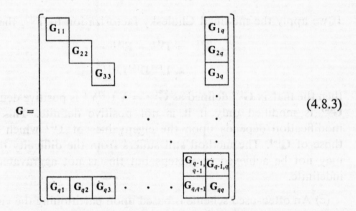

Marquardt scheme (Chapter II, Method (e)). We note that methods based upon performing an eigensystem analysis of **G** are completely unsatisfactory.

(b) It may be the case that the method of conjugate gradients is preferred. In the following we shall describe a modified conjugate-gradient method based upon the Lanczos scheme. This modified algorithm has the feature of giving a matrix $\bar{\mathbf{G}}^{(k)}$ such that the direction of search satisfies

$$\bar{\mathbf{G}}^{(k)}\mathbf{p}^{(k)} = -\,\mathbf{g}^{(k)}.$$

As mentioned in Section 4.6 the conjugate-gradient method for the solution of (4.8.1) involves the formation of a tri-diagonal matrix $\mathbf{T}^{(k)}$ such that

$$\mathbf{V}^T\mathbf{G}^{(k)}\mathbf{V} = \mathbf{T}^{(k)}, \qquad \mathbf{V}^T\mathbf{V} = \mathbf{I}.$$

If we apply the modified Cholesky factorization to $\mathbf{T}^{(k)}$, that is, form

$$\begin{aligned}\bar{\mathbf{T}}^{(k)} &= \mathbf{T}^{(k)} + \mathbf{E}^{(k)}\\ &= \mathbf{L}^{(k)}\mathbf{D}^{(k)}\mathbf{L}^{(k)T},\end{aligned}$$

then the matrix $\bar{\mathbf{G}}^{(k)}$ defined as $\bar{\mathbf{G}}^{(k)} = \mathbf{V}\bar{\mathbf{T}}^{(k)}\mathbf{V}^T$ is positive definite. The matrix $\mathbf{G}^{(k)}$ is modified only if it is not positive definite. This is because the modification depends upon the eigenvalues of $\mathbf{T}^{(k)}$ which are identical to those of $\mathbf{G}^{(k)}$. The method still suffers from the difficulty that convergence may not be achieved in n steps but this is not aggravated by $\mathbf{G}^{(k)}$ being indefinite.

(c) An often-used scheme is based upon partitioning the variables into two sets and minimizing the objective function with respect to one set while keeping constant those remaining. The method proceeds in a cyclic way with the partitioning varying at each stage. If the Hessian matrix is known, Newton's method can be applied to perform the sub-optimization, where the matrix used in (4.8.1) is the relevant sub-matrix of **G**. The number of variables over which to optimize and the order in which they are selected is usually suggested by the structure of **G**. For example, if **G** were block diagonal the unknown variables can be chosen cyclicly to coincide with the block structure. In this form the method is directly analogous to the block Gauss–Seidel iteration mentioned in Section 4.7 except that the diagonal block associated with the set of variables which are currently being optimized is *recomputed* at each new point.

If the objective function is of a form similar to (4.8.2) then a useful partition is defined by $\{\mathbf{x}_j\}_{j=1}^{q-1}$ and **y**. Once the **y**-variables are fixed the problem separates into $q-1$ unconstrained problems in the $\mathbf{x}_j$-variables—this result indicates that pre-processing the Hessian matrix may convey benefits for iterative as well as direct methods.

Schechter (1962, 1968, 1970) has presented and analyzed a class of these partitioning algorithms for some convex functions and Elkin (1968) has extended the methods to the non-convex case.

(d) The SOR process can be further generalized by constructing a combined Newton-SOR method. The Hessian is computed and several steps of the SOR algorithm are used to obtain an approximate solution of the equations (4.8.1) at which the Hessian is re-evaluated. The reader is referred to Ortega and Rheinboldt (1970, pp. 214–222) for a comprehensive review of such methods. Results indicate that Newton-SOR-type methods exhibit only a linear rate of convergence except under special circumstances.

4.9. Methods Using Only First Derivatives

In the dense case quasi-Newton methods are generally regarded as the most efficient methods for the minimization of functions in which only first derivatives are available. Unfortunately these methods are not easily adapted to the solution of sparse problems. The reason for this becomes evident when one considers the complementary DFP modification formula (see Chapter III, Section 3.3, formula (b)); viz

$$\mathbf{B}^{(k+1)} = \mathbf{B}^{(k)} + \frac{1}{\alpha^{(k)}\mathbf{y}^{(k)T}\mathbf{p}^{(k)}}\,\mathbf{y}^{(k)}\mathbf{y}^{(k)T} + \frac{1}{\mathbf{g}^{(k)T}\mathbf{p}^{(k)}}\,\mathbf{g}^{(k)}\mathbf{g}^{(k)T}.$$

In general the vectors $\mathbf{y}^{(k)}$ and $\mathbf{g}^{(k)}$ will not have a significant number of zero elements. This implies that the matrix $\mathbf{B}^{(k)}$ will be dense even when $\mathbf{G}^{(k)}$ itself is sparse. For example, if $F(\mathbf{x})$ is quadratic, the exactly computed $\mathbf{B}^{(k)}$ will have zero elements only at the nth iteration.

If the sparsity pattern of $\mathbf{G}$ is known, it can be imposed upon both $\mathbf{B}^{(k)}$ and $\mathbf{B}^{(k+1)}$ by altering the modification rule so that a zero value is assigned to those elements which are known to be zero in $\mathbf{G}$. At a given stage this procedure can only reduce the error norm $\|\mathbf{G}^{(k)} - \mathbf{B}^{(k)}\|$. Unfortunately elements of $\mathbf{B}^{(k)}$ corresponding to zero elements in $\mathbf{G}$ will not, in general, be small since $\mathbf{B}^{(k)}$ is a poor element-by-element approximation to $\mathbf{G}^{(k)}$ (cf. Murray, 1972c). This implies that setting elements to zero could alter the properties of $\mathbf{B}^{(k)}$ to such an extent that a deterioration in the rate of convergence results. There is the added difficulty of ensuring that $\mathbf{B}^{(k)}$ is positive definite when elements are altered.

Schubert (1970) has suggested a quasi-Newton method for the solution of nonlinear equations which takes advantage of sparsity in the Jacobian matrix by modifying only the non-zero elements. His modification requires a rank-n change every iteration. We have not seen any report of this approach being applied to minimization problems although it may be possible to design similar quasi-Newton minimization methods to allow for sparsity. We believe, however, that such methods will differ from their dense counterparts to such an extent that their relative efficiency, vis-a-vis alternative approaches, will be lost.

An algorithm which adapts quite naturally to large-scale problems is the discrete Newton method described in Chapter II, Section 2.3. This method computes an additional n gradients at points $\mathbf{x}^{(k)} + h\mathbf{e}_j$, $j = 1, 2, \ldots, n$ and uses them to compute a finite-difference approximation to $\mathbf{G}^{(k)}$. The method is not recommended for large n in the dense case because the reduction in the number of iterations seldom compensates for the increase in the number of gradient evaluations. Fortunately, when $\mathbf{G}^{(k)}$ is sparse a considerable reduction can be made in the number of gradient subroutine calls required. To illustrate this, consider the approximation of a tri-diagonal Hessian matrix:

$$\mathbf{G} = \begin{bmatrix} \times & \times & & & & & \\ \times & \times & \times & & & & \\ & \times & \times & \times & & & \\ & & \times & \times & \times & & \\ & & & \times & \times & \times & \\ & & & & \times & \times & \times \\ & & & & & \times & \times \end{bmatrix}.$$

If the differences $\mathbf{y}_j = (\mathbf{g}(\mathbf{x}^{(k)} + h\mathbf{e}_j) - \mathbf{g}(\mathbf{x}^{(k)}))/h$ are computed for $j = 1$ and $j = 4$, we have $\mathbf{y}_1{}^T = (\times, \times, 0, 0, 0, 0, 0)$ and $\mathbf{y}_4{}^T = (0, 0, \times, \times, \times, 0, 0)$ respectively. Consequently if we form the difference

$$\mathbf{y} = (\mathbf{g}(\mathbf{x}^{(k)} + h(\mathbf{e}_1 + \mathbf{e}_4)) - \mathbf{g}(\mathbf{x}^{(k)}))/h$$

the resulting vector is $(\times, \times, \times, \times, \times, 0, 0,)$, whose first two elements are those of $\mathbf{y}_1$ and third, fourth and fifth elements are those of $\mathbf{y}_4$. In general we can form the difference

$$\left\{\mathbf{g}\left(\mathbf{x}^{(k)} + h \sum_{i=0}^{2} \mathbf{e}_{3i+1}\right) - \mathbf{g}(\mathbf{x}^{(k)})\right\} \Big/ h$$

and obtain estimates of three columns for just a single gradient evaluation. Indeed the whole matrix can be approximated for only three gradient evaluations irrespective of the size of n. This technique forms the basis of a method described by Gill and Murray (1973b) to solve a class of problems for which it is known that the Hessian has a given bandwidth. The number of additional gradients required is related only to the bandwidth and is independent of n. Symmetrization of the approximation can be performed economically as in the dense case. Curtis, Powell and Reid (1974) first drew attention to this type of technique for arbitrarily sparse Jacobian matrices occurring in the solution of nonlinear equations; the same principles can be applied when the Hessian is arbitrarily sparse.

In Section 4.6 we discussed the conjugate-gradient method for solving a set of symmetrical linear equations and remarked that the method could be interpreted as minimizing a quadratic function. Fletcher and Reeves (1964) have demonstrated how the method can be adapted to minimize more general functions. The Fletcher–Reeves algorithm is based upon using the iteration (4.6.3) to minimize a quadratic function which is re-approximated at every step, the approximation being obtained by taking $\mathbf{g}^{(k)}$ as the gradient of the quadratic function. Thus we have

$$\left.\begin{array}{l}\text{(i) define } \mathbf{p}^{(0)} = -\mathbf{g}^{(0)};\\ \text{(ii) for } k = 0, 1, \ldots, n-1 \text{ define}\\ \quad \mathbf{x}^{(k+1)} = \mathbf{x}^{(k)} + \alpha^{(k)}\mathbf{p}^{(k)}, \text{ with } \alpha^{(k)} \text{ minimizing}\\ \quad F(\mathbf{x}^{(k)} + \alpha\mathbf{p}^{(k)}) \text{ with respect to } \alpha,\\ \quad \beta^{(k)} = \|\mathbf{g}^{(k+1)}\|_2{}^2/\|\mathbf{g}^{(k)}\|_2{}^2,\\ \quad \mathbf{p}^{(k+1)} = -\mathbf{g}^{(k+1)} + \beta^{(k)}\mathbf{p}^{(k)}.\end{array}\right\} \tag{4.9.1}$$

The process is restarted every n iterations and, as in the algorithm for linear equations, requires only two additional vectors. This algorithm has the property that n-step convergence is achieved on a quadratic function, but on general functions the method is widely known to be inferior to alternative methods. Our experience is that on sparse problems with banded matrices the conjugate-gradient algorithm requires more iterations, function and gradient evaluations, and is less robust than the discrete Newton-type method discussed earlier. However, the conjugate-gradient scheme has the advantages of simplicity and minimal storage requirements. The final choice of method will depend upon the density and structure of the non-zero elements of $\mathbf{G}^{(k)}$.

4.10. Methods Using No Derivatives

The problems in this category divide into two groups: those for which gradients are unavailable and those for which they are undefined (for example, the derivatives may be discontinuous). In the former group the best method available in the dense case is the quasi-Newton method with finite-difference approximations to the gradient (see Chapter III, Section 3.6) but, as we indicated in Section 4.9, the efficiency of such methods is impaired when they are adapted for sparse problems. One possibility is to take the finite-difference approximation one stage further in the Newton-type method and approximate both first and second derivatives. Since we are approximating **G** element by element, the number of function evaluations required is directly proportional to the number of non-zero elements. Another approach is to use a finite-difference approximation in the conjugate-gradient algorithm (4.9.1), together with the type of rule used in the quasi-Newton method (Gill, Murray and Pitfield, 1972) for switching between forward and central differences. However, we emphasize that there are problems with cancellation and truncation error in both these approaches, particularly when **G** is ill-conditioned; but these difficulties are almost inevitable with any non-gradient algorithm. Numerical experience with both these approaches has confirmed their expected behaviour, which is very similar to that of their gradient analogues on a computer with half the word length.

When derivatives are not defined, a direct search method must be used. Many of the better direct search algorithms, such as the simplex method (Spendley, Hext and Himsworth, 1962) are unsuitable for large problems due to their considerable storage requirements which are independent of any structure in the problem. There are other methods which require a small amount of storage; and the reader is referred to Chapter VII for further details.

Part III
Linearly Constrained Minimization

4.11. General Problems

In our discussion of the solution of unconstrained problems two alternative classes of method emerged: those in which a sequence $\{\mathbf{x}^{(k)}\}$ is computed by taking advantage of sparsity using the basic strategy of the methods for dense problems; and those in which a possibly inferior rate of convergence is acceptable because the structure of the problem can be exploited to reduce the work required for each iteration. We would always choose the former sequence if it could be effortlessly computed and thus we shall regard it as being an *ideal* or *prototype* sequence. This concept can be extended to the linearly constrained case as follows.

DEFINITION 4.1. *An ideal algorithm is one which moves from a minimum on one subspace to the minimum on another subspace when solving a convex quadratic problem.*

DEFINITION 4.2. *The sequence of points* $\{\mathbf{x}^{(k)}\}$ *generated by an ideal algorithm is defined as an ideal sequence.*

An ideal sequence can be computed using either of the two alternative Newton-type techniques discussed in Chapter II, Section 2.4. We shall consider the applicability of each of these methods to the case where the matrices **G** and $\hat{\mathbf{A}}$ are large and sparse.

We shall consider Method I in the following form in which the computation of **Z** is based on method (a) of Section 2.8. Let the rows of $\mathbf{V}^T$ be $n-t$ inactive constraints such that

$$\mathbf{T} = \begin{bmatrix} \hat{\mathbf{A}}^T \\ \mathbf{V}^T \end{bmatrix}$$

is non-singular, and let the $n-t$ columns of the matrix **Z** be defined by

$$\mathbf{T}\mathbf{z}_j = \mathbf{e}_{t+j}, \qquad j = 1, 2, \ldots, n-t.$$

Then compute $\mathbf{p}^{(k)} = \mathbf{Z}\mathbf{p}_A{}^{(k)}$ where $\mathbf{p}_A{}^{(k)}$ is such that

$$\mathbf{G}_A{}^{(k)}\mathbf{p}_A{}^{(k)} = -\mathbf{g}_A{}^{(k)} \tag{4.11.1}$$

with $\mathbf{G}_A{}^{(k)} = \mathbf{Z}^T\mathbf{G}^{(k)}\mathbf{Z}$ and $\mathbf{g}_A{}^{(k)} = \mathbf{Z}^T\mathbf{g}^{(k)}$. If necessary, the Lagrange multipliers are computed (see Section 2.8) using either

$$\mathbf{T}^T \begin{bmatrix} \boldsymbol{\omega}^{(k)} \\ \mathbf{0} \end{bmatrix} = \mathbf{G}^{(k)}\mathbf{p}^{(k)} + \mathbf{g}^{(k)}, \qquad \text{(second-order multipliers)},$$

or

$$\mathbf{T}^T \begin{bmatrix} \boldsymbol{\lambda}^{(k)} \\ \mathbf{0} \end{bmatrix} = \mathbf{g}^{(k)}, \qquad \text{(first-order multipliers)}.$$

The difficulty with this approach is that although the Lagrange multipliers and columns of **Z** can be computed efficiently using sparse matrix techniques, it is not easy to compute $\mathbf{p}_A{}^{(k)}$ because the coefficient matrix of (4.11.1) is a product of three matrices, which usually results in $\mathbf{G}_A{}^{(k)}$ being a large dense matrix. Thus the interaction of the curvature and constraint information makes solution of (4.11.1) impossible by any technique which requires the matrix $\mathbf{G}_A{}^{(k)}$ explicitly. This implies that unless there are special circumstances (some of which are discussed in Sections 4.12–4.16) we cannot use direct methods or iterative methods of the SOR or Newton-SOR type. The inadequacy of direct methods implies in turn that we are not in general able to devise ideal methods in the sparse case. The only efficient method of solving the equations (4.11.1) in the general sparse case is that of conjugate gradients, because we can efficiently obtain products of the form $\mathbf{G}_A{}^{(k)}\mathbf{v}$ by forming successively $\mathbf{v}_1 = \mathbf{Z}\mathbf{v}$, $\mathbf{v}_2 = \mathbf{G}\mathbf{v}_1$ and $\mathbf{v}_3 = \mathbf{Z}^T\mathbf{v}_2$. The elements of $\mathbf{v}_3$ and $\mathbf{v}_1$ can be formed one by one and consequently it is not necessary to store more than one column of $\mathbf{Z}$ at one time. The modification of the conjugate-gradient algorithm which gives a related positive-definite matrix $\mathbf{G}_A^{(k)}$ can be applied just as in the unconstrained case. If the Hessian matrix is unavailable, the Fletcher–Reeves algorithm can be applied by using the conjugate-gradient iteration with the projected gradient. The algorithm is of the form

(i) define $\mathbf{p}_A^{(0)} = -\mathbf{g}_A^{(0)}$;

(ii) for $k = 0, 1, 2, \ldots, n-1$ define

$$\begin{aligned}\mathbf{p}^{(k)} &= \mathbf{Z}\mathbf{p}_A^{(k)},\\ \mathbf{x}^{(k+1)} &= \mathbf{x}^{(k)} + \alpha^{(k)}\mathbf{p}^{(k)},\\ \beta^{(k)} &= \|\mathbf{g}_A^{(k+1)}\|_2^2/\|\mathbf{g}_A^{(k)}\|_2^2,\\ \mathbf{p}_A^{(k+1)} &= -\mathbf{g}_A^{(k+1)} + \beta^{(k)}\mathbf{p}_A^{(k)}.\end{aligned}$$

This algorithm is very similar to that given by Goldfarb (1969) which extends the gradient-projection method of Rosen (1960) to the Fletcher–Reeves algorithm. If $\mathbf{P}$ is the matrix

$$\bar{\mathbf{P}} = \mathbf{I} - \hat{\mathbf{A}}(\hat{\mathbf{A}}^T\hat{\mathbf{A}})^{-1}\hat{\mathbf{A}}^T$$

and we define $\mathbf{y}_p = \bar{\mathbf{P}}\mathbf{y}$, then the Fletcher–Reeves algorithm becomes

(i) define $\mathbf{p}^{(0)} = -\mathbf{g}_p^{(k)}$;

(ii) for $k = 0, 1, \ldots, n-1$ define

$$\begin{aligned}\mathbf{x}^{(k+1)} &= \mathbf{x}^{(k)} + \alpha^{(k)}\mathbf{p}^{(k)},\\ \beta^{(k)} &= \|\mathbf{g}_p^{(k+1)}\|_2^{\,2}/\|\mathbf{g}_p^{(k)}\|_2^{\,2},\\ \mathbf{p}^{(k+1)} &= -\mathbf{g}_p^{(k+1)} + \beta^{(k)}\mathbf{p}^{(k)}.\end{aligned}$$

The implementation of Method II of Chapter II involves the same difficulties as Method I. The reader will recall from (2.4.9) and (2.4.10) that the method requires the computation of $\mathbf{p}^{(k)}$ such that

$$\mathbf{G}^{(k)}\mathbf{p}^{(k)} = \hat{\mathbf{A}}\boldsymbol{\omega}^{(k)} - \mathbf{g}^{(k)}, \tag{4.11.2}$$

where $\boldsymbol{\omega}^{(k)}$ is such that

$$\hat{\mathbf{A}}^T\mathbf{G}^{(k)-1}\hat{\mathbf{A}}\boldsymbol{\omega}^{(k)} = \hat{\mathbf{A}}^T\mathbf{G}^{(k)-1}\mathbf{g}^{(k)}. \tag{4.11.3}$$

In this case efficiency demands that a direct method be used to solve (4.11.2) and a conjugate-gradient method for (4.11.3).

It is difficult to add to the comparison between Methods I and II given in

Chapter II. When **G** and **A** are large and sparse each method is suitable for a different class of problem; Method I is effective for problems for which there are a large number of constraints in the basis and Method II for problems in which there are few constraints in the basis. An implication of this result is that the conditions for dropping a constraint from the basis should be more stringent for Method I than for Method II.

We note that in either case the situation is not completely satisfactory for general sparse problems because the conjugate-gradient method is not the most effective way of solving a set of linear equations. However, there exist categories of problems for which it is possible to use either Method I or Method II to formulate an ideal algorithm. In the next five sections we shall consider these types of problem in detail.

4.12. Large-scale Linear Programming

Currently the most important application of large-scale linearly constrained optimization occurs in linear programming (*LP*) where the function is linear and given by $F(\mathbf{x}) = \mathbf{c}^T\mathbf{x}$. As mentioned previously at the end of Section 2.8, Method I is identical to the simplex method if n constraints are kept in the basis. If at a point $\mathbf{x}^{(k)}$ the matrix of n active constraints is defined as $\hat{\mathbf{A}}$, the Lagrange multipliers are given by the solution of the $n \times n$ set of equations

$$\hat{\mathbf{A}}\boldsymbol{\lambda} = \mathbf{c}. \tag{4.12.1}$$

If all the Lagrange multipliers are positive then $\mathbf{x}^{(k)}$ is the solution; otherwise the objective function can be reduced by computing a direction of search parallel to all the constraints except one with a negative Lagrange multiplier, $(\lambda_s < 0)$. A direction $\mathbf{p}^{(k)}$ satisfying these properties can be computed by solving the $n \times n$ set of linear equations

$$\hat{\mathbf{A}}^T\mathbf{p}^{(k)} = \mathbf{e}_s. \tag{4.12.2}$$

(We note that this is the statement of Theorem 2.5 with $\mathbf{T} = \hat{\mathbf{A}}^T$. When $n-1$ constraints are active the matrix **Z** is a single vector which is parallel to $\mathbf{p}^{(k)}$.) The algorithm then proceeds as described in Sections 2.5, 2.6 and 2.8 of Chapter II. The simplex method essentially involves the solution of two sets of linear equations (4.12.1) and (4.12.2), which in many applications are large and sparse. Any of the techniques described in Sections 4.3 and 4.5 can be used to compute both the initial and updated form of the basis. Most practical implementations use a direct method in product form together with a pre-processing technique.

Due to the historical development of *LP* problems from operational research applications in which the variables are non-negative,these problems are often defined in an alternative way known as the *canonical form*, viz

$$\underset{\mathbf{x}}{\text{minimize}}\ \mathbf{c}^T\mathbf{x}$$

subject to the constraints $\mathbf{A}\mathbf{x} = \mathbf{b}, \mathbf{x} \geqslant \mathbf{0}$.

The matrix $\mathbf{A}$ is now $m \times n$ with $m < n$. If the original problem does not conform to this standard form it can be made to do so by the introduction of slack variables. In this event the resulting matrix $\mathbf{A}$ will have a special structure, involving columns which are columns of the identity matrix. This does not seriously increase the storage requirements since in large-scale applications the matrix $\mathbf{A}$ will be stored in packed form.

We shall now show that the active constraint strategy outlined earlier for the standard problem leads directly to the revised simplex method given by Dantzig (1963), the difference being that now columns are exchanged in a basis matrix instead of rows. If $\hat{\mathbf{A}}^T$ is the matrix of constraints active at a point $\mathbf{x}^{(k)}$ which is an estimate of the solution of the canonical problem, then $\hat{\mathbf{A}}^T$ must be made up of the m rows of $\mathbf{A}\mathbf{x} = \mathbf{b}$ and $n - m$ rows of the identity matrix. This is because the constraints $\mathbf{A}\mathbf{x} = \mathbf{b}$ are *always* active and the remaining constraints have been selected from $\mathbf{x} \geqslant \mathbf{0}$. If we assume without loss of generality that the first $n - m$ variables x_j are such that $x_j = 0$, then

$$\mathbf{A}^T = \begin{bmatrix} \mathbf{I}_{n-m} & \mathbf{0} \\ & \mathbf{A} & \end{bmatrix}$$

$$= \begin{bmatrix} \mathbf{I}_{n-m} & \mathbf{0} \\ \bar{\mathbf{B}} & \hat{\mathbf{B}} \end{bmatrix}, \qquad (4.12.3)$$

where $\bar{\mathbf{B}}$ is an $m \times (n - m)$ matrix and $\hat{\mathbf{B}}$ is an $m \times m$ matrix known as the *column basis*. The vector $\mathbf{x}^{(k)}$ is known as a basic feasible solution if exactly $n - m$ entries are zero and the remainder are positive, where the positive entries are defined as the m – vector $\hat{\mathbf{x}}$. With the particular form (4.12.3) of the active constraints, the equations (4.12.1) for the Lagrange multipliers become

$$\begin{bmatrix} \mathbf{I}_{n-m} & \bar{\mathbf{B}}^T \\ \mathbf{0} & \hat{\mathbf{B}}^T \end{bmatrix} \boldsymbol{\lambda} = \mathbf{c} = \begin{bmatrix} \bar{\mathbf{c}} \\ \hat{\mathbf{c}} \end{bmatrix}, \text{ say.}$$

Since we are interested in the signs of Lagrange multipliers associated with inequality constraints alone, we must inspect the quantities

$$\bar{c}_j - \mathbf{a}_j^T\boldsymbol{\pi},$$

where $\boldsymbol{\pi}$ is the solution of the equations

$$\hat{\mathbf{B}}^T\boldsymbol{\pi} = \hat{\mathbf{c}}$$

and $\mathbf{a}_j$ is the jth column of $\bar{\mathbf{B}}$. The quantities π_j are known as the *simplex multipliers* or *reduced costs.*

We propose to move off precisely one constraint, $x_s = 0$ say, for which $\lambda_s < 0$, and so the direction of search $\mathbf{p}^{(k)}$ will have zero elements corresponding to all $x_j^{(k)} = 0, j = 1, \ldots, s-1, s+1, \ldots, n-m$ and non-zero values corresponding to the elements of $\hat{\mathbf{x}}$. If we define the vector of non-zero values of $\mathbf{p}^{(k)}$ corresponding to the elements of $\hat{\mathbf{x}}$ as $\mathbf{y}$, then on inspection of (4.12.1) and (4.12.3) we see that $\mathbf{y}$ satisfies the equations

$$\hat{\mathbf{B}}\mathbf{y} = -\mathbf{a}_s,$$

where $\mathbf{a}_s$ is the sth column of $\bar{\mathbf{B}}$. The step to the nearest constraint $x_r = 0$ is determined by

$$\theta_r = -\frac{\hat{x}_r}{y_r} = \min_{y_r < 0}\left\{-\frac{\hat{x}_i}{y_i}\right\},$$

and if columns $\mathbf{a}_s$ and $\mathbf{a}_r$ are exchanged in the column basis then we have the new value of $\hat{\mathbf{x}}$ as

$$\hat{x}_i = \hat{x}_i + \theta_r y_i, \qquad i \neq r,$$
$$\hat{x}_r = \theta_r.$$

For further details of the solution of *LP* problems the reader is referred to Dantzig (1963).

4.13. Simple Constraints

If all the constraints on the variables are "simple" constraints of the form $x_j \geqslant 0$, Method I can be implemented efficiently. In this case the constraint matrix $\hat{\mathbf{A}}$ is made up of columns of $\mathbf{I}_n$, and $\mathbf{Z}$ can be taken as the columns of $\mathbf{I}_n$ which are not in $\hat{\mathbf{A}}$. This implies that $\mathbf{G}_A{}^{(k)}$ will consist of the rows and columns of $\mathbf{G}^{(k)}$ which correspond to variables x_j such that $x_j > 0$. Since, by assumption, $\mathbf{G}^{(k)}$ is sparse, the matrix $\mathbf{G}_A{}^{(k)}$ can be factorized using any of the methods of Section 4.3 for factorizing a symmetric matrix. (We note that Method II does not simplify in this case since the matrix $\hat{\mathbf{A}}^T\mathbf{G}^{(k)-1}\hat{\mathbf{A}}$ is made up of the rows and columns of $\mathbf{G}^{(k)-1}$ corresponding to the variables $x_j = 0$. In general the matrix $\mathbf{G}^{(k)-1}$ will be a dense matrix even if $\mathbf{G}^{(k)}$ is sparse.)

4.14. Problems with a Small Number of Variables Appearing Nonlinearly in $F(\mathbf{x})$

In general the dimension of the matrix $\mathbf{G}_A{}^{(k)}$ associated with Method I is not known in advance since it will vary from iteration to iteration. However, in some applications it is possible to obtain a lower bound on the number of constraints that must be active in order that $\mathbf{G}_A^{(k)}$ be positive definite.

THEOREM 4.1. *Let $F(\mathbf{x})$ be of the form*

$$F(\mathbf{x}) = \hat{F}(\hat{\mathbf{x}}) + \sum_{j=\mu+1}^{n} c_j x_j \tag{4.14.1}$$

where $\hat{\mathbf{x}}$ is the vector $(x_1, \ldots, x_\mu)^T$. If $\mathring{\mathbf{x}}$ is a point such that $\mathbf{G}_A(\mathring{\mathbf{x}})$ is positive definite then there must be at least $n - \mu$ constraints active at $\mathring{\mathbf{x}}$.

Proof. Assume that $n - \mu - j$ constraints are active at $\mathring{\mathbf{x}}$, where $1 \leqslant j \leqslant n - \mu$. By definition, $\mathbf{G}_A = \mathbf{Z}^T\mathbf{G}\mathbf{Z}$, where $\mathbf{Z}$ is of dimension $n \times (\mu + j)$. If $\mathbf{G}_A$ is positive definite, then $\mathbf{G}_A$ must be of rank $\mu + j$.

The matrix $\mathbf{G}$ is of the form

$$\mathbf{G} = \begin{bmatrix} \mathbf{G}_1 & \mathbf{0} \\ \mathbf{0} & \mathbf{0} \end{bmatrix}, \tag{4.14.2}$$

with $\mathbf{G}_1$ a $\mu \times \mu$ matrix, and consequently $\text{rank}(\mathbf{G}) \leqslant \mu$. It is a well-known result that the rank of a product of matrices cannot exceed the rank of each of its factors, and therefore $\text{rank}(\mathbf{G}_A) \leqslant \mu$, which contradicts our earlier statement that $\text{rank}(\mathbf{G}_A) = \mu + j$, $j > 0$. ∎

COROLLARY. *Let $\mathbf{x}^{(0)}$ be a point with more than $n - \mu$ constraints active and let Method I be applied to the linearly constrained problem with $F(\mathbf{x})$ given by* (4.14.1). *If a constraint is deleted only when $\mathbf{G}_A^{(k)}$ is positive definite then*

$$\dim(\mathbf{G}_A^{(k)}) \leqslant \mu.$$

This corollary implies that for a problem with, say, 2000 linear variables and 50 nonlinear variables, $\mathbf{G}_A^{(k)}$ will never be larger than a 51×51 matrix which can always be factorized in-core. Any of the methods discussed in Chapters II and III which determine the search direction from (4.11.1) can be applied to problems of this form. Murtagh and Saunders (1973) have presented an algorithm for solving the canonical problem:

$$\underset{\mathbf{x}}{\text{minimize}}\, F(\mathbf{x})$$

subject to the constraints $\mathbf{A}\mathbf{x} = \mathbf{b}$, $\mathbf{x} \geqslant \mathbf{0}$, when the Hessian matrix of $F(\mathbf{x})$ is of the form (4.14.2). The algorithm is essentially Method I with the matrix $\mathbf{Z}$ determined using the variable reduction method (*b*) of Section 2.8.

There are other important applications where the dimension of $\mathbf{G}_A{}^{(k)}$ remains small. The refinement of linear models often involves adding small but nonlinear terms to the objective function. If the original linear model, in which the solution is characterized by the constraints, is valid, then one would expect almost the same number of constraints to be active at the solution of the refined model. We would also expect the old solution to be a good initial (and feasible) estimate of the solution of the new model. However, unlike the cases considered in Sections 4.12 and 4.13, $\mathbf{G}^{(k)}$ need not be sparse, and it is then advisable to use a method for which it is not necessary to compute $\mathbf{G}^{(k)}$.

4.15. Problems with a Small Number of Constraints

Method II is ideally suited to problems for which $\mathbf{G}^{(k)}$ is sparse and there are few constraints on the variables. In this case $\hat{\mathbf{A}}^T\mathbf{G}^{(k)-1}\hat{\mathbf{A}}$ (or some approximation to it) will be sufficiently small for equations (4.11.3) to be solved directly.

4.16. Structured Problems

There are important types of structured problems for which ideal methods can be constructed. Gill and Murray (1973b) have suggested an algorithm for the solution of problems (for example in the calculus of variations and in optimal control) where $\mathbf{G}$ is a block tri-diagonal matrix of the form

$$\begin{bmatrix} \mathbf{G}_{11} & \mathbf{G}_{12} & & & & \\ \mathbf{G}_{21} & \mathbf{G}_{22} & \mathbf{G}_{23} & & & \\ & \mathbf{G}_{32} & \mathbf{G}_{33} & \mathbf{G}_{34} & & \\ & & \cdot & \cdot & \cdot & \\ & & & \cdot & \cdot & \cdot \\ & & & & \cdot & \cdot & \mathbf{G}_{q-1,q} \\ & & & & & \mathbf{G}_{q,q-1} & \mathbf{G}_{qq} \end{bmatrix} \tag{4.16.1}$$

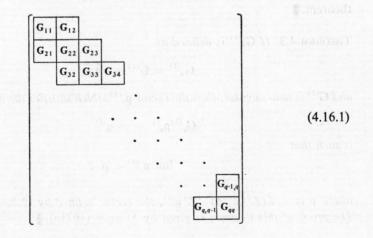

and the matrix of constraints is of the form

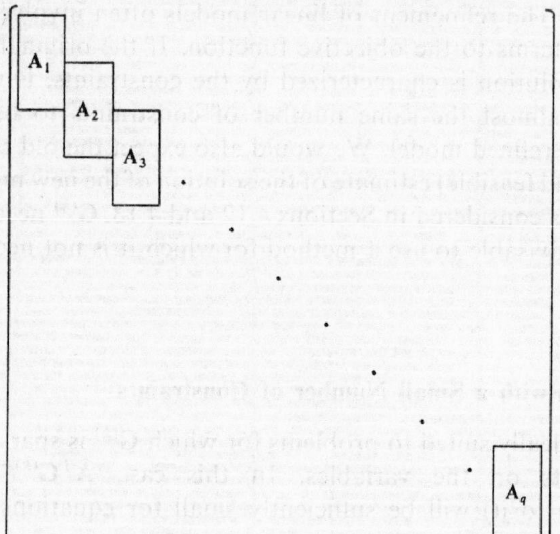

(4.16.2)

with the column dimension of $\mathbf{G}_{ij}$ being equal to the column dimension of $\mathbf{A}_j$ and $\mathbf{G}_{ij} = \mathbf{G}_{ji}{}^T, j = 1, \ldots, q$. The method is based upon the following two theorems.

THEOREM 4.2. *If the matrix* $\mathbf{Z}^T\mathbf{G}^{(k)}\mathbf{Z}$ *is positive definite, there exists a constant* $\bar{v}$ *such that the matrix* $\mathbf{G}^{(k)} + v\hat{\mathbf{A}}\hat{\mathbf{A}}^T$ *is positive definite for all* $v > \bar{v}$.

The reader is referred to Hestenes (1966, pp. 10–11) for a proof of this theorem. ▮

THEOREM 4.3. *If* $\mathbf{G}_v{}^{(k)}$ *is defined as*

$$\mathbf{G}_v{}^{(k)} = \mathbf{G}^{(k)} + v\hat{\mathbf{A}}\hat{\mathbf{A}}^T$$

and $\mathbf{G}^{(k)}$ *is non-singular, then the vector* $\mathbf{p}_v{}^{(k)}$ *which satisfies the equations*

$$\mathbf{G}_v{}^{(k)}\mathbf{p}_v{}^{(k)} = -\,\mathbf{g}^{(k)} \tag{4.16.3}$$

is such that

$$\lim_{v\to\infty} \mathbf{p}_v{}^{(k)} = \mathbf{p}$$

where $\mathbf{p}$ *is* $-\,\mathbf{Z}(\mathbf{Z}^T\mathbf{G}^{(k)}\mathbf{Z})^{-1}\mathbf{Z}^T\mathbf{g}^{(k)}$, *the vector defined by* (2.5.1) *and* (4.11.1). *The proof of this theorem is given by Murray* (1971a). ▮

The vector $\mathbf{p}_\nu^{(k)}$ which corresponds to a *bounded* value $\nu^{(k)}$, say, can be used as an approximation to $\mathbf{p}$ and can be computed without forming $\mathbf{G}_A^{(k)}$, but it is not entirely satisfactory because it contains a component perpendicular to the constraints. However, the vector $\mathbf{p}^{(k)} = \mathbf{Z}\mathbf{Z}^T\mathbf{p}_\nu^{(k)}$ can be used as the direction of search, this being a vector parallel to the constraints.

The point of using (4.16.3) to compute $\mathbf{p}^{(k)}$ is that with $\mathbf{G}^{(k)}$ of the form (4.16.1) and $\hat{\mathbf{A}}^T$ made up of rows from (4.16.2), $\mathbf{G}_\nu^{(k)}$ is a block tri-diagonal matrix and $\mathbf{p}_\nu^{(k)}$ can be efficiently computed using the Cholesky factorization. If $\mathbf{Z}^T\mathbf{G}^{(k)}\mathbf{Z}$ is not positive definite then no value of $\bar{\nu}$ defined in Theorem 4.2. exists. In this situation the modified Cholesky factorization can be applied, giving a vector $\mathbf{p}_\nu^{(k)}$ satisfying

$$(\mathbf{G}_\nu^{(k)} + \mathbf{E}_\nu^{(k)})\,\mathbf{p}_\nu^{(k)} = -\,\mathbf{g}^{(k)},$$

where $\mathbf{E}_\nu^{(k)}$ is a diagonal matrix. We have adhered to the principle of altering the search direction only if $\mathbf{Z}^T\mathbf{G}^{(k)}\mathbf{Z}$ is not positive definite. The search direction obtained will not now be identical to that obtained by modifying $\mathbf{Z}^T\mathbf{G}^{(k)}\mathbf{Z}$ to $\mathbf{Z}^T\overline{\mathbf{G}}^{(k)}\mathbf{Z}$, even as ν tends to infinity. However, this represents only a difference in weight given to the direction of negative curvature: if $\mathbf{Z}^T\mathbf{G}^{(k)}\mathbf{Z}$ is only slightly indefinite, the two directions of search are very similar. The value of ν is not critical, its significance being similar to that of the parameter required for the ideal penalty function discussed in Chapter VIII by Fletcher. It is advisable to choose $\nu^{(k)}$ to be larger than that strictly necessary for $\mathbf{G}_\nu^{(k)}$ to be positive definite since this improves the approximation of $\mathbf{p}_\nu^{(k)}$ to $\mathbf{p}$ of Theorem 4.3. If the constraints are normalized so that $\|\mathbf{A}\|_\infty$ is of the order of unity, a sensible choice of $\nu^{(k)}$ is given by $\nu^{(k)} = (\|\mathbf{G}^{(k)}\|_\infty + \varepsilon)\delta^{-1}$ where ε is the relative machine precision and δ lies in the range $[\varepsilon^{\frac{1}{3}}, \varepsilon^{\frac{1}{2}}]$. On the rare occasions when $\nu^{(k)}$ is not large enough to make $\mathbf{G}_\nu^{(k)}$ positive definite, the alteration produced by the modified Cholesky factorization generally gives a small change to the search direction over that which would be obtained by choosing larger values of ν.

The effectiveness of the technique lies in the fact that the matrix $\mathbf{Z}(\mathbf{Z}^T\mathbf{G}^{(k)}\mathbf{Z})^{-1}\mathbf{Z}^T$ is being approximated by a matrix $\mathbf{Z}\mathbf{Z}^T\mathbf{G}_\nu^{(k)-1}$ which can be shown to be in error by a term of the order of $1/\nu$. Similar accuracy is achieved by using a finite-difference approximation to $\mathbf{Z}^T\mathbf{G}^{(k)}\mathbf{Z}$ (a technique which is known to give good results in practice). The system of equations (4.16.3) is mildly ill-conditioned but this tends to affect $\mathbf{p}_\nu^{(k)}$ in those figures which differ from those of $\mathbf{p}$ due to the truncation error caused by using a small value of ν. In any event an improved value of $\mathbf{p}_\nu^{(k)}$ can be obtained by using an extrapolation procedure. Murray (1971a) has shown that

$$\mathbf{p}_\nu^{(k)} = \mathbf{p} + \nu^{-1}\mathbf{v}_1 + \nu^{-2}\mathbf{v}_2 + O(1/\nu^3), \qquad (4.16.4)$$

where $\mathbf{v}_1$ and $\mathbf{v}_2$ are vectors which are independent of ν. If (4.16.3) is solved for two different values of ν, the expansion (4.16.4) can be used to compute an approximate value of $\mathbf{v}_1$ and hence $\mathbf{p}$. The result of such an extrapolation is still pre-multiplied by $\mathbf{ZZ}^T$ in order to guarantee a feasible direction, but if sufficient extrapolations are performed this precaution is unnecessary.

The method just described can be extended so that finite differences of the gradient vector can be used as an estimate of the Hessian matrix (see Section 4.9). Our experience is that the discrete version is as effective as the original method since the finite-difference truncation error can be made to be of the same order as the truncation error in $\mathbf{G}_\nu^{(k)}$, and such errors do not lead to a significant deterioration in the effectiveness of the method.

The method can be applied to problems with structure other than that of (4.16.1) and (4.16.2). The conditions for such an extension are that $\mathbf{G}^{(k)}$ and $\hat{\mathbf{A}}\hat{\mathbf{A}}^T$ are sparse and that the zero/non-zero structure of $\hat{\mathbf{A}}\hat{\mathbf{A}}^T$ is very similar to that of $\mathbf{G}^{(k)}$. This occurs for example if the objective function is given by (4.8.2) and the constraints are of the form

$$\mathbf{A}_j^T\mathbf{x}_j + \mathbf{D}_j^T\mathbf{y} \geqslant \mathbf{b}_j, \qquad j = 1, 2, \ldots, q-1, \tag{4.16.5}$$

where $\mathbf{A}_j^T$ is an $m_j \times n_j$ matrix, $\mathbf{D}_j^T$ an $m_j \times n_q$ matrix,

$$n = \sum_{j=1}^{q} n_j$$

and

$$m = \sum_{j=1}^{q-1} m_j.$$

These are known as *dual-angular* problems and the matrix of constraints, $\mathbf{A}^T$, is of the form (4.1.2).

4.17. Decomposition Techniques

In the linearly constrained case, non-ideal methods are usually of the form in which the original "master" problem is solved utilizing the solutions of a number of smaller problems. For this reason non-ideal methods in the constrained case are often referred to as *decomposition methods*. In every case, the smaller problem is suggested by the structure of the constraints or objective function. We shall describe the three principal methods in this class which we judge to be the most useful in the context of reliable numerical software. Numerous other methods have been proposed; the reader is referred to the paper of Geoffrion (1970a, b) for an extensive review of decomposition techniques for large-scale problems.

(i) *The Method of Partitioning*

Consider the dual-angular problem defined by the objective function (4.8.2) and constraints (4.16.5). For a given value $\mathbf{y} = \hat{\mathbf{y}}$ of the $\mathbf{y}$-variables the problem can be separated to $q-1$ independent problems since the minimum value of the objective function coincides with the sum of the minimum value of each of the terms in the summation. Thus the problem for the $\mathbf{x}_j$-variables is given by

$$f_0(\hat{\mathbf{y}}) + \sum_{j=1}^{q-1} \underset{\mathbf{x}_j}{\text{minimize}} \{f_j(\mathbf{x}_j, \hat{\mathbf{y}}): \quad \text{subject to } \mathbf{A}_j{}^T\mathbf{x}_j \geqslant \mathbf{b}_j - \mathbf{D}_j{}^T\hat{\mathbf{y}}\}.$$

Following the solution of these $q-1$ problems, $\mathbf{y}$ must be re-estimated. We shall illustrate the method for computing a new value of $\mathbf{y}$ in the linear case with $q = 2$. This gives a master problem of the form

$$\left.\begin{aligned} &\underset{\mathbf{x},\,\mathbf{y}}{\text{minimize}}\ \mathbf{c}_0{}^T\mathbf{y} + \mathbf{c}_1{}^T\mathbf{x} \\ &\text{subject to the constraints } \mathbf{A}^T\mathbf{x} + \mathbf{D}^T\mathbf{y} \geqslant \mathbf{b}. \end{aligned}\right\} \tag{4.17.1}$$

For a fixed value, $\hat{\mathbf{y}}$, of the $\mathbf{y}$-variables the separated problem becomes

$$\text{minimize } \{\mathbf{c}_0{}^T\hat{\mathbf{y}} + \mathbf{c}_1{}^T\mathbf{x}, \quad \text{subject to } \mathbf{A}^T\mathbf{x} \geqslant \mathbf{b} - \mathbf{D}^T\hat{\mathbf{y}}\}. \tag{4.17.2}$$

Let $\hat{\mathbf{A}}^T$ and $\overline{\mathbf{A}}^T$ be the matrices of active and inactive constraints, respectively, at the solution $\hat{\mathbf{x}}$ of (4.17.2). If $\hat{\mathbf{D}}$, $\overline{\mathbf{D}}$, $\hat{\mathbf{b}}$ and $\overline{\mathbf{b}}$ denote the corresponding partitions of $\mathbf{D}$ and $\mathbf{b}$ we have $\hat{\mathbf{A}}^T\hat{\mathbf{x}} = \hat{\mathbf{b}} - \hat{\mathbf{D}}^T\hat{\mathbf{y}}$ and $\overline{\mathbf{A}}^T\hat{\mathbf{x}} > \overline{\mathbf{b}} - \overline{\mathbf{D}}^T\hat{\mathbf{y}}$. The method of partitioning suggested by Rosen (1963) involves using the relations

$$\hat{\mathbf{A}}^T\mathbf{x} = \hat{\mathbf{b}} - \hat{\mathbf{D}}^T\mathbf{y} \tag{4.17.3}$$

and

$$\overline{\mathbf{A}}^T\mathbf{x} > \overline{\mathbf{b}} - \overline{\mathbf{D}}^T\mathbf{y} \tag{4.17.4}$$

to eliminate the $\mathbf{x}$-variables from (4.17.1). Since $\hat{\mathbf{A}}^T$ is non-singular (4.17.3) gives

$$\mathbf{x} = \hat{\mathbf{A}}^{-T}(\hat{\mathbf{b}} - \hat{\mathbf{D}}^T\mathbf{y}), \tag{4.17.5}$$

and if $\mathbf{x}$ is substituted into the objective function of (4.17.1) and inequality constraints (4.17.4) we have the problem

$$\underset{\mathbf{y}}{\text{minimize}} \{\mathbf{c}_0{}^T\mathbf{y} + \mathbf{c}_1{}^T\hat{\mathbf{A}}^{-T}(\hat{\mathbf{b}} - \hat{\mathbf{D}}^T\mathbf{y})\} \tag{4.17.6}$$

subject to the constraints

$$(\overline{\mathbf{D}}^T - \overline{\mathbf{A}}^T\hat{\mathbf{A}}^{-T}\hat{\mathbf{D}}^T)\,\mathbf{y} \geqslant \overline{\mathbf{b}} - \overline{\mathbf{A}}^T\hat{\mathbf{A}}^{-T}\hat{\mathbf{b}}.$$

This is a linear problem in the y-variables alone and can be solved using standard techniques. We note that from (4.12.1) the objective function (4.17.6) can be written as

$$(\mathbf{c}_0{}^T - \hat{\boldsymbol{\lambda}}^T\hat{\mathbf{D}}^T)\,\mathbf{y} + \hat{\boldsymbol{\lambda}}^T\hat{\mathbf{b}},$$

where $\hat{\boldsymbol{\lambda}}$ are the Lagrange multipliers at the solution of problem (4.17.2).

It is clear now how a typical iteration of the general q-block problem should proceed. From an initial feasible solution $(\mathbf{x}, \mathbf{y})$, $q - 1$ linear programs are solved with $\mathbf{y}$ fixed. Using the vectors of Lagrange multipliers at the solutions of these problems, a single *LP* in the $\mathbf{y}$ variables is constructed and solved to obtain an improved estimate of $\mathbf{y}$.

In the nonlinear case the matrix of active constraints of the sub-problem may not be square and consequently an elimination technique of the form (4.17.5) cannot be used. However, other schemes can be constructed; for example, Grigoriadis (1971) has suggested a scheme which, in the case where $q = 2$, gives the y-variables in the form

$$\mathbf{x} = (\hat{\mathbf{A}}^T)^+(\hat{\mathbf{b}} - \hat{\mathbf{D}}^T\mathbf{y}), \tag{4.17.7}$$

where $(\hat{\mathbf{A}}^T)^+$ denotes the pseudo-inverse of $\hat{\mathbf{A}}^T$. The method used to solve the linearly constrained problem in the x-variables determines the set of active constraints $\hat{\mathbf{A}}^T$. The value of $\mathbf{x}$ given by (4.17.7) can be substituted into the function (4.8.2) to obtain a linearly constrained problem in the y-variables. Other schemes have been proposed based on alternative methods of eliminating the x-variables; see, for example, Grigoriadis and Ritter (1969).

(ii) *Dualization Techniques*

This technique is especially useful for problems in which there are coupling constraints, for example

$$\mathbf{A}_j{}^T\mathbf{x}_j \geqslant \mathbf{b}_j, \qquad j = 1, 2, \ldots, q-1, \tag{4.17.8}$$

and

$$\sum_{j=1}^{q-1} \mathbf{D}_j{}^T\mathbf{x}_j \geqslant \mathbf{b}_q, \tag{4.17.9}$$

where $\mathbf{x}_j$ are n_j-vectors, $\mathbf{A}_j{}^T$ is an $m_j \times n_j$ matrix, $\mathbf{D}_j{}^T$ is an $m_q \times n_j$ matrix,

$$\sum_{j=1}^{q-1} n_j = n \quad \text{and} \quad \sum_{j=1}^{q} m_j = m.$$

Dualization involves including the "complicating" constraint (4.17.9) into the Lagrangian function

$$F_\lambda(\mathbf{x}) = F(\mathbf{x}) + \boldsymbol{\lambda}_q{}^T\left(\mathbf{b}_q - \sum_{j=1}^{q-1} \mathbf{D}_j{}^T\mathbf{x}_j\right). \tag{4.7.10}$$

It can be shown that if: (i) $F(\mathbf{x})$ is a *convex* function, (ii) $\hat{\mathbf{x}}$ minimizes $F_\lambda(\mathbf{x})$ subject to the constraints (4.17.8) and (iii) $\boldsymbol{\lambda}_q$ is such that

$$\boldsymbol{\lambda}_q{}^T\left(\mathbf{b}_q - \sum_{j=1}^{q-1} \mathbf{D}_j{}^T\mathbf{x}_j\right) = 0,$$

then $\hat{\mathbf{x}}$ solves the master problem. If $F(\mathbf{x})$ has a block-diagonal Hessian matrix then the minimization of $F_\lambda(\mathbf{x})$ subject to the constraints (4.17.8) is a separable problem since the Hessian of $F(\mathbf{x})$ is exactly that of $F_\lambda(\mathbf{x})$. The elements of the vector $\boldsymbol{\lambda}_q$ are the Kuhn–Tucker multipliers associated with the constraints (4.17.9) (see Chapter I) and consequently $(\boldsymbol{\lambda}_q)_j \geqslant 0$, $j = 1, 2, \ldots, m_q$. A value of $(\boldsymbol{\lambda}_q)_j = 0$ corresponds to an inactive constraint and $(\boldsymbol{\lambda}_q)_j > 0$ corresponds to an active constraint. A typical strategy is to approximate $\boldsymbol{\lambda}_q$, solve the set of linearly constrained sub-problems defined by (4.17.10) and re-estimate the values of $\boldsymbol{\lambda}_q$. A scheme similar to that used in the ideal penalty function method (see Chapter VIII) can be used to estimate the values of $\boldsymbol{\lambda}_q$. Alternatively $\boldsymbol{\lambda}_q$ could be computed as part of the vector of first- or second-order Lagrange multipliers. This is a relatively efficient scheme since the block-angular structure of $\mathbf{A}$ is amenable to column methods of matrix factorization.

The fundamental disadvantage of this method is that $F(\mathbf{x})$ must be convex for a bounded minimum of $F_\lambda(\mathbf{x})$ to exist. For example, $F_\lambda(\mathbf{x})$ will not possess a finite minimum if the Lagrangian incorporates a constraint which excludes a region wherein $F(\mathbf{x})$ is unbounded. Convexity is almost impossible to verify numerically and consequently the method is unsuitable for use in a general numerical software library.

(iii) *Dantzig–Wolfe Decomposition*

This method was originally formulated for linear-programming problems in canonical form with block-angular constraints. We shall briefly illustrate the technique for the single block problem

$$\underset{\mathbf{x}}{\text{minimize}}\, \{\mathbf{c}^T\mathbf{x}\} \quad \text{subject to} \quad \mathbf{A}_1\mathbf{x} = \mathbf{b}_1, \qquad \mathbf{D}_1\mathbf{x} = \mathbf{b}_2, \qquad \mathbf{x} \geqslant \mathbf{0}, \tag{4.17.11}$$

and go on to discuss the extension of the method to problems with non-linear objective functions.

Consider the region $\Pi_1 = \{\mathbf{x} : \mathbf{A}_1\mathbf{x} = \mathbf{b}_1, \mathbf{x} \geqslant \mathbf{0}\}$; Π_1 is a closed convex polyhedron with a finite number l, say, of vertices. If these vertices are known and denoted by the vectors $\{\mathbf{v}_j\}_{j=1}^{l}$ then any $\mathbf{x} \in \Pi_1$ can be written as a convex linear combination of the $\mathbf{v}_j$, i.e.

$$\mathbf{x} = \sum_{j=1}^{l} \rho_j \mathbf{v}_j, \quad \text{with} \quad \sum_{j=1}^{l} \rho_j = 1.$$

If this expansion is substituted into (4.17.11) we obtain the equivalent problem

$$\left.\begin{aligned}&\underset{\boldsymbol{\rho}}{\text{minimize}}\ \sum_{j=1}^{l}\rho_j\mathbf{c}^T\mathbf{v}_j,\\ &\text{subject to}\sum_{j=1}^{l}\rho_j\mathbf{D}_1\mathbf{v}_j=\mathbf{b}_2,\qquad\sum_{j=1}^{l}\rho_j=1,\qquad\boldsymbol{\rho}\geqslant\mathbf{0},\end{aligned}\right\}\tag{4.17.12}$$

which is a problem only in the variables ρ_j. The most important property of this problem is that the row dimension of the constraints is much smaller than in the original problem. The reader will recall from Section 4.12 that this is a desirable situation since it is the number of rows which determines the dimension of the column basis when solving problems in canonical form. In practice it is not necessary to compute all the vertices of Π_1 since a vertex associated with a column in the basis of the problem (4.17.12) can be generated as it is required (see Dantzig, 1963).

The extension of the method to the nonlinear case (Dantzig 1963, Chapter 24) is to approximate the function

$$F\left(\sum_{j=1}^{l}\rho_j\mathbf{v}_j\right)\quad\text{by}\quad\sum_{j=1}^{l}\rho_jF(\mathbf{v}_j).$$

This process is best illustrated by the one-dimensional example depicted in Fig. 4.2, where we have four vertices $\mathbf{v}_j$.

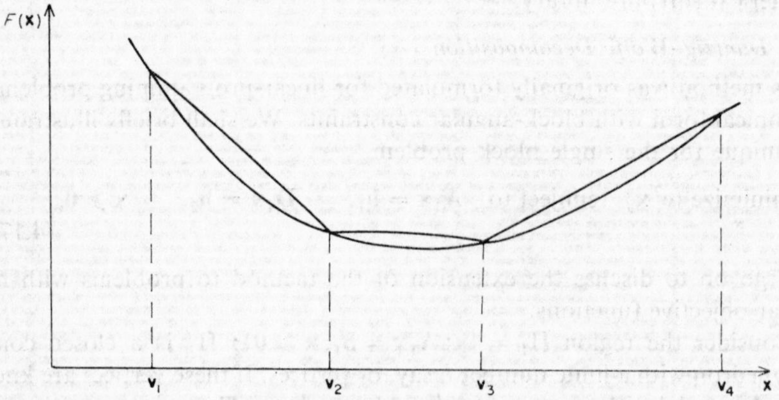

FIG. 4.2.

This method has two fundamental disadvantages; a large number of additional "grid points" $\{\mathbf{v}_j\}$ must be added in order to obtain any degree of accuracy in the approximation; and the convergence depends critically upon the convexity of $F(\mathbf{x})$.

4.18. Concluding Remarks

Over the years a proliferation of algorithms for large-scale optimization has occurred due to the need to take advantage of various problem structures. Our objective in this chapter has been to give a representative selection of these algorithms in order to emphasize the basic qualities needed for the fast and efficient solution of large problems.

The considerable effort involved in producing computer implementations of large-scale methods has meant that numerical experience of many of the techniques presented here is limited. In particular the effect of fill-in and rate of convergence can be determined only by experiment and a comparative evaluation is difficult; our presentation has, therefore, been less selective than in other chapters.

Lack of computational experience also led us to exclude exploratory research—no matter how promising that research may be. (For example, in Chapters I and II great stress was laid on the importance of representing the null-space of a matrix as part of an orthogonal factorization. Methods for maintaining the orthogonal factorization in product form as rows are exchanged are at an early stage of development. It is known how such product forms can be computed and stored, but the most efficient method has yet to be shown numerically stable.)

Obviously a considerable amount of research remains to be done and this chapter constitutes only a state-of-the-art assessment. However, we believe that the unknown rate of convergence and strict convexity conditions associated with decomposition methods makes the adaptation of standard algorithms to cater for sparsity a more promising approach.

Chapter V

Reduced-gradient and Projection Methods for Nonlinear Programming

R. W. H. SARGENT

Department of Chemical Engineering and Chemical Technology, Imperial College of Science and Technology

5.1. Introduction

Methods for minimizing a function subject to nonlinear constraints can be divided broadly into two classes—those which set up an equivalent unconstrained minimization problem by adding a penalty term to either the objective function or the Lagrangian function, and those which seek to generate a sequence of feasible-descent steps. The penalty-function methods will be described by D. M. Ryan and R. Fletcher, and this chapter will deal with the second class of methods, which build on the ideas described by P. E. Gill and W. Murray for linearly constrained problems.

We shall be concerned with the general nonlinear problem:

$$\min_{\mathbf{x}} \{F(\mathbf{x}) : \mathbf{c}(\mathbf{x}) \geqslant \mathbf{0}\}, \tag{5.1.1}$$

where $\mathbf{x} \in E^n, \mathbf{c}(\mathbf{x}) \in E^m, F(\mathbf{x}) \in E^1$. We shall assume that no analytical expressions for $F(\mathbf{x})$ and $\mathbf{c}(\mathbf{x})$ are available, but that computer subroutines are provided which evaluate these functions and their gradients for a given vector $\mathbf{x}$; this of course implies that they are single-valued functions of their arguments. In order to develop the methods we shall further assume that $F(\mathbf{x})$ and $\mathbf{c}(\mathbf{x})$ are in the class C^2, mainly so that we can use Taylor expansions to second order, but this does not of course imply that the resulting methods are inapplicable if these assumptions are not satisfied.

Gill and Murray have shown that effective methods exist for dealing with linear constraints and for generating quadratic approximations to general functions from gradient values. A natural approach to the nonlinear programming problem is therefore to generate a sequence of quadratic programming problems, making a local linear approximation to the constraints and quadratic approximation to the objective function based on the current estimate $\mathbf{x}^{(k)}$ of the solution, and then taking the solution of this quadratic program as the new estimate $\mathbf{x}^{(k+1)}$ of the solution to the nonlinear problem.

An immediate question is whether such a sequence of estimates will in fact converge to a solution of the nonlinear program, and one can also ask whether it is in fact worth the effort of finding a complete solution of each quadratic program, rather than being content with an improvement on the current estimate. We shall therefore examine the various elements of the quadratic programming problem, with a view to seeing how they are best combined with successive approximations to the nonlinear objective and constraint functions.

5.2. Minimization Subject to Equality Constraints

The original problem may include equality constraints, and in any case many algorithms select a set of active constraints to be treated as equalities, so it is worth examining methods for dealing with the equality constrained problem

$$\min_{\mathbf{x}} \{F(\mathbf{x}) : \mathbf{c}(\mathbf{x}) = \mathbf{0}\}, \qquad m < n. \tag{5.2.1}$$

Reduced-gradient Methods

It is easier to develop the basic ideas by first considering the linearly constrained problem

$$\min_{\mathbf{x}} \{F(\mathbf{x}) : \mathbf{A}^T\mathbf{x} - \mathbf{b} = \mathbf{0}\}, \qquad m < n. \tag{5.2.2}$$

An obvious approach to solving this problem is to use the m linear equality constraints to eliminate m of the variables x_i, $i = 1, 2, \ldots, n$, so leaving an unconstrained problem in the remaining $(n - m)$ variables. Accordingly we partition $\mathbf{A}$ and $\mathbf{x}$:

$$\mathbf{A} = \begin{bmatrix} \mathbf{A}_1 \\ \mathbf{A}_2 \end{bmatrix}, \qquad \mathbf{x} = \begin{bmatrix} \mathbf{x}_1 \\ \mathbf{x}_2 \end{bmatrix}, \tag{5.2.3}$$

so that $\mathbf{x}_1$ has m elements and the matrix $\mathbf{A}_1$ is an $m \times m$ non-singular matrix. Such a partitioning is always possible if the constraints are linearly independent, and we shall assume that any redundant linearly-dependent constraints have already been deleted from (5.2.2).

It will be convenient to introduce a vector $\mathbf{y}$, similarly partitioned, and defined by the equations

$$\left.\begin{aligned}\mathbf{y}_1 &= \mathbf{A}^T\mathbf{x} - \mathbf{b},\\ \mathbf{y}_2 &= \mathbf{x}_2.\end{aligned}\right\} \tag{5.2.4}$$

Thus $\mathbf{y}_2$ is the reduced set of $(n - m)$ unconstrained variables, and $\mathbf{y}_1$ is the vector of residuals of the linear constraint equations, which must of course be zero if the constraints are satisfied. Equations (5.2.4) represent a one-to-one transformation from $\mathbf{x}$-space to $\mathbf{y}$-space, which can be written in matrix form:

$$\begin{bmatrix}\mathbf{y}_1\\ \mathbf{y}_2\end{bmatrix} = \begin{bmatrix}\mathbf{A}_1{}^T & \mathbf{A}_2{}^T\\ \mathbf{0} & \mathbf{I}\end{bmatrix}\begin{bmatrix}\mathbf{x}_1\\ \mathbf{x}_2\end{bmatrix} - \begin{bmatrix}\mathbf{b}\\ \mathbf{0}\end{bmatrix}$$

with its inverse transformation:

$$\begin{bmatrix}\mathbf{x}_1\\ \mathbf{x}_2\end{bmatrix} = \begin{bmatrix}(\mathbf{A}_1{}^{-1})^T & -(\mathbf{A}_2\mathbf{A}_1{}^{-1})^T\\ \mathbf{0} & \mathbf{I}\end{bmatrix}\begin{bmatrix}\mathbf{y}_1\\ \mathbf{y}_2\end{bmatrix} + \begin{bmatrix}(\mathbf{A}_1{}^{-1})^T\,\mathbf{b}\\ \mathbf{0}\end{bmatrix}. \tag{5.2.5}$$

The transformation is illustrated for two variables and one constraint in Fig. 5.1a.

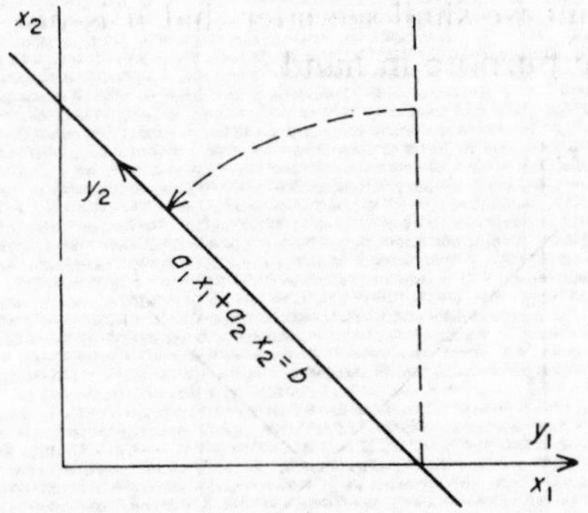

FIG. 5.1a.

Clearly this is only one possible transformation to a set of co-ordinates $\mathbf{y}$ where the subset $\mathbf{y}_1$ measures departure from the constraints and the subset $\mathbf{y}_2$ measures position within the constraint space. More generally we may use a transformation of the form

$$\left.\begin{aligned}\mathbf{y}_1 &= \mathbf{U}(\mathbf{A}^T\mathbf{x} - \mathbf{b}),\\ \mathbf{y}_2 &= \mathbf{V}^T\mathbf{x} - \mathbf{v},\end{aligned}\right\} \tag{5.2.6}$$

which for convenience we shall write as

$$\left.\begin{aligned} \mathbf{y} = \mathbf{T}\mathbf{x} - \mathbf{d}, \qquad \mathbf{x} = \mathbf{T}^{-1}(\mathbf{y} + \mathbf{d}), \\ \text{with} \qquad \mathbf{T}^T = [\mathbf{A}\mathbf{U}^T \quad \mathbf{V}]. \end{aligned}\right\} \tag{5.2.7}$$

Here, $\mathbf{y}_1 = \mathbf{0}$ if and only if the constraints are satisfied, provided that $\mathbf{U}$ is a non-singular $m \times m$ matrix. We also require $\mathbf{y}_2$ to span the constraint space, and this will be so if the columns of $\mathbf{A}$ and $\mathbf{V}$ together span the whole space. Within these restrictions many choices of $\mathbf{U}$ and $\mathbf{V}$ are possible, and we shall naturally seek choices which make it easy to obtain the inverse transformation.

A particularly simple inversion is obtained if we choose $\mathbf{U}$ and $\mathbf{V}$ so that the **y**-co-ordinates form an orthonormal system. We then have

$$\left.\begin{aligned} &\mathbf{T}^T\mathbf{T} = \mathbf{I}, \\ &\text{and it follows that} \\ &\mathbf{A}^T\mathbf{V} = \mathbf{0}, \qquad \mathbf{V}^T\mathbf{V} = \mathbf{I}, \\ &\mathbf{U}^T\mathbf{U} = (\mathbf{A}^T\mathbf{A})^{-1}, \qquad \mathbf{V}\mathbf{V}^T = \mathbf{I} - \mathbf{A}(\mathbf{A}^T\mathbf{A})^{-1}\mathbf{A}^T, \\ &\mathbf{x} = \mathbf{T}^T(\mathbf{y} + \mathbf{d}). \end{aligned}\right\} \tag{5.2.8}$$

This transformation is illustrated in Fig. 5.1b. For $n > 2$ it is not uniquely specified by (5.2.8), but we shall see later that it is not necessary to make a specific choice for the purpose in hand.

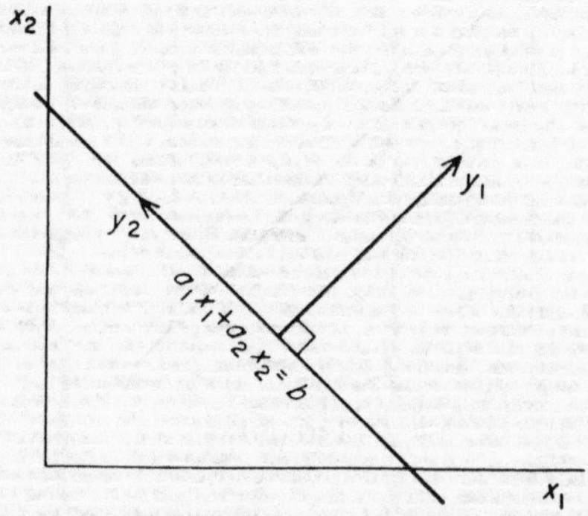

FIG. 5.1b.

To solve the minimization problem we are interested in the properties of the mapping of the objective function from **x**-space into **y**-space: $F(\mathbf{x}) \to f(\mathbf{y})$. For this section we shall denote the corresponding gradients by ∇F and ∇f, where it is understood that the differential operator ∇ is in the appropriate co-ordinates; we also partition ∇F and ∇f to conform with the partitions of $\mathbf{x}$ and $\mathbf{y}$

$$\nabla F = \begin{bmatrix} \nabla_1 F \\ \nabla_2 F \end{bmatrix}, \qquad \nabla f = \begin{bmatrix} \nabla_1 f \\ \nabla_2 f \end{bmatrix}.$$

By the chain rule we have

$$\frac{\partial F}{\partial x_j} = \sum_{i=1}^{n} \frac{\partial f}{\partial y_i}\frac{\partial y_i}{\partial x_j},$$

and hence, using (5.2.7):

$$\nabla F = \mathbf{T}^T \nabla f = \mathbf{A}\,\mathbf{U}^T \nabla_1 f + \mathbf{V}\nabla_2 f. \tag{5.2.9}$$

Now to solve the constrained minimization problem (5.2.2) we set $\mathbf{y}_1 = \mathbf{0}$ and seek a stationary point of $f(\mathbf{y})$ with respect to the $\mathbf{y}_2$-co-ordinates, obtaining $\nabla_2 f = \mathbf{0}$. Thus from (5.2.9) it follows that

$$\left.\begin{aligned} \nabla F(\hat{\mathbf{x}}) &= \mathbf{A}\boldsymbol{\lambda}, \\ \text{where} \qquad \boldsymbol{\lambda} &= \mathbf{U}^T\, \nabla_1 f(\hat{\mathbf{y}}) \end{aligned}\right\} \tag{5.2.10}$$

and $\hat{\mathbf{x}}, \hat{\mathbf{y}}$ are the co-ordinates of the point which solves problem (5.2.2). We recognize $\boldsymbol{\lambda}$ as the vector of Lagrange multipliers for this problem, and from (5.2.10) we can obtain a very simple interpretation of their significance. For this purpose let us define $\mathbf{c} = \mathbf{A}^T\mathbf{x} - \mathbf{b}$, so that from (5.2.6) we have $\mathbf{y}_1 = \mathbf{U}\mathbf{c}$, and consider the mapping $f(\mathbf{y}_1, \mathbf{y}_2) \to \phi(\mathbf{c}, \hat{\mathbf{y}}_2)$. The chain rule gives

$$\left.\begin{aligned} \frac{\partial \phi}{\partial c_j} &= \sum_{i=1}^{n} \frac{\partial f}{\partial y_i}\frac{\partial y_i}{\partial c_j}, \\ \text{which can be written as} \qquad & \\ \nabla_1 \phi &= \mathbf{U}^T \nabla_1 f + \nabla_2 f, \end{aligned}\right\} \tag{5.2.11}$$

but at the constrained minimum $\mathbf{c} = \mathbf{0}$, $\mathbf{y}_2 = \hat{\mathbf{y}}_2$ and $\nabla_2 f = \mathbf{0}$, so from (5.2.10) and (5.2.11) we have

$$\boldsymbol{\lambda} = \nabla_1 \phi(\mathbf{0}, \hat{\mathbf{y}}_2). \tag{5.2.12}$$

Thus $\boldsymbol{\lambda}$ measures the rate of change of the minimum value of the objective function as the constraint residuals change from zero. It is this property of Lagrange multipliers which make them useful in determining whether to leave a constraint in inequality constrained problems.

Most unconstrained minimization algorithms make use of gradients, which means that we shall require values of $\nabla_2 f$. However the computer subroutine provides ∇F for given values of $\mathbf{x}$, so that for each gradient evaluation we need to transform from $\mathbf{y}$ to $\mathbf{x}$ variables, evaluate ∇F, then transform this back to ∇f. Often it will be more efficient not to introduce the y-co-ordinates explicitly, but to find expressions for the vectors required in terms of the **x**-co-ordinates. Thus a step $\boldsymbol{\delta y}$ in the constraint space coinciding with $\nabla_2 f$ is given by

$$\boldsymbol{\delta y} = \begin{bmatrix} \boldsymbol{\delta y}_1 \\ \boldsymbol{\delta y}_2 \end{bmatrix} = \begin{bmatrix} \mathbf{0} \\ \nabla_2 f \end{bmatrix} = \begin{bmatrix} \mathbf{0} & \mathbf{0} \\ \mathbf{0} & \mathbf{I} \end{bmatrix} \nabla f.$$

Using (5.2.7) and (5.2.9) the image of $\boldsymbol{\delta y}$ in **x**-space, known as the "reduced gradient" is given by

$$\mathbf{g}_R(\mathbf{x}) = \mathbf{T}^{-1}\boldsymbol{\delta y} = \mathbf{T}^{-1} \begin{bmatrix} \mathbf{0} & \mathbf{0} \\ \mathbf{0} & \mathbf{I} \end{bmatrix} (\mathbf{T}^{-1})^T \, \nabla F(\mathbf{x}). \tag{5.2.13}$$

Similarly, from (5.2.9) and (5.2.10) we obtain the expression for the Lagrange multipliers:

$$\boldsymbol{\lambda} = [\mathbf{U}^T \quad \mathbf{0}] \, \nabla f(\hat{\mathbf{y}}) = [\mathbf{U}^T \quad \mathbf{0}] \, (\mathbf{T}^{-1})^T \, \nabla F(\hat{\mathbf{x}}). \tag{5.2.14}$$

The reduced gradient lies in the constraint space, so if we start with a point $\mathbf{x}^{(0)}$ satisfying the constraints and use successive values of $\mathbf{g}_R^{(k)}$ as gradients in an unconstrained minimization algorithm, all points $\mathbf{x}^{(k)}$ will satisfy the constraints, and if the algorithm is successful they will converge to the constrained minimum $\hat{\mathbf{x}}$. Equation (5.2.14) then provides the Lagrange multipliers if these are required. An initial feasible point is easily obtained by choosing any vector $\mathbf{y}_1$ with $\mathbf{y} = \mathbf{0}$ and carrying out the inverse transformation in (5.2.7).

The original reduced-gradient method, due to Wolfe (1967), used the simple variable-elimination method described by (5.2.5). In this system we have from (5.2.5), (5.2.13) and (5.2.14):

$$\left.\begin{aligned} \mathbf{g}_R(\mathbf{x}) &= \begin{bmatrix} (\mathbf{A}_2\mathbf{A}_1^{-1})^T(\mathbf{A}_2\mathbf{A}_1^{-1}) & -(\mathbf{A}_2\mathbf{A}_1^{-1})' \\ -(\mathbf{A}_2\mathbf{A}_1^{-1}) & \mathbf{I} \end{bmatrix} \nabla F(\mathbf{x}), \\ \boldsymbol{\lambda} &= [\mathbf{A}_1^{-1} \quad \mathbf{0}] \, \nabla F(\mathbf{x}). \end{aligned}\right\} \tag{5.2.15}$$

For the orthonormal transformation given by (5.2.8) we have

$$\left.\begin{aligned} \mathbf{g}_R(\mathbf{x}) &= \left(\mathbf{I} - \mathbf{A}(\mathbf{A}^T\mathbf{A})^{-1}\mathbf{A}^T\right) \nabla F(\mathbf{x}), \\ \boldsymbol{\lambda} &= (\mathbf{A}^T\mathbf{A})^{-1}\mathbf{A}^T \, \nabla F(\mathbf{x}). \end{aligned}\right\} \tag{5.2.16}$$

In this case the reduced gradient is simply the orthogonal projection of the gradient ∇F onto the constraint space. It will be seen that the expressions in (5.2.16) merely involve **A** and do not depend on the explicit choice of **U** and **V**, as indicated previously.

It should be noted that the reduced gradient is a vector-valued function of position, since it depends on the gradient $\nabla F(\mathbf{x})$. However the matrix which transforms $\nabla F(\mathbf{x})$ to $\mathbf{g}_R(\mathbf{x})$ depends only on the constraint gradients (and the arbitrary matrices **U** and **V**), and is therefore a fixed constant matrix if the constraints are linear.

The concept of the reduced gradient can still be used if the constraints are nonlinear by modifying the transformation to

$$\left.\begin{aligned} \mathbf{y}_1 &= \mathbf{Uc}(\mathbf{x}), \\ \mathbf{y}_2 &= \mathbf{V}^T\mathbf{x} - \mathbf{v}. \end{aligned}\right\} \tag{5.2.17}$$

All the relations concerning gradients and Lagrange multipliers then remain unchanged, except of course that the matrix **A** must be evaluated at the current **x**. The reduced gradient now lies in the tangent hyperplane to the constraint manifold, so that any finite step along it will in general leave the manifold.

To deal with this problem Arrow, Hurwicz and Uzawa (1958) proposed a continuous steepest-descent method based on integrating the system of differential equations:

$$\frac{d\mathbf{x}}{d\alpha} = -\mathbf{g}_R(\mathbf{x}), \qquad \mathbf{x}(0) = \mathbf{x}_0, \tag{5.2.18}$$

where $\mathbf{x}_0$ is an initial feasible point. It should be noted that since the transformation is now nonlinear, finding an initial feasible point is no longer a trivial matter. Of course (5.2.17) must usually be integrated numerically, and since we are not interested in the whole trajectory but only its limit point, stability is a more important consideration than accuracy. Standard explicit methods, such as the Runge–Kutta methods would normally require prohibitively small steplengths, and the best choice would seem to be a low order predictor-corrector method. Arrow, Hurwicz and Uzawa do not discuss the practical implementation of their algorithm, but Branin and Hoo (1972) report some success with a similar approach to unconstrained problems, extending the idea to a continuous version of Newton and quasi-Newton methods.

A more direct approach is to make an initial step along the reduced-gradient direction and then use a Newton-type correction procedure to return to a point satisfying the nonlinear constraints, according to the scheme:

$$\left.\begin{aligned} &\text{for } r = 0: && \mathbf{s}^{(k,0)} = \mathbf{x}^{(k+1,1)} - \mathbf{x}^{(k)} = -\alpha^{(k)}\,\mathbf{g}_R(\mathbf{x}^{(k)}); \\ &\text{for } r \geqslant 1: && \mathbf{T}(\mathbf{x}^{(k+1,r)})\,\mathbf{s}^{(k,r)} = -\begin{bmatrix} \mathbf{Uc}(\mathbf{x}^{(k+1,r)}) \\ \mathbf{0} \end{bmatrix}, \\ &\text{where} && \mathbf{s}^{(k,r)} = \mathbf{x}^{(k+1,r+1)} - \mathbf{x}^{(k+1,r)}. \end{aligned}\right\} \tag{5.2.19}$$

The essential idea is illustrated in Fig. 5.2.

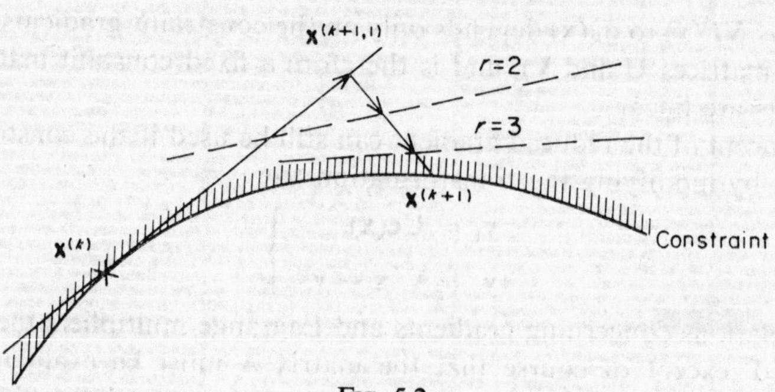

FIG. 5.2.

For the variable-elimination method the correction formula reduces to

$$\mathbf{A}_1(\mathbf{x}^{(k+1,r)})\,\mathbf{s}_1{}^{(k,r)} = -\,\mathbf{c}(\mathbf{x}^{(k+1,r)}); \qquad \mathbf{s}_2{}^{(k,r)} = \mathbf{0}, \tag{5.2.20}$$

while for the orthonormal transformation we obtain

$$\mathbf{s}^{(k,r)} = -\,\mathbf{A}(\mathbf{A}^T\mathbf{A})^{-1}\,\mathbf{c}(\mathbf{x}^{(k+1,r)}) \tag{5.2.21}$$

where obviously $\mathbf{A}$ is evaluated at $\mathbf{x}^{(k+1,r)}$.

In fact it is hardly worth re-evaluating the gradients for each iteration of the correction procedure, for the constituent matrices for the correction must be evaluated at $\mathbf{x}^{(k)}$ in order to compute $\mathbf{g}_R(\mathbf{x}^{(k)})$ and can then be used systematically at each iteration of the correction. Although this simplified Newton procedure has only linear convergence, the saving per iteration is more than enough to justify its use. In fact Abadie and Carpentier (1969), who applied this technique in conjunction with the variable-elimination method, suggest an approximate correction to the stored value of $\mathbf{A}_1^{-1}$, according to the formula:

$$\mathbf{A}_1^{-1}(\mathbf{x}^{(k+1,r)}) \simeq 2\mathbf{A}_1^{-1}(\mathbf{x}^{(k)}) - \mathbf{A}_1^{-1}(\mathbf{x}^{(k)})\mathbf{A}_1(\mathbf{x}^{(k+1,r)})\,\mathbf{A}_1^{-1}(\mathbf{x}^{(k)}). \tag{5.2.22}$$

However, if one *is* going to re-evaluate $\mathbf{A}_1$ it would seem preferable to recompute its triangular factors rather than use this approximation.

It is well known that the steepest-descent method is inefficient, but a similar technique can be used in conjunction with other methods. With linear constraints any conjugate-direction or quasi-Newton method using the reduced gradients will generate a search direction $\mathbf{p}^{(k)}$ lying in the constraint manifold. For nonlinear constraints the curvature prevents the successive vectors from lying in a linear manifold, but a similarly constructed search direction will be close to the tangent hyperplane if the curvature is not too great, and in any case the iterative correction procedure will correct for this additional inherited effect of the constraint curvature. Abadie and Carpentier

(1969) in fact incorporated the Fletcher–Reeves conjugate-gradient procedure in one version of their "generalized reduced gradient" (GRG) procedure, referred to above.

Finally we note that the correction procedure can be used to find an initial feasible point, although convergence can be proved only for a sufficiently good initial guess, as is usual for Newton-type procedures. On succeeding iterations the distance of the initial point $\mathbf{x}^{(k+1,1)}$ from the constraint manifold can be controlled by reducing $\alpha^{(k)}$ and hence this can always be chosen small enough to ensure convergence of the correction procedure.

Projection Methods

A solution $\hat{\mathbf{x}}$ of the equality constrained problem (5.2.1) corresponds to a stationary point of its Lagrangian function:

$$L(\mathbf{x}, \boldsymbol{\lambda}) = F(\mathbf{x}) - \boldsymbol{\lambda}^T \mathbf{c}(\mathbf{x}). \tag{5.2.23}$$

Thus we have

$$\left.\begin{aligned} \mathbf{g}(\hat{\mathbf{x}}) - \mathbf{A}(\hat{\mathbf{x}})\boldsymbol{\lambda} &= \mathbf{0}, \\ \mathbf{c}(\hat{\mathbf{x}}) &= \mathbf{0}. \end{aligned}\right\} \tag{5.2.24}$$

This system of nonlinear equations could be solved by standard techniques, but it is better to construct methods which take account of the special structure of the system. We wish to make local approximations to the functions about a current point $\mathbf{x}$, so we consider the problem of finding the step $\mathbf{s}$ from this point which attains the feasible point with the lowest value of the objective function within a distance δ from $\mathbf{x}$:

$$\min_{\mathbf{s}} \{F(\mathbf{x}+\mathbf{s}) : \mathbf{c}(\mathbf{x}+\mathbf{s}) = \mathbf{0}, \quad \mathbf{s}^T\mathbf{s} \leqslant \delta^2\}. \tag{5.2.25}$$

If this problem has a solution this must satisfy the conditions:

$$\left.\begin{aligned} \mathbf{g}(\mathbf{x}+\mathbf{s}) - \mathbf{A}(\mathbf{x}+\mathbf{s})\,\boldsymbol{\lambda} + \mu\mathbf{s} &= \mathbf{0}, \\ \mathbf{c}(\mathbf{x}+\mathbf{s}) \qquad &= \mathbf{0}. \end{aligned}\right\} \tag{5.2.26}$$

The Kuhn–Tucker multiplier μ is either zero, in which case the step-size constraint has not affected the problem, or $\mu > 0$ and $\|\mathbf{s}\| = \delta$. We now choose δ small enough to justify replacing the nonlinear constraints by their second-order Taylor expansions:

$$\left.\begin{aligned} F(\mathbf{x}+\mathbf{s}) &= F(\mathbf{x}) + \mathbf{s}^T\mathbf{g}(\mathbf{x}) + \tfrac{1}{2}\mathbf{s}^T\mathbf{G}(\mathbf{x})\,\mathbf{s}, \\ c_j(\mathbf{x}+\mathbf{s}) &= c_j(\mathbf{x}) + \mathbf{s}^T\mathbf{a}_j(\mathbf{x}) + \tfrac{1}{2}\mathbf{s}^T\mathbf{G}_j(\mathbf{x})\,\mathbf{s}, \quad j = 1, 2, \ldots, m. \end{aligned}\right\} \tag{5.2.27}$$

Differentiating and substituting the result in the first equation of (5.2.26) gives

$$(\mathbf{g}(\mathbf{x}) + \mathbf{G}(\mathbf{x})\,\mathbf{s}) - \sum_{j=1}^{m} (\mathbf{a}_j(\mathbf{x}) + \mathbf{G}_j(\mathbf{x})\,\mathbf{s})\,\lambda_j + \mu\mathbf{s} = \mathbf{0}. \tag{5.2.28}$$

If we write

$$\mathbf{W}(\mathbf{x}) = \mathbf{G}(\mathbf{x}) - \sum_{j=1}^{m} \lambda_j \mathbf{G}_j(\mathbf{x}) \quad \text{and} \quad \overline{\mathbf{W}}(\mathbf{x}) = \mathbf{W}(\mathbf{x}) + \mu\mathbf{I},$$

this can be rearranged to give

$$\left.\begin{aligned} \overline{\mathbf{W}}(\mathbf{x})\,\mathbf{s} &= \mathbf{A}(\mathbf{x})\,\boldsymbol{\lambda} - \mathbf{g}(\mathbf{x}), \\ \mathbf{c}(\mathbf{x} + \mathbf{s}) &= \mathbf{0}. \end{aligned}\right\} \tag{5.2.29}$$

Choice of a value of $\mu > 0$ implicitly fixes the step size $\delta = \|\mathbf{s}\|$, and the larger the value of μ, the smaller the step size. It is interesting to note however that in principle the system (5.2.29) has a solution $(\mathbf{s}, \boldsymbol{\lambda})$ for any chosen μ, so this indirect method of fixing δ ensures that the constraint set is always attainable, no matter how far $\mathbf{x}$ is from this set. Thus, to be sure of the validity of our second-order approximation, $\mathbf{x}$ must be close to the constraint manifold.

System (5.2.29) is somewhat simpler to solve than system (5.2.26) since its first equation is linear in $\mathbf{s}$ for given μ and $\boldsymbol{\lambda}$, but we still have to choose $\boldsymbol{\lambda}$ so that the resulting $\mathbf{s}$ satisfies the nonlinear constraint equations, and the quadratic approximation to the constraints makes no essential simplification here. However if δ is small enough to justify a linear approximation to the constraints, this difficulty disappears and we obtain a set of linear equations to determine $\boldsymbol{\lambda}$. By substituting for $\mathbf{s}$ from the first equation of (5.2.29) into this linear approximation we obtain the system:

$$\left.\begin{aligned} \overline{\mathbf{W}}\,\mathbf{s} &= \mathbf{A}\,\boldsymbol{\lambda} - \mathbf{g}, \\ (\mathbf{A}^T\overline{\mathbf{W}}^{-1}\mathbf{A})\,\boldsymbol{\lambda} &= \mathbf{A}^T\overline{\mathbf{W}}^{-1}\mathbf{g} - \mathbf{c}, \end{aligned}\right\} \tag{5.2.30}$$

where it is understood that $\mathbf{c}, \mathbf{A}, \mathbf{g}, \overline{\mathbf{W}}$ are all evaluated at $\mathbf{x}$.

To be consistent we should also neglect the second-order constraint terms in $\overline{\mathbf{W}}$, which would then give the system:

$$\left.\begin{aligned} \overline{\mathbf{G}}\,\mathbf{s} &= \mathbf{A}\,\boldsymbol{\lambda} - \mathbf{g}, \\ (\mathbf{A}^T\overline{\mathbf{G}}^{-1}\mathbf{A})\,\boldsymbol{\lambda} &= \mathbf{A}^T\overline{\mathbf{G}}^{-1}\mathbf{g} - \mathbf{c}, \end{aligned}\right\} \tag{5.2.31}$$

where we have written $\overline{\mathbf{G}} = \mathbf{G}(\mathbf{x}) + \mu\mathbf{I}$.

If the constraints are in fact linear, equations (5.2.31) provide a Newton-type procedure for solving the problem. The first step gives a point satisfying the constraints, and the remaining steps are similar to an unconstrained Newton procedure within the constraint space. Convergence is assured for a sufficiently large value of μ, and this unconstrained procedure is recognizable as the well known Levenberg–Marquardt algorithm, first proposed for use in unconstrained least-squares problems by Levenberg (1944).

As μ becomes large, $\overline{\mathbf{G}} \to \mu\mathbf{I}$ and $\overline{\mathbf{W}} \to \mu\mathbf{I}$, and equations (5.2.30) and (5.2.31) both tend to the form

$$\left.\begin{aligned} \mathbf{s} &= \mu^{-1}(\mathbf{A}\boldsymbol{\lambda} - \mathbf{g}) \\ \mu^{-1}(\mathbf{A}^T\mathbf{A})\,\boldsymbol{\lambda} &= \mu^{-1}\mathbf{A}^T\mathbf{g} - \mathbf{c}. \end{aligned}\right\} \qquad (5.2.32)$$

When the point $\mathbf{x}$ satisfies the constraints we have $\mathbf{c} = \mathbf{0}$ and (5.2.32) then gives

$$\left.\begin{aligned} \boldsymbol{\lambda} &= (\mathbf{A}^T\mathbf{A})^{-1}\mathbf{A}^T\mathbf{g}, \\ \mathbf{s} &= -\,\mu^{-1}\{\mathbf{I} - \mathbf{A}(\mathbf{A}^T\mathbf{A})^{-1}\mathbf{A}^T\}\,\mathbf{g}. \end{aligned}\right\} \qquad (5.2.33)$$

Comparison of (5.2.33) with (5.2.16) shows that this first-order approximation for the constrained steepest-descent direction $\mathbf{s}$ is just the orthogonal projection of the objective function gradient onto the constraint space.

Putting $\mathbf{c} = \mathbf{0}$ in (5.2.30) or (5.2.31) produces a similar kind of formula; for example, (5.2.30) gives

$$\left.\begin{aligned} \boldsymbol{\lambda} &= (\mathbf{A}^T\overline{\mathbf{W}}^{-1}\mathbf{A})^{-1}\mathbf{A}^T\overline{\mathbf{W}}^{-1}\mathbf{g}, \\ \mathbf{s} &= \{\mathbf{I} - \overline{\mathbf{W}}^{-1}\mathbf{A}(\mathbf{A}^T\overline{\mathbf{W}}^{-1}\mathbf{A})^{-1}\mathbf{A}^T\}\,\overline{\mathbf{W}}^{-1}\mathbf{g}. \end{aligned}\right\} \qquad (5.2.34)$$

This is also a projection onto the constraint space, for it is easily verified that any component of $\mathbf{g}$ orthogonal to the constraint space (of form $\mathbf{Az}$) is annihilated by the matrix operator. Indeed, if we transform to a new system of co-ordinates: $\mathbf{y} = \overline{\mathbf{W}}^{-\frac{1}{2}}\mathbf{x}$, with corresponding transformations of $\mathbf{c}, \mathbf{A}, \mathbf{g}, \mathbf{s}$, equations (5.2.34) reduce to the form (5.2.33) in the new co-ordinates. Since the metric $\overline{\mathbf{W}}^{-\frac{1}{2}}$ of this transformation depends on the point $\mathbf{x}$, it is reasonable to call projections of the type defined by (5.2.30) and (5.2.31) "variable-metric" projections.

Although these formulae have been developed in terms of the true Hessian matrices of the various functions, and are indeed usable in this form, they are more often used with approximations to these matrices, obtained by quasi-Newton techniques. In particular, equations (5.2.30) involving $\mathbf{W}(\mathbf{x})$ would normally make prohibitive demands on storage, if not computation time, if all the $\mathbf{G}_j(\mathbf{x})$ matrices had to be separately evaluated. However it is easy to generate a quasi-Newton approximation to $\mathbf{W}$ itself, for we note that it is the Hessian matrix of the Lagrangian function (5.2.23), whose gradient is simply $(\mathbf{g} - \mathbf{A}\boldsymbol{\lambda})$.

The use of the Levenberg–Marquardt rule is not the only means of limiting the step size. The basic objective is to choose a step size such that the Lagrangian function (5.2.23) is well approximated by terms up to second order, and we might equally well choose $\mathbf{s}$ to make the second-order terms themselves suitably small, by requiring that $\frac{1}{2}\mathbf{s}^T \mathbf{W}(\mathbf{x})\,\mathbf{s} \leqslant \delta^2$. The analogue of (5.2.28) is then

$$(\mathbf{g}(\mathbf{x}) + \mathbf{G}(\mathbf{x})\,\mathbf{s}) - \sum_{j=1}^{m} (\mathbf{a}_j(\mathbf{x}) + \mathbf{G}_j(\mathbf{x})\,\mathbf{s})\,\lambda_j + \mu \mathbf{W}\mathbf{s} = \mathbf{0}, \tag{5.2.35}$$

leading to the system

$$\left.\begin{aligned} \mathbf{W}\mathbf{s} &= \alpha(\mathbf{A}\boldsymbol{\lambda} - \mathbf{g}), \\ \mathbf{c}(\mathbf{x} + \mathbf{s}) &= \mathbf{0}, \end{aligned}\right\} \tag{5.2.36}$$

where we have written $\alpha = 1/(1 + \mu)$, so that $0 < \alpha \leqslant 1$, and the step-size decreases from its unconstrained value as α decreases from unity. The version analogous to (5.2.30), corresponding to linearizing the constraints, is then

$$\left.\begin{aligned} \mathbf{W}\,\mathbf{s} &= \alpha(\mathbf{A}\boldsymbol{\lambda} - \mathbf{g}), \\ \alpha(\mathbf{A}^T\mathbf{W}^{-1}\mathbf{A})\,\boldsymbol{\lambda} &= \alpha\mathbf{A}^T\mathbf{W}^{-1}\mathbf{g} - \mathbf{c}. \end{aligned}\right\} \tag{5.2.37}$$

It is of some interest to compare these two alternative methods of limiting the step size by comparing (5.2.30) and (5.2.37). Of course for $\mu = 0$ and $\alpha = 1$ both formulae give the same result: a variable-metric projection of $\mathbf{x}$ onto the constraint manifold plus a variable-metric projection of the gradient $\mathbf{g}$. For (5.2.37), as α decreases from unity the only effect is to scale down the distance travelled in the constraint space along the projected gradient, as shown in Fig. 5.3a. For (5.2.30) on the other hand, as μ increases from zero both projections rotate towards the orthogonal projections, also producing a decrease in step-size, as shown in Fig. 5.3b.

In one sense system (5.2.37) may seem more logical, for the step size is measured in the same metric as appears in the projection, but in fact this interpretation only makes sense if $\mathbf{W}$ is positive-definite. It must of course be non-singular for the inverse $\mathbf{W}^{-1}$ to exist, but if it is not also positive definite we are not assured of obtaining a decrease in the objective function for sufficiently small α. In contrast, $\overline{\mathbf{W}}$ is always positive definite for sufficiently large μ, so there are no difficulties about inverses and descent steps.

For Newton-type methods, which actually evaluate $\mathbf{G}$, and if necessary the $\mathbf{G}_j$, for use in the formulae, there is thus an over-riding advantage in using the Levenberg–Marquardt rule. However, if a quasi-Newton method is used to approximate $\mathbf{G}$ or $\mathbf{W}$ it is possible to use a scheme which ensures that the approximation remains positive-definite. Of course, if the true matrix is not

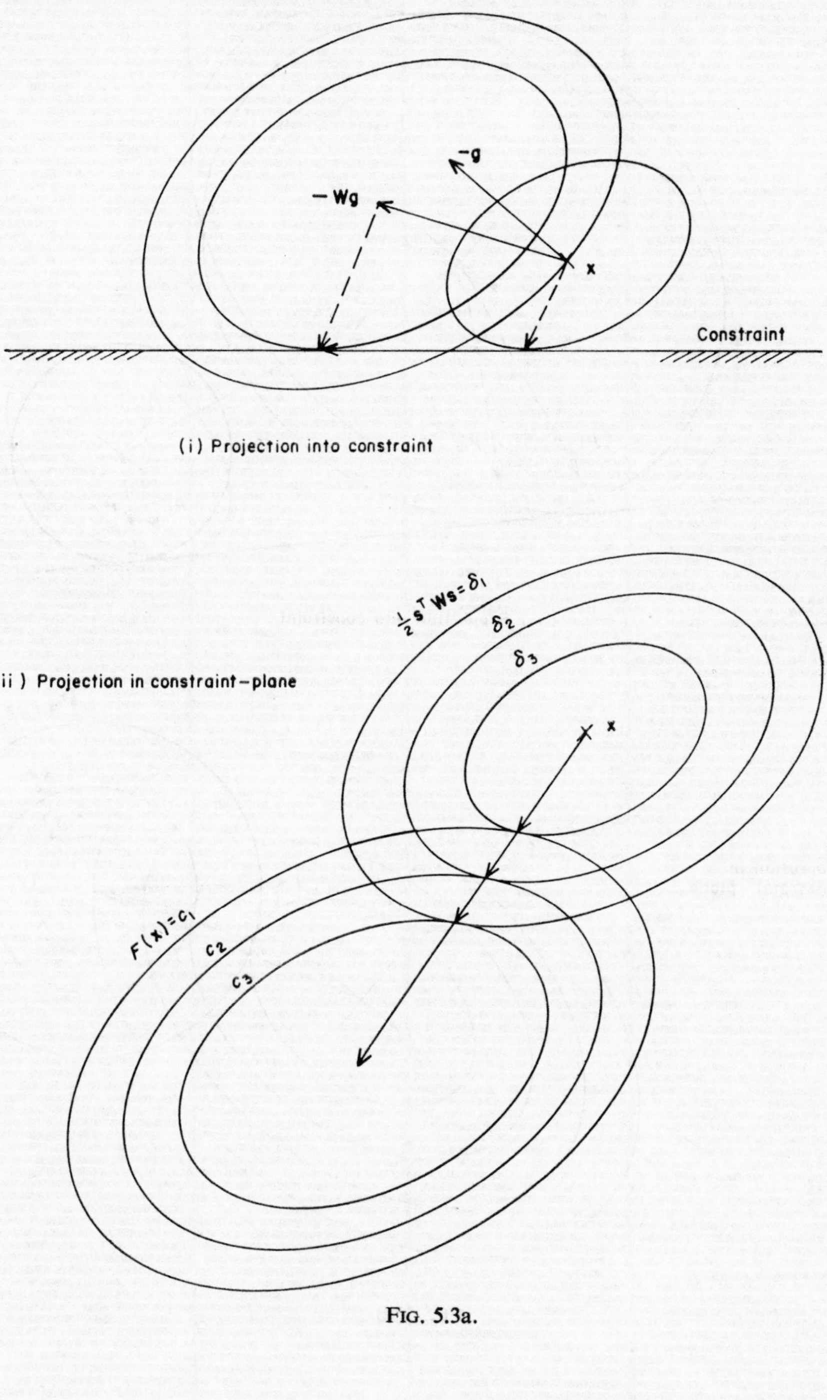
-g
− Wg
x
Constraint
(i) Projection into constraint
(ii) Projection in constraint-plane
½ sᵀWs = δ₁
δ₂
δ₃
x
F(x)=c₁
c₂
c₃

FIG. 5.3a.

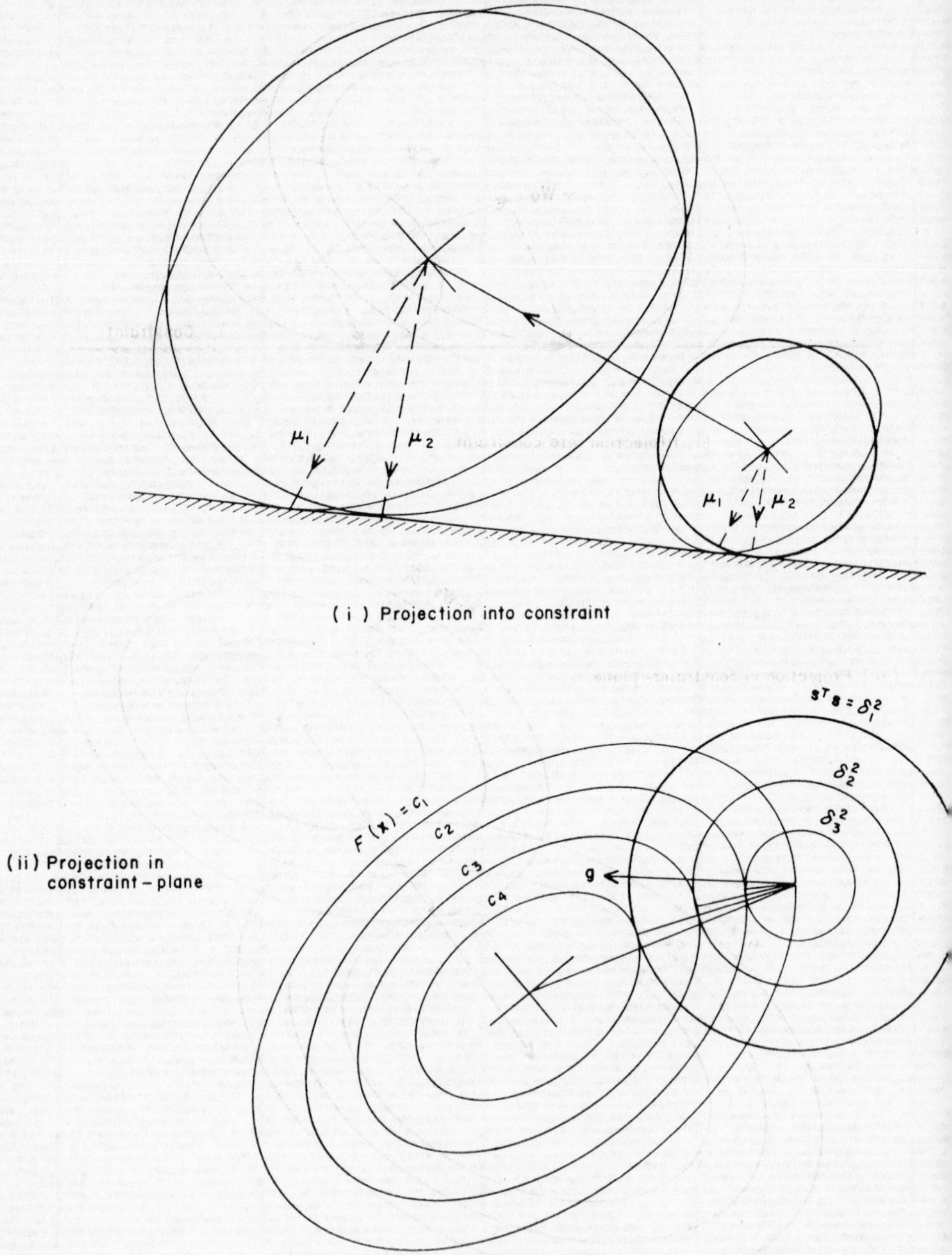
μ1
μ2
μ1
μ2
(i) Projection into constraint
s^T s = δ1^2
δ2^2
δ3^2
F (x) = C1
C2
C3
C4
g
(ii) Projection in constraint – plane

FIG. 5.3b.

positive-definite, such an approximating scheme is imposing an artificial modification very similar to that imposed by the Levenberg–Marquardt rule, and there is no theoretical basis for choosing between them. Some quasi-Newton methods require minimization of the objective function along the successive search directions, and this provides a quite different reason for choosing system (5.2.36) or its analogues. However, to secure convergence of any of the schemes a simple decrease of the function at each step is not sufficient, and it is necessary to impose a stronger "stability condition" of the type:

$$F^{(k)} - F^{(k+1)} \geqslant \delta|\mathbf{g}^{(k)T}\mathbf{s}^{(k)}|, \tag{5.2.38}$$

where $\mathbf{s}^{(k)} = \mathbf{x}^{(k+1)} - \mathbf{x}^{(k)}$ and $0 < \delta < 1$. From the above discussion it is clear that this can always be satisfied with a suitably small step provided that the underlying matrix is positive definite. Both conditions are achieved using a single parameter, μ, in the Levenberg–Marquardt scheme, while the use of α to control step size requires separate attention to the problem of maintaining positive definiteness of the matrix.

We now have complete schemes for dealing with linearly constrained problems, based on either (5.2.31) or the analogue of (5.2.37) (with $\mathbf{W}$ replaced by $\mathbf{G}$). However for nonlinear constraints these schemes replace the curved constraint manifold by its tangent hyperplane, and as for the reduced gradient methods we have the problem of following the curved constraint. In effect this means returning to the schemes (5.2.29) or (5.2.36), but we can again use the linearized schemes, (5.2.30) and (5.2.37) respectively, as the basis for a Newton-type correction procedure.

For the solution of (5.2.36), where $\mathbf{x} = \mathbf{x}^{(k)}$, $\mathbf{s} = \mathbf{s}^{(k)}$, the scheme used is:

$$\left.\begin{aligned}
&\text{for } r = 0:\\
&\qquad \alpha^{(k)}(\mathbf{A}^T\mathbf{W}^{-1}\mathbf{A})\,\boldsymbol{\lambda}^{(k,0)} = \alpha^{(k)}\mathbf{A}^T\mathbf{W}^{-1}\mathbf{g} - \mathbf{c}(\mathbf{x}^{(k)}),\\
&\qquad \mathbf{W}\,\mathbf{s}^{(k,0)} = \alpha^{(k)}(\mathbf{A}\boldsymbol{\lambda}^{(k,0)} - \mathbf{g}),\\
&\qquad \mathbf{x}^{(k+1,1)} = \mathbf{x}^{(k)} + \mathbf{s}^{(k,0)};\\
&\text{for } r \geqslant 1:\\
&\qquad \alpha^{(k)}(\mathbf{A}^T\mathbf{W}^{-1}\mathbf{A})\,\delta\boldsymbol{\lambda}^{(k,r)} = -\,\mathbf{c}(\mathbf{x}^{(k+1,r)}),\\
&\qquad \mathbf{W}\,\delta\mathbf{s}^{(k,r)} = \alpha^{(k)}\mathbf{A}\delta\boldsymbol{\lambda}^{(k,r)},\\
&\qquad \mathbf{x}^{(k+1,r+1)} = \mathbf{x}^{(k+1,r)} + \delta\mathbf{s}^{(k,r)},\\
&\qquad \boldsymbol{\lambda}^{(k,r+1)} = \boldsymbol{\lambda}^{(k,r)} + \delta\boldsymbol{\lambda}^{(k,r)}.
\end{aligned}\right\} \tag{5.2.39}$$

It suffices to use a simplified Newton scheme, in which $\mathbf{g}$, $\mathbf{A}$, $\mathbf{W}$ in (5.2.39) are all evaluated at the point $\mathbf{x}^{(k)}$. The analogous scheme for solving (5.2.29) is obtained from (5.2.39) by setting $\alpha^{(k)} = 1$ and replacing $\mathbf{W}$ by $\overline{\mathbf{W}}$.

If the correction procedure converges (within say 10 iterations), we set $\mathbf{x}^{(k+1)} = \mathbf{x}^{(k+1,r)}$ and $\mathbf{s}^{(k)} = \mathbf{x}^{(k+1)} - \mathbf{x}^{(k)}$ and test the stability condition (5.2.38). If this is not satisfied, or if the correction procedure does not converge, the whole step is repeated with a smaller value of $\alpha^{(k)}$ (or a larger value of $\mu^{(k)}$). As with the reduced-gradient methods, the correction procedure can also be used to obtain an initial feasible point.

Since the correction procedure is iterative, one must set a tolerance for the convergence and this can be either on the step size $\|\delta\mathbf{s}^{(k,r)}\| \leqslant \varepsilon$, or on the residual $\|\mathbf{c}(\mathbf{x}^{(k+1,r)})\| \leqslant \varepsilon$, or indeed one can insist on both. It can be argued that there is little point in iterating to high accuracy on this correction when far from the solution, and hence that one should start with a relatively large ε in the test and reduce this as the constrained minimum is approached. Unfortunately there are hidden pitfalls in this idea, for proof of convergence relies on the generation of a sequence of descent steps in a compact space, achieved by satisfying the stability condition (5.2.38) at each step. If at any time a violation of the constraints larger than the final acceptable tolerance is allowed, it is possible to find a point where the objective function has a lower value than at any feasible point, and then condition (5.2.38) actually prevents recovery to an acceptable point. What one would like to do is to allow an increase in the objective function if this results in a decrease in the constraint violation, and one way of achieving this is to add a penalty term to the objective function if the constraints are violated; for example one could replace $F(\mathbf{x})$ by the penalty function:

$$P(\mathbf{x}, r) = F(\mathbf{x}) + r[c(\mathbf{x})^T \mathbf{c}(\mathbf{x})]. \qquad (5.2.40)$$

By making r sufficiently large we can make the minimum of $P(\mathbf{x}, r)$ arbitrarily close to the constrained minimum of $F(\mathbf{x})$, and hence use an unconstrained minimization technique applied to $P(\mathbf{x}, r)$; such methods will be discussed by Ryan. However, we know that the Lagrangian has a stationary point at the constrained minimum, and much smaller values of r ensure that this stationary point is in fact a minimum. Thus if the step size is chosen to satisfy the stability condition (5.2.38) applied to the Lagrangian of $P(\mathbf{x}, r)$, the so-called "augmented Lagrangian function", this will force convergence without the need to insist on feasibility at each step. This is the idea behind the "augmented Lagrangian" methods to be described by Fletcher, and also his "exact penalty function" method.

Unfortunately, although there is a finite threshold value of r to achieve this result, there is no *a priori* way of obtaining a suitable lower bound for it—it clearly depends on the curvature of the objective and constraint functions at the solution. Nevertheless, even if we do not rely completely on the penalty term to satisfy the constraints, it may still be useful to replace $F(\mathbf{x})$ by $P(\mathbf{x}, r)$ if the constraints are strongly curved, for then the initial projection step will not cause such a strong violation of the constraints and less work will be required in the correction procedure. This device should not be so necessary with the projections employing $\mathbf{W}$ since this already incorporates constraint curvature information.

In conclusion, it should be pointed out that the distinction between reduced-gradient and projection methods is artificial, for although the motivating ideas may seem different both approaches lead to methods of the same type. Indeed any given method can be derived using either approach, as we have shown in the case of the orthogonal-projection method. In both cases the step at each iteration is a projection of the current point into the constraint manifold, combined with a similar projection of the objective function gradient. The essence of the choice between methods is the choice of metric for the projection, and this point will be taken up again after considering inequality constraints.

5.3. Inequality Constraints—Active Set Strategies

Most strategies for solving a linear inequality-constrained problem start with a feasible point, seek a feasible search direction from this point, then move along this direction until either the objective function passes through a minimum or a new constraint is encountered; the process is repeated from this new point. A simple illustration is given in Fig. 5.4.

One method of finding a feasible direction from a given point $\mathbf{x}^{(k)}$ is to find the set of constraints satisfied as equalities at $\mathbf{x}^{(k)}$ and project the objective function gradient $\mathbf{g}^{(k)}$ into this set. If the projection gives a non-zero step this defines a feasible direction; if not we are at a stationary point in the constraint space and the Lagrange multipliers can be used to test if we can decrease the objective function by leaving any of the constraints. If the constraints are of the form $\mathbf{A}^T\mathbf{x} \geqslant \mathbf{b}$, equation (5.2.12) shows that this will be so for any constraint corresponding to a negative λ_j, and since λ_j is the rate of change of the objective function it is logical to drop the constraint with the most negative λ_j. We then repeat the process with the reduced set of constraints, continuing until either a non-zero projection is obtained, or all λ_j are positive. The latter condition indicates that $\mathbf{x}^{(k)}$ is a Kuhn–Tucker point and the algorithm is terminated. The set of constraints treated as equalities in determining the feasible direction is called the active set of constraints at point $\mathbf{x}^{(k)}$.

As Powell has pointed out in Chapter I, such an algorithm must converge since constraints are not dropped from the active set unless a stationary point has been attained in this set, and since the next step reduces the objective function value below its value at this point, one cannot return to it. The objective function will normally have only a finite number of stationary points with distinct values in each active set, and the total number of possible active sets is finite, so the process must terminate.

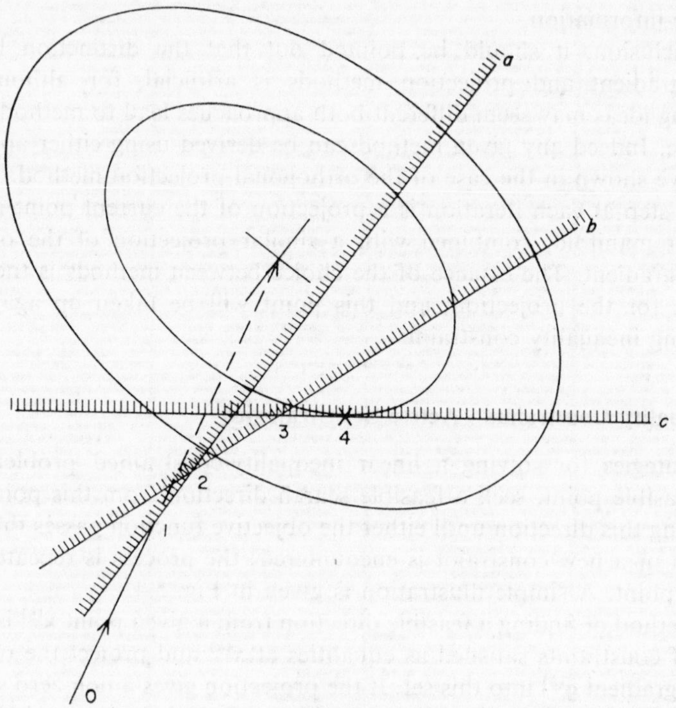

FIG. 5.4.

We note that the active set need not be constituted afresh at each iteration, since the search direction lies in the current active set and all constraints in it will therefore be satisfied as equalities at the new point; there will only be an addition to this if the step along the search direction encounters a new constraint. The idea of minimizing the objective function along the search direction derives from the use of steepest-descent or quasi-Newton methods which require this, but it is of course not an essential feature; the step can be of the length prescribed by the projection algorithm used unless this is truncated by encountering a new constraint.

For nonlinear constraints, the basic projection step before correction will normally give a non-feasible point, so one must include the correction iterations as part of the step. There then arises the problem that one or more new constraints may be encountered before the correction procedure converges, and hence while the point is still infeasible. Rosen (1961), who first proposed active set strategies for nonlinear-programming problems in connection with the orthogonal gradient-projection procedure, (cf. equations (5.2.33)), suggested reducing $\alpha^{(k)}$ $(= \mu^{-1})$ until the final corrected step came within the desired tolerance of the nearest newly-encountered constraint, as shown in Fig. 5.5. However this process would seem to require iteration on $\alpha^{(k)}$ and it is better to add the new constraint to the active set as soon as it is violated, so that the correction procedure itself obtains the required solution; indeed one can also treat any further violated constraints in the same way. It is just possible to obtain n constraints in the active set in this process, which of course have a unique point of intersection so that the projected correction step is zero; only in such a case will it then be necessary to reduce $\alpha^{(k)}$ (or $\mu^{(k)}$ in the relevant algorithms) to obtain successful correction to a feasible point. Abadie and Carpentier (1969) use this strategy in their generalized reduced-gradient method, and so do Sargent and Murtagh (1973) in their variable-metric projection method based on equations (5.2.34).

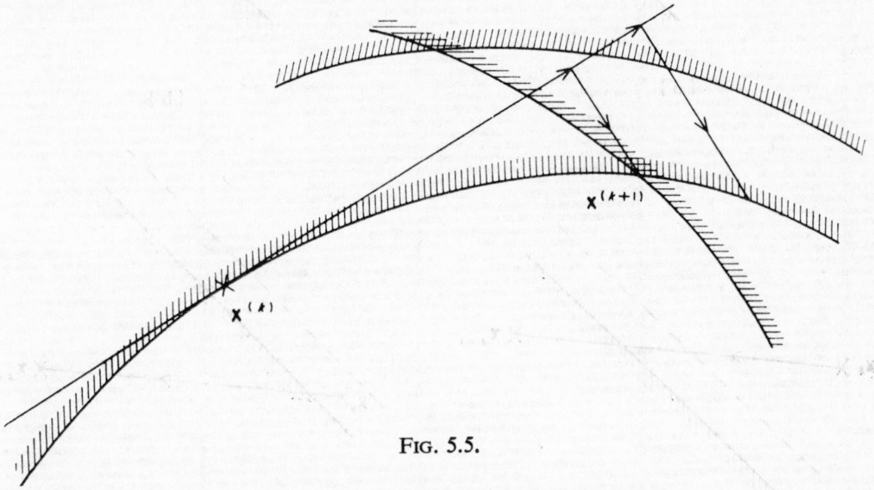

FIG. 5.5.

Sargent and Murtagh (1973) also use slightly different rules for adding a constraint, which are illustrated in Fig. 5.6. For any point $\mathbf{x}$ (whether at the start of an iteration or during the correction procedure) a projection step $\mathbf{s}$ is computed for the current active set. If the new point $(\mathbf{x} + \mathbf{s})$ is feasible with respect to inactive constraints, as in Figs 5.6a or 5.6b, the step is made without changing the active set. If on the other hand a new constraint j is violated at $(\mathbf{x} + \mathbf{s})$ the action depends on $\mathbf{c}_j(\mathbf{x})$. If $\|\mathbf{c}_j(\mathbf{x})\|$ is larger than a specified tolerance the new point is $\mathbf{x} + \alpha\mathbf{s}$, where α is chosen so that the point is on the linearization of $\mathbf{c}_j(\mathbf{x})$ about $\mathbf{x}^{(k)}$; otherwise constraint j is added to the active set and the projection step recomputed. If several new constraints are violated the nearest constraint (that is the one with the smallest value of α) is selected. This rule avoids computing intersection points of search directions with nonlinear constraints, and occasionally saves needless addition of constraints to the active set.

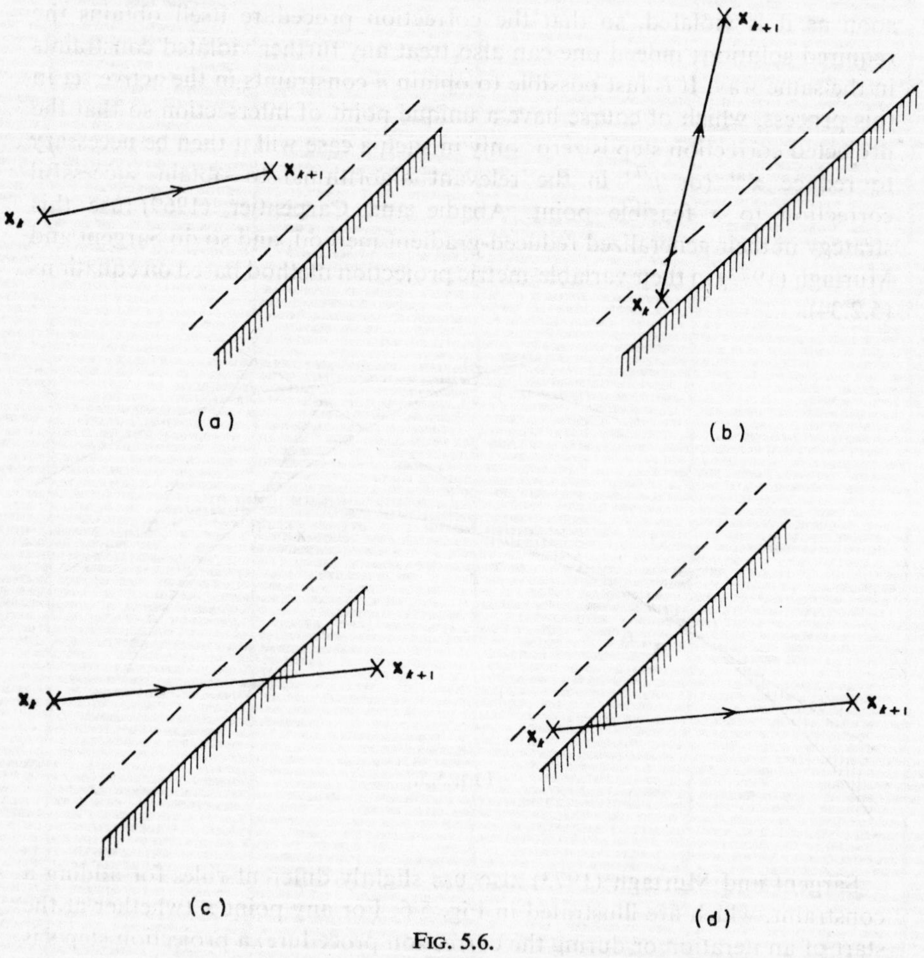

FIG. 5.6.

Rosen (1961) in fact did not drop the constraint with the most negative Lagrange multiplier, but used instead a first-order estimate of the change in objective function due to the change in projected step when the constraint is dropped. The variable-metric analogue of this formula c.f. Sargent and Murtagh (1973), corresponding to (5.2.37) is

$$\Delta F_j \simeq \mathbf{g}^{(k)\,T} \Delta \mathbf{s}_j = \lambda_j^{\,2}/m_{jj}, \tag{5.3.1}$$

where $\Delta\mathbf{s}_j$ is the change in step due to dropping constraint j from the active set and ΔF_j is the corresponding change in the objective function; λ_j is the Lagrange multiplier, as given by (5.3.37), and m_{jj} is the corresponding diagonal element of the matrix $(\mathbf{A}^T\mathbf{W}^{-1}\mathbf{A})^{-1}$. Rosen's formula is of course obtained by setting $\mathbf{W} = \mathbf{I}$. Thus the constraint to be dropped is the one among those with negative λ_j which has the largest value of (λ_j^2/m_{jj}); we note in this connection that $m_{jj} > 0$ if $\mathbf{W}$ is positive definite and the active constraints are linearly independent.

This appears to be a better criterion, and since it is valid for every $\mathbf{x}^{(k)}$ it can be used to test whether it is advantageous to drop a constraint at every iteration, rather than waiting until a stationary point is attained in the current set. We can even use it to drop all but the minimum active set required to obtain a feasible direction. Note that dropping a constraint changes the projection, and hence the magnitudes, and perhaps also the signs, of the λ_j for the remaining constraints; thus the constraints must be dropped one at a time, recomputing the λ_j each time, until no negative λ_j remain.

Several authors have used such a strategy, and Sargent and Murtagh (1973) in their algorithm test for dropping constraints in this way every time a constraint is added to the active set, whether this is in the basic step of the iteration or during the correction procedure. This further decreases the chances of building up a set of n active constraints and makes the best possible step at every stage.

Again Powell has pointed out that "zigzagging" can occur when constraints are dropped before waiting to attain a constrained stationary point, and that this may slow down convergence or even prevent it. Various *ad hoc* devices have been suggested for dealing with zigzagging, but the only "anti-zigzagging rule" which enables one to *prove* convergence is the one proposed by Zoutendijk (1960): "If a constraint previously dropped from an active set is added again, it is retained in the active set until a constrained stationary point is attained". In fact it seems that variable-metric projection algorithms are much less prone to zigzagging, and although the Zoutendijk rule is incorporated in our algorithm (Sargent and Murtagh, 1973) it seems to be rarely activated.

The combination of active set selection and projection is in effect attempting to solve the problem:

$$\left.\begin{aligned} &\mathbf{W}\,\mathbf{s} = \alpha(\mathbf{A}\boldsymbol{\lambda} - \mathbf{g}),\\ &\mathbf{c}(\mathbf{x}+\mathbf{s}) \geqslant \mathbf{0}, \qquad \boldsymbol{\lambda} \geqslant \mathbf{0},\\ &\boldsymbol{\lambda}^T\,\mathbf{c}(\mathbf{x}+\mathbf{s}) = 0, \end{aligned}\right\} \tag{5.3.2}$$

where $\mathbf{W}, \mathbf{A}, \mathbf{g}$ are all evaluated at $\mathbf{x} = \mathbf{x}^{(k)}$, $\alpha = \alpha^{(k)}$ is fixed, and $\mathbf{A}$ here represents the complete set of constraints. We note that since all $c_j(\mathbf{x}+\mathbf{s})$

and λ_j must be non-negative, the final equation in (5.3.2), known as the complementarity condition, ensures that $\lambda_j c_j(\mathbf{x}+\mathbf{s}) = 0$ for each $j = 1, 2, \ldots, m$, so that λ_j and $c_j(\mathbf{x}+\mathbf{s})$ cannot both be non-zero at the same time; a non-zero λ_j indicates that constraint j is active at the solution of (5.3.2).

By making a local linear approximation to the constraint functions, we can develop a simplified Newton procedure to solve (5.3.2), by solving the sequence of problems:

$$\left.\begin{aligned} &\mathbf{W}(\mathbf{x}^{(k+1,r)} - \mathbf{x}^{(k)}) = \alpha(\mathbf{A}\boldsymbol{\lambda}^{(k+1,r)} - \mathbf{g}) \\ &\boldsymbol{\phi}^{(k+1,r)} = \mathbf{c}^{(k+1,r-1)} + \mathbf{A}^T(\mathbf{x}^{(k+1,r)} - \mathbf{x}^{(k+1,r-1)}) \\ &\boldsymbol{\phi}^{(k+1,r)} \geqslant \mathbf{0}, \qquad \boldsymbol{\lambda}^{(k+1,r)} \geqslant \mathbf{0}, \\ &[\boldsymbol{\lambda}^{(k+1,r)}]^T[\boldsymbol{\phi}^{(k+1,r)}] = 0, \end{aligned}\right\} \quad (5.3.3)$$

for $r \geqslant 1$, where $\mathbf{x}^{(k+1,0)} \equiv \mathbf{x}^{(k)}$.

This is exactly equivalent to solving the sequence of quadratic programming problems:

$$\left.\begin{aligned} &\min_{\mathbf{s}} \{\alpha\mathbf{g}^T\mathbf{s} + \tfrac{1}{2}\mathbf{s}^T\mathbf{W}\mathbf{s}\} \\ &\text{subject to} \\ &\boldsymbol{\phi} = [\mathbf{c}^{(k+1,r-1)} - \mathbf{A}^T(\mathbf{x}^{(k+1,r-1)} - \mathbf{x}^{(k)})] + \mathbf{A}^T\mathbf{s} \geqslant \mathbf{0}, \\ &\mathbf{x}^{(k+1,r)} = \mathbf{x}^{(k)} + \mathbf{s}. \end{aligned}\right\} \quad (5.3.4)$$

The Sargent and Murtagh (1973) strategy usually achieves the solution of (5.3.2) via (5.3.3). However it fails to do so if the procedure stops at an infeasible point because the active set has built up to n constraints, and the solution then has to be restarted with a smaller value of α. Also, as with all active set strategies considered so far, it requires an initial feasible point for convergence to be guaranteed, and for nonlinear constraints the finding of such a point is not a trivial problem. It is possible to add further refinements to deal with both of these problems, but the resulting algorithm becomes rather cumbersome and a simpler, more direct approach is available, as described by Sargent (1973).

In this approach we first eliminate $\mathbf{x}^{(k+1,r)}$ from (5.3.3) to yield a "linear complementarity problem":

$$\left.\begin{aligned} &\boldsymbol{\phi} = \mathbf{q} + \mathbf{M}\boldsymbol{\lambda}, \\ &\boldsymbol{\phi} \geqslant \mathbf{0}, \qquad \boldsymbol{\lambda} \geqslant \mathbf{0}, \\ &\boldsymbol{\lambda}^T\boldsymbol{\phi} = 0, \end{aligned}\right\} \quad (5.3.5)$$

where we have written

$$\left.\begin{aligned} &\boldsymbol{\phi} \equiv \boldsymbol{\phi}^{(k+1,r)}, \qquad \boldsymbol{\lambda} \equiv \boldsymbol{\lambda}^{(k+1,r)}, \qquad \mathbf{M} = \alpha\mathbf{A}^T\mathbf{W}^{-1}\mathbf{A}, \\ &\mathbf{q} = \mathbf{c}^{(k+1,r-1)} - \mathbf{A}^T(\mathbf{x}^{(k+1,r-1)} - \mathbf{x}^{(k)} + \alpha\mathbf{W}^{-1}\mathbf{g}). \end{aligned}\right\} \quad (5.3.6)$$

From the form (5.3.4) we know that there exists a unique solution to the problem provided that the constraints are consistent, and it can be shown that this will be so for all r provided that they are consistent at $\mathbf{x}^{(k)}$ and α is chosen sufficiently small. Further, there is an algorithm due to Lemke (1968) which provides a straightforward procedure for finding this solution or demonstrating that no solution exists.

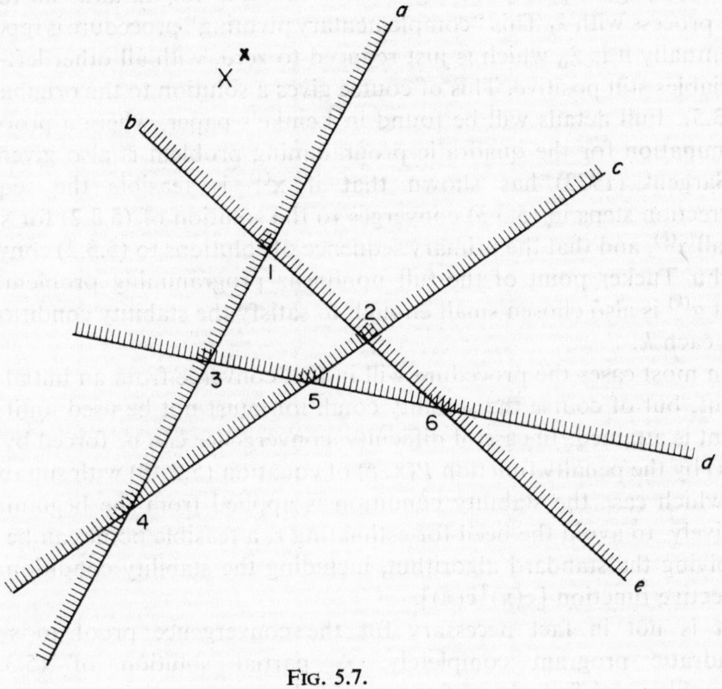

FIG. 5.7.

Thus the strategy is to start with an arbitrary α (e.g. $\alpha = 1$) and use the Lemke algorithm to solve the sequence of problems (5.3.3) until the convergence criterion is satisfied. If no solution is indicated at any stage, the process is repeated with a smaller value of α.

The Lemke algorithm for solving (5.3.5) adds a slack vector:

$$\left.\begin{aligned} &\boldsymbol{\phi} = \mathbf{q} + \mathbf{m}_0\lambda_0 + \mathbf{M}\boldsymbol{\lambda}, \\ &\boldsymbol{\phi} \geqslant \mathbf{0}, \qquad \boldsymbol{\lambda} \geqslant \mathbf{0}, \qquad \lambda_0 \geqslant 0, \\ &\boldsymbol{\lambda}^T\boldsymbol{\phi} = 0, \end{aligned}\right\} \tag{5.3.7}$$

where usually $\mathbf{m}_0{}^T = [1, 1, \ldots 1]$.

We start with $\boldsymbol{\lambda} = \mathbf{0}$, $\lambda_0 = 0$, and then increase λ_0 until we just have $\boldsymbol{\phi} \geqslant \mathbf{0}$. At this point we have $\phi_j = 0$ for some constraint j, so the appropriate value of λ_0 is obtained by solving the jth equation for λ_0; this is achieved by the pivot operation of linear programming, putting λ_0 on the left-hand side of the jth equation and ϕ_j on the right-hand side. Since $\phi_j = 0$ we can now increase λ_j from zero without violating the "complementarity condition" $\boldsymbol{\lambda}^T\boldsymbol{\phi} = 0$. Thus we increase λ_j until some ϕ_k is just reduced to zero. We again pivot, solving the kth equation for λ_j, and can then repeat the process with λ_k This "complementary pivoting" procedure is repeated until eventually it is λ_0 which is just reduced to zero, with all other left-hand side variables still positive. This of course gives a solution to the original problem (5.3.5). Full details will be found in Lemke's paper, where a proof of finite termination for the quadratic programming problem is also given.

Sargent (1973) has shown that if $\mathbf{x}^{(k)}$ is feasible the sequence of correction steps in (5.3.3) converges to the solution of (5.3.2) for sufficiently small $\alpha^{(k)}$, and that the primary sequence of solutions to (5.3.2) converges to a Kuhn–Tucker point of the full nonlinear programming problem provided that $\alpha^{(k)}$ is also chosen small enough to satisfy the stability condition (5.2.38) for each k.

In most cases the procedure will in fact converge from an initial infeasible point, but of course the stability condition must not be used until a feasible point is attained. In case of difficulty, convergence can be forced by replacing $F(\mathbf{x})$ by the penalty function $P(\mathbf{x}, r)$ of equation (5.2.40) with suitably large r, in which case the stability condition is applied from the beginning. Alternatively, to avoid the need for estimating r, a feasible point can be found by applying the standard algorithm, including the stability condition, with the objective function $[\mathbf{c}(\mathbf{x})^T\mathbf{c}(\mathbf{x})]$.

It is not in fact necessary for the convergence proof to solve each quadratic program completely. A partial solution of (5.3.5), with everything satisfied except for some of the non-negativity conditions on the λ_j, corresponds to a feasible solution with some constraints held as equalities. Such a solution suffices, provided that these constraints are held as equalities in the remaining iterations of the current correction cycle. This is simply achieved in the Lemke algorithm by first pivoting the corresponding λ_j to the left-hand side, and then ignoring them. Any equality constraints in the original problem are dealt with similarly.

In all the equations developed in the paper the implicit assumption has been made that inverses of matrices exist wherever they are required. This is ensured by making a "non-degeneracy assumption" for the constraints, which requires that for every point $\mathbf{x}$, every set of n gradient vectors $\mathbf{a}_j(\mathbf{x})$ is a linearly independent set. For linear constraints, any degeneracy among them can be eliminated at the outset by making small perturbations of the original set, as is done in linear programming. For nonlinear constraints there is a chance that an active set of linear approximations becomes degenerate, but since the gradients are a function of **x** this situation will normally be resolved by changing the step, for example by reducing $\alpha^{(k)}$. In the algorithms described, all that is necessary is to use a test for linear dependence before adding a constraint in order to take the appropriate action.

It is perhaps worth adding a final comment on the use of slack variables. In linear programming all general inequality constraints are converted to equalities by the addition of slack variables, so that the only inequalities left in the problem are non-negativity conditions on the extended set of variables. This technique was adopted by Wolfe (1967) in his reduced-gradient method, and also by Abadie and Carpentier (1969) in their extension of this method to deal with nonlinear constraints. Sargent and Murtagh (1973) dealt with linear inequalities as such, but advocated the use of slack variables for converting nonlinear constraints to equalities. They point out that, since slack variables appear only linearly, the Hessian matrices G and W have null rows and columns which may cause difficulties unless special precautions are taken to maintain positive-definiteness of their approximations. Since, as we have seen, it is perfectly possible to deal with linear and nonlinear inequalities directly, there appears to be no good reason for enlarging the problem and adding extra complications by using slack variables.

5.4. Summary

The ingredients of a nonlinear programming algorithm are as follows.

1. An active set strategy for selecting a set of constraints to be treated as equalities in the current step.
2. A projection formula for predicting a step in the active set.
3. Formulae for updating the matrices associated with the projection formula.
4. A correction procedure to follow nonlinear constraints.
5. A stability test to ensure convergence.

It will be clear from the discussion that I favour an active set strategy which does not rely on an initial feasible point. The use of the Lemke algorithm effectively combines the active set strategy with the projection formula, but there is not as yet sufficient experience to judge whether it is better to solve the quadratic program completely at each step or not.

The simplest correction procedure is the simplified Newton method, which does not require re-evaluation of gradients during the correction. Its operation may be aided by adding a penalty term to the objective function.

There is no real distinction between reduced-gradient and projection methods. All methods require storage of a transformation matrix or projection matrix of some sort, and the quasi-Newton methods require in addition the storage of a Hessian matrix approximation. For very large problems there may therefore be some merit in using a reduced-gradient (elimination of variables) or orthogonal projection, combined with a conjugate-gradient algorithm, as in Abadie's GRG method. Otherwise there is every advantage in using the variable-metric projection methods based on a quasi–Newton approximation to **W** or **W**, storing the matrices **W** and $\mathbf{A}^T\mathbf{W}^{-1}\mathbf{A}$ or their equivalents. Clearly one would store and update triangular factors rather than inverses.

Chapter VI

Penalty and Barrier Functions

D. M. Ryan

Operations Research Group,
Atomic Energy Research Establishment

6.1. Introduction

To avoid confusion in nomenclature in this chapter, we shall use the term "Transformation Method" to describe any method which solves the nonlinear programming problem

$$P1: \quad \text{minimize} \quad F(\mathbf{x}), \quad \mathbf{x} \in E^n$$
$$\text{subject to} \quad c_i(\mathbf{x}) \geqslant 0, \quad i = 1, \ldots, m,$$

by transforming the constrained optimization problem into one or more unconstrained optimization problems. In Section 6.2, the general concept of a transformation method will be introduced and we shall consider in some detail the properties of basic transformation functions and the behaviour of algorithms that use them. Throughout this discussion we shall avoid an emphasis of the mathematical aspects of the theory but we shall attempt to identify properties of transformation methods from a practical or computational point of view. It will be seen in Sections 6.4 and 6.5 that these properties can be considered as either desirable in that they establish the convergence of the algorithms, or undesirable in that they adversely affect the computational behaviour of the methods. Many recent contributions to the theory and implementation of transformation methods have been motivated by the computational weaknesses of the basic approach. These contributions can be recognized as attempts to eliminate or at least reduce the effect of computational weaknesses. In Section 6.7, we shall introduce four such contributions and will examine the properties of the resulting algorithms in the light of the results of Sections 6.4 and 6.5.

Before developing the concept of transformation methods, we consider briefly some properties of problem *P1* and then introduce the Kuhn–Tucker first-order necessary conditions for its solution. The feasible region of *P1* will be written as

$$R = \{\mathbf{x} : \mathbf{c}(\mathbf{x}) \geqslant \mathbf{0}\}.$$

The interior of the feasible region will be written as

$$R_0 = \{\mathbf{x} : \mathbf{c}(\mathbf{x}) > \mathbf{0}\}.$$

We shall assume throughout that the problem functions are continuous and also, mainly for computational convenience, that they are differentiable. We shall also assume a local solution, $\mathbf{x}^*$, exists and that at least one constraint is active at $\mathbf{x}^*$ (i.e. J, the active constraint set at $\mathbf{x}^*$, is non-empty). With care, we can consider the problem

$$P2: \quad \text{minimize} \quad F(\mathbf{x}), \quad \mathbf{x} \in E^n$$
$$\text{subject to} \quad c_i(\mathbf{x}) = 0, \quad i \in J \quad (\text{i.e. } i = 1, \ldots, t),$$

to be an "equivalent" problem to *P1*. The solution of *P2* is the solution of *P1* only if we ensure that the constraints, $c_i(\mathbf{x}) \geqslant 0, i \notin J$, are also strictly satisfied at the solution of *P2*. In general this need not be the case. Problem *P2* can be interpreted as the problem of minimizing $F(\mathbf{x})$ subject to an active constraint set.

For problem *P1*, we can write the Lagrangian as

$$L(\mathbf{x}, \boldsymbol{\lambda}) = F(\mathbf{x}) - \sum_{i=1}^{m} \lambda_i c_i(\mathbf{x}),$$

and following similar arguments to those used by Powell in Chapter I (see also Kuhn and Tucker, 1951; Hestenes, 1966; Fiacco and McCormick, 1968; and Lootsma, 1970) we can establish the Kuhn–Tucker first-order necessary conditions for $\mathbf{x}^*$ to be a local minimum of *P1*.

Kuhn–Tucker First-order Conditions

If $\mathbf{x}^*$ is a local solution of *P1* and the constraints $c_i(\mathbf{x}), i \in J$, satisfy "constraint qualifications" then there exists $\boldsymbol{\lambda}^* \in E^m$ such that

$$\mathbf{g}(\mathbf{x}^*) - \sum_{i=1}^{m} \lambda_i^* \mathbf{a}_i(\mathbf{x}^*) = \mathbf{0}, \tag{6.1.1}$$

$$\lambda_i^* \geqslant 0, \quad i \in J, \tag{6.1.2}$$

and

$$\lambda_i^* = 0, \quad i \notin J. \tag{6.1.3}$$

where $\mathbf{g}(\mathbf{x})$ and $\mathbf{a}_i(\mathbf{x}), i = 1, \ldots, m$, are the gradients of the problem functions.

This result can be extended to equality constraints by requiring that they also satisfy the "constraint qualifications". The multipliers corresponding to the equality constraints are unrestricted in sign.

Since Kuhn and Tucker (1951) first discussed necessary and sufficient conditions for constrained optimality, many alternative constraint qualifications have been proposed. One of the strongest, most widely known and probably most useful in any practical sense is the assumption used by Powell that the gradients of active constraints be linearly independent at $\mathbf{x}^*$. Under this assumption we also obtain the stronger result that the multipliers $\boldsymbol{\lambda}^*$ are unique. The importance of the Kuhn–Tucker conditions in relation to transformation methods lies in the fact that they or at least expressions of the same form, appear naturally in the formulation of transformation methods. The conditions under which the Kuhn–Tucker conditions hold also enable us to establish some very attractive and useful results concerning the methods.

6.2. Transformation Methods

The first use of a transformation appears as early as 1943 when Courant reported the use of a similar concept as a method for solving simple problems of constrained motion. It was not until 1955 that the idea was rediscovered. This time the initial developments were motivated by the concept of minimizing $F(\mathbf{x})$ with an unconstrained minimization method while maintaining *implicit* control over the violations of constraints by "penalizing" the objective function at points which violate or perhaps tend to violate the constraints. This is in contrast to methods such as those discussed by Sargent in Chapter V, which minimize the objective function and *explicitly* accommodate constraints in the determination of feasible descent steps.

Suppose then that we define a transformation of *P1* as

$$T(\mathbf{x}, \mathbf{r}) = F(\mathbf{x}) + \Phi(\mathbf{c}(\mathbf{x}), \mathbf{r})$$

where $\mathbf{r}$ in general, is a vector of *controlling parameters* and Φ is a real-valued function whose action of imposing the "penalty" is controlled by $\mathbf{r}$. We denote a local minimum of $T(\mathbf{x}, \mathbf{r})$, when it exists by $\mathbf{x}(\mathbf{r})$. The attractions are obvious—with a suitable choice of Φ and its control, $\mathbf{r}$, we could use an efficient *unconstrained* algorithm (e.g. Davidon–Fletcher–Powell method) to completely solve the *constrained* problem.

Two approaches are possible. The first and traditional approach has been to choose Φ and a sequence $\{\mathbf{r}^{(k)}\}$ such that $\mathbf{x}(\mathbf{r}^{(k)})$ is determined in some way and $\mathbf{x}(\mathbf{r}^{(k)}) \to \mathbf{x}^*$ as $k \to \infty$. We shall refer to these methods as sequential transformation methods. The second and more recent approach has been to choose Φ, some $\mathbf{r}^*$ and δ such that for $\|\mathbf{r} - \mathbf{r}^*\| < \delta$ then $\mathbf{x}(\mathbf{r}) = \mathbf{x}^*$. We shall restrict our attention in this paper to sequential methods; methods of the second type will be mentioned briefly in Section 6.7 and are discussed in detail by Fletcher in his chapter.

The sequential methods have also been referred to by Fiacco and McCormick (1968) as Sequential Unconstrained Minimization Techniques commonly abbreviated to SUMT. Two major classes of such methods can be identified. The first, the *barrier-function methods* (also known as interior-point methods), are characterized by their property of preserving constraint feasibility at all times. This is a useful property when solving problems in which the objective function is only defined on R. It also has the reassuring feature that, should the algorithm be terminated prematurely, a feasible solution is always returned.

The second class of sequential methods, the *penalty-function methods* (also referred to as exterior-point methods) are characterized by their use of infeasible points. The term "penalty function" has also been widely used to refer collectively to both types of sequential transformation methods.

In Sections 6.4 and 6.5 we shall consider, in some detail, the properties of barrier-function and penalty-function methods. In particular, we shall attempt to identify their strengths and weaknesses from both the theoretical and computational points of view. From these properties we will be able to recognize the motivation and justification behind the more recent extensions of transformation methods.

6.3. Barrier Functions

The transformation, $T(\mathbf{x}, \mathbf{r})$, is defined so that a barrier is constructed at the boundary of the feasible region R, and the solution, $\mathbf{x}^*$, is approached from the interior of R (i.e. R_0 is non-empty) by modifying the barrier using the controlling parameter. We note in passing that R_0 being non-empty implies that the barrier function is not a suitable transformation for equality constraints.

Let us define $\Phi(\mathbf{c}(\mathbf{x}), r)$ as

$$\Phi(\mathbf{c}(\mathbf{x}), r) = r \sum_{i=1}^{m} \phi_i(c_i(\mathbf{x}))$$

where r is a positive scalar and $\phi_i(t)$ is defined continuously on the interval $t > 0$. Let $\phi_i(t) \to \infty$ as $t \to 0_+$. For computational convenience we also assume ϕ_i is differentiable. It is interesting to note that from a practical point of view the conditions imposed on $\phi_i(t)$ are not of great importance provided one such function can be found. The conditions that must be considered important in establishing the transformation method are those that the problem functions must satisfy. The barrier-function transformation is then

$$B(\mathbf{x}, r) = F(\mathbf{x}) + r \sum_{i=1}^{m} \phi_i(c_i(\mathbf{x})), \qquad r > 0. \tag{6.3.1}$$

$B(\mathbf{x}, r)$ is defined on R_0 and $B(\mathbf{x}, r) \to \infty$ as $c_i(\mathbf{x}) \to 0$ for any i. If $c_i(\mathbf{x}^*) = 0$, then as $\mathbf{x} \to \mathbf{x}^*$, the growth of $\phi_i(c_i(\mathbf{x}))$ can be controlled or "cancelled" by decreasing r.

Examples

(i) Inverse barrier function (Carrol, 1961)

$$\phi_i(c_i(\mathbf{x})) = (c_i(\mathbf{x}))^{-1}. \tag{6.3.2}$$

(ii) Log barrier function (Frisch, 1955)

$$\phi_i(c_i(\mathbf{x})) = -\log(c_i(\mathbf{x})). \tag{6.3.3}$$

We can interpret the behaviour of (6.3.1) in the following way. Assume $c_\alpha(\mathbf{x}^*) = 0$ for some α. If r is decreased, then $\phi_\alpha(c_\alpha(\mathbf{x}))$ can be increased without increasing $B(\mathbf{x}, r)$. This implies that $c_\alpha(\mathbf{x})$ can be decreased, so permitting $\mathbf{x}(r)$ to approach $\mathbf{x}^*$. As a by-product of the convergence $\mathbf{x}(r) \to \mathbf{x}^*$, we would also expect $F(\mathbf{x}(r))$ to decrease towards $F(\mathbf{x}^*)$. This observation forms the basis of the computational procedure.

Basic Algorithm

(i) Select a sequence $\{r^{(k)}\}$ which is monotonic decreasing and null as $k \to \infty$ (e.g. $r^{(k)} = 10^{1-k}$, $k = 1, 2, \ldots$). Find $\mathbf{x}^{(0)} \in R_0$ and set $k = 0$.

(ii) $k = k + 1$.

(iii) Minimize $B(\mathbf{x}, r^{(k)})$ to find $\mathbf{x}(r^{(k)}) = \mathbf{x}^{(k)}$ starting the unconstrained minimization from $\mathbf{x}^{(k-1)}$. Return to (ii) if convergence is not satisfied.

Convergence tests in step (iii) are usually based on magnitudes of quantities such as $(F(\mathbf{x}^{(k)}) - F(\mathbf{x}^{(k-1)}))$ and $\|\mathbf{x}^{(k)} - \mathbf{x}^{(k-1)}\|$. In practice, k seldom exceeds say 10 before computer rounding error becomes significant. We shall see later that there are also other factors which limit the number of iterations of the basic algorithm that can be performed.

6.4. Barrier-Function Strengths

We shall now examine some properties of the basic algorithm which can be considered as either theoretically or computationally desirable properties of any transformation method. In general, the results can be considered as strengths of the methods.

Barrier-Function Convergence

Under mild topological conditions and for r sufficiently small, Fiacco and McCormick (1968) have shown that a sequence of minimizing points $\{\mathbf{x}^{(k)}\}$, produced by the basic algorithm and corresponding to $\{r^{(k)}\}$, exist and $\mathbf{x}^{(k)} \to \mathbf{x}^*$ as $k \to \infty$. Furthermore, it is easy to establish the following results which confirm the earlier observation concerning the behaviour of the barrier-function transformation (6.3.1).

(i) $\lim_{k\to\infty} r^{(k)} \sum_{i=1}^{m} \phi_i(c_i(\mathbf{x}^{(k)})) = 0.$

(ii) $\lim_{k\to\infty} F(\mathbf{x}^{(k)}) = F(\mathbf{x}^*)$ and $\{F(\mathbf{x}^{(k)})\}$ is monotonic decreasing.

(iii) $\lim_{k\to\infty} B(\mathbf{x}^{(k)}, r^{(k)}) = F(\mathbf{x}^*).$

(iv) $\left\{\sum_{i=1}^{m} \phi_i(c_i(\mathbf{x}^{(k)}))\right\}$ is monotonic increasing.

To give some idea of the generality of the basic algorithm, the topological conditions required amount to continuity of the problem functions and an assumption that $\mathbf{x}^*$ is in the closure of R_0. The last condition implies that the barrier-function approach will not converge to local minima which are isolated points of the feasible region. In establishing convergence of the basic algorithm, we do not require assumptions as strong as Kuhn–Tucker constraint qualifications. Indeed, the barrier-function method will converge to a local minimum at which the Kuhn–Tucker first-order conditions fail to hold. The generality of these convergence results suggest that the basic algorithm has wide applicability.

Lagrange Multiplier Estimates

A further aspect of transformation methods which has recently become more useful is the provision of "structural information" about the solution of the problem. With further assumptions on the smoothness of the barrier function (see Fiacco and McCormick, 1968), it is possible to derive estimates of the Lagrange multipliers appearing in (6.1.1), (6.1.2) and (6.1.3). We shall not comment further on the assumptions required except to say that both the inverse barrier function (6.3.2) and the log barrier function (6.3.3) satisfy them. By definition of $\mathbf{x}(r)$ we have

$$\nabla B(\mathbf{x}(r), r) = \mathbf{g}(\mathbf{x}(r)) + r \sum_{i=1}^{m} \frac{d\phi_i(c_i(\mathbf{x}(r)))}{dc_i} \mathbf{a}_i(\mathbf{x}(r)) = \mathbf{0}$$

and we define

$$\lambda_i(r) = -r\frac{d\phi_i(c_i(\mathbf{x}(r)))}{dc_i} \tag{6.4.1}$$

to give

$$\mathbf{g}(\mathbf{x}(r)) - \sum_{i=1}^{m} \lambda_i(r)\,\mathbf{a}_i(\mathbf{x}(r)) = \mathbf{0}. \tag{6.4.2}$$

If $\mathbf{a}_i(\mathbf{x}^*)$ are linearly independent, then as $\mathbf{x}(r) \to \mathbf{x}^*$, $\boldsymbol{\lambda}(r) \to \boldsymbol{\lambda}^*$ as $r \to 0$. This follows immediately from (6.3.5) using continuity. It is also possible to show under weaker Kuhn–Tucker constraint qualifications (see Osborne and Ryan, 1970) that $\{\boldsymbol{\lambda}^{(k)}\}$ corresponding to $\{\mathbf{x}^{(k)}\}$ and $\{r^{(k)}\}$ is bounded and that limit points of $\{\boldsymbol{\lambda}^{(k)}\}$ satisfy the Kuhn–Tucker conditions (6.1.1), (6.1.2) and (6.1.3). If $\{\boldsymbol{\lambda}^{(k)}\}$ has no finite limit point, then the Kuhn–Tucker conditions do not hold at $\mathbf{x}^*$.

If the Kuhn–Tucker conditions do hold at $\mathbf{x}^*$, the estimates of Lagrange multipliers provided by (6.4.1) at successive values of $r^{(k)}$ together with the corresponding constraint values can be used to identify constraints which are becoming active and also constraints which are remaining inactive. For active constraints we have

$$\lim_{k\to\infty} c_i(\mathbf{x}^{(k)}) = 0$$

and from (6.1.2)

$$\lim_{k\to\infty} \lambda_i^{(k)} = \lambda_i^* \geqslant 0.$$

For inactive constraints we have

$$\lim_{k\to\infty} c_i(\mathbf{x}^{(k)}) = c_i^* > 0$$

and from (6.1.3)

$$\lim_{k\to\infty} \lambda_i^{(k)} = 0.$$

Simple tests can be devised to monitor convergence of these sequences and so determine active and inactive constraint sets. The use of such structural information is discussed further in Section 6.7.

An Error Estimate or Bound

Under stronger conditions on the problem functions it is possible to derive an estimate of $(F(\mathbf{x}(r)) - F(\mathbf{x}^*))$. At $\mathbf{x}(r)$ we have

$$\mathbf{g}(\mathbf{x}(r)) = \sum_{i\in J} \lambda_i(r)\,\mathbf{a}_i(\mathbf{x}(r)) + O(r), \tag{6.4.3}$$

where the $O(r)$ term represents the contribution from inactive constraints. Taking the scalar product of (6.4.3) with $(\mathbf{x}(r) - \mathbf{x}^*)$ and using the first-order Taylor expansions about $\mathbf{x}^*$, we obtain

$$F(\mathbf{x}(r)) - F(\mathbf{x}^*) = \sum_{i \in J} \lambda_i(r) c_i(\mathbf{x}(r)) + O(\max [r\|\mathbf{x}(r) - \mathbf{x}^*\|, \ \|\mathbf{x}(r) - \mathbf{x}^*\|^2]). \tag{6.4.4}$$

If the condition of *strict complementarity*, $\lambda_i^* > 0, i \in J$, holds, it is possible to show for the log barrier function that the first term on the right-hand side of (6.4.4) dominates and the order term can be ignored (see Osborne and Ryan, 1970). When the active constraint set is unknown, the sum in (6.4.4) can be extended over all constraints. In this case we would expect

$$\sum_{i=1}^{m} \lambda_i(r) c_i(\mathbf{x}(r))$$

to be a bound for the error $(F(\mathbf{x}(r)) - F(\mathbf{x}^*))$. It can be shown that if *P1* is a convex programming problem, this bound becomes strict.

Robustness

Mifflin (1972) has established under much stronger conditions on the problem functions that the basic algorithm, using the log barrier function, will converge even when $B(\mathbf{x}, r)$ is "minimized" only to within a predetermined tolerance of $B(\mathbf{x}(r), r)$. The rate of convergence with respect to r is, however, adversely affected by the magnitude of the tolerance. The importance of this result lies in the observation that inexact minimizations are an unavoidable consequence of any numerical implementation of the basic algorithm. Using this result we can claim that the basic algorithm exhibits a certain robustness in overcoming this form of systematic error.

6.5. Barrier-Function Weaknesses

In contrast to the four desirable properties of barrier-transformation methods discussed in Section 6.4 it is also possible to identify a number of undesirable properties of the methods. These weaknesses of the basic algorithm are of a computational nature and are most serious when the controlling parameter is small. In this section we shall consider three such weaknesses.

Repeated Unconstrained Minimizations

The basic sequential transformation method requires repeated unconstrained minimization of $B(\mathbf{x}, r)$ with no strong indication of how $\{r^{(k)}\}$ should be chosen. The choice of $r^{(1)}$ and the rate at which $r^{(k)}$ tends to zero can seriously affect the computational effort required to find the solution $\mathbf{x}^*$. We must therefore seek a compromise between the use of a few very difficult minimizations when $r^{(k)}$ is chosen to converge rapidly and a larger number of less difficult minimizations when $r^{(k)}$ is chosen to converge slowly.

It can be shown (see Lootsma, 1972) that for the inverse barrier function (6.3.2)

$$\|\mathbf{x}(r) - \mathbf{x}^*\| = O(r^{\frac{1}{2}})$$

and for the log barrier function (6.3.3)

$$\|\mathbf{x}(r) - \mathbf{x}^*\| = O(r). \tag{6.5.1}$$

If the log barrier function is chosen, we can use (6.5.1) to "justify" the generating relation

$$r^{(k)} = 10^{1-k}, \qquad k = 1, 2, \ldots,$$

as a suitable choice of controlling parameter sequence since successive values of $r^{(k)}$ yield an extra decimal place of accuracy in $\mathbf{x}^{(k)}$.

The choice of $r^{(1)}$ remains an open question, however, and one possible approach is to choose $r^{(1)}$ so that $B(\mathbf{x}, r^{(1)})$ is well scaled in the sense that neither

$$F(\mathbf{x}^{(0)}) \quad \text{nor} \quad r^{(1)} \sum_{i=1}^{m} \phi_i(c_i(\mathbf{x}^{(0)}))$$

dominates. An alternative approach might be to choose $r^{(1)}$ which minimizes the magnitude of the gradient of the transformation function $B(\mathbf{x}, r)$ at $\mathbf{x}^{(0)}$.

Unconstrained Minimization Difficulties

The direct application of a typical unconstrained minimization algorithm to minimize the transformation function is seldom satisfactory, especially when the controlling parameter becomes small and the minimizing point of the transformation function approaches the boundary of the feasible region. Three associated difficulties can be distinguished.

(i) The unconstrained minimization algorithm, in general, assumes the objective function is defined on E^n or at least on a subset of E^n which contains the minimum as an interior point. Although this is true of the barrier transformation function, it is also true that $\mathbf{x}(r)$ approaches the *boundary* of R as r decreases. This implies that linear search procedures within the algorithm will need to be modified to accommodate attempts to evaluate $B(\mathbf{x}, r)$ at infeasible points. The simple expedient of setting the function value to "infinity" is unlikely to be sufficient if this value is then used to determine an interpolating function to perform the linear search or if the function value is used to compute or update derivative information about $B(\mathbf{x}, r)$.

(ii) The linear search procedures incorporated in many unconstrained algorithms are usually performed by fitting quadratic or cubic extrapolation and interpolation functions to function values and sometimes gradient values. It is impractical to expect such functions to model accurately the behaviour of the barrier function with its singularity at the boundary of the feasible region. This problem has been examined by Murray (1969b) and Fletcher and McCann (1969) who propose and numerically evaluate a number of alternative models incorporating singularities.

(iii) A third difficulty in minimizing $B(\mathbf{x}, r)$ using a standard unconstrained minimization algorithm arises in the specification of convergence criteria which are satisfactory for all values of the controlling parameter. As r decreases, the transformation function becomes extremely steep-valleyed and in a very small neighbourhood of $\mathbf{x}(r)$, the magnitude of the gradient of $B(\mathbf{x}, r)$ can take very large values. In these circumstances it is practically impossible to reduce the gradient magnitude numerically and this implies that a convergence criterion based solely on gradient magnitudes is unsuitable. Care must also be taken to avoid premature convergence resulting from the use of tests based on objective function improvement or steplengths in successive iterations of the unconstrained algorithm.

Ill-conditioning of the Hessian Matrix

A third weakness of the barrier transformation is related to the ill-conditioned nature of its Hessian matrix. The normal quasi–Newton minimization algorithm determines the kth descent search direction $\mathbf{p}^{(k)}$ by implicitly solving the system of linear equations

$$\mathbf{B}^{(k)}\,\mathbf{p}^{(k)} = -\nabla_x B(\mathbf{x}^{(k)}, r) \tag{6.5.2}$$

where $\mathbf{B}^{(k)}$ is an approximation to the Hessian of $B(\mathbf{x}^{(k)}, r)$. It is not unreasonable to expect that if (6.5.2) is poorly conditioned, the performance of the unconstrained algorithm may be seriously impaired by the use of the resulting $\mathbf{p}^{(k)}$. It has been shown by several authors (see Murray, 1969b, 1971a; Fletcher and McCann, 1969; and Lootsma, 1969, 1970) that if t constraints are active at $\mathbf{x}^*$, then t eigenvalues of $\nabla^2 B(\mathbf{x}(r), r)$ vary with r^{-1} and the remaining eigenvalues are positive and independent of r. This implies that as r decreases the condition number of $\nabla^2 B(\mathbf{x}(r), r)$ varies with r^{-1} and the system (6.5.2) becomes increasingly ill-conditioned. This result reflects the well-known difficulties of minimizing functions whose minima lie in steep-sided valleys. In practical terms, the effect of this ill-conditioning is seen in numerical evidence that successive minimizations of $B(\mathbf{x}, r)$ do not become significantly easier as r decreases, despite the evidence of (6.5.1) that this should be so.

In summary, we have seen that although barrier-function methods are well supported by theory and require very little structure on the problem to ensure theoretical convergence, they do suffer from serious computational weaknesses which become more critical as the controlling parameter decreases.

6.6. Penalty Functions

The penalty function transformation, in contrast to the barrier-function transformation discussed in Section 6.3, is defined to impose an increasing penalty on the objective function as constraint violation increases. The controlling parameter is used effectively to increase the magnitude of the penalty. Let us define $\Phi(\mathbf{c}(\mathbf{x}), r)$ as

$$\Phi(\mathbf{c}(\mathbf{x}), r) = \frac{1}{r} \sum_{i=1}^{m} \psi_i(c_i(\mathbf{x}))$$

where r is a positive scalar and $\psi_i(t)$ is defined and continuous on $-\infty < t < \infty$. Let $\psi_i(t) \to \infty$ as $t \to -\infty$, $\psi_i(t) = 0$, $t > 0$ for inequality constraints and $\psi_i(t) \to \infty$ as $t \to \infty$ for equality constraints. For computational convenience we can again require that the penalty function be differentiable. The penalty-function transformation now becomes

$$P(\mathbf{x}, r) = F(\mathbf{x}) + \frac{1}{r} \sum_{i=1}^{m} \psi_i(c_i(\mathbf{x})), \quad r > 0. \tag{6.6.1}$$

$P(\mathbf{x}, r)$ is defined on E^n and $P(\mathbf{x}, r) \to \infty$ as constraint violation increases.

Examples

1. Inequality constraints:
   (i) quadratic loss function
   $$\psi_i(c_i(\mathbf{x})) = [\min(0, c_i(\mathbf{x}))]^2,$$
   (ii) Zangwill's (1967) loss function
   $$\psi_i(c_i(\mathbf{x})) = -\min(0, c_i(\mathbf{x})).$$
2. Equality constraints:
   (i) $$\psi_i(c_i(\mathbf{x})) = (c_i(\mathbf{x}))^2, \tag{6.6.2}$$
   (ii) $$\psi_i(c_i(\mathbf{x})) = |c_i(\mathbf{x})|.$$

The interpretation of the behaviour of penalty-function transformations as r decreases is similar to that given for barrier functions. In particular, the basic algorithm can again be applied and equivalent theoretical results can be established to ensure convergence (see Fiacco and McCormick, 1968; Lootsma, 1972). The only difference in the basic algorithm for penalty functions is that we no longer require a feasible initial point $\mathbf{x}^{(0)}$ in step (i).

It is also possible to identify computational difficulties similar to those discussed for barrier functions in Section 6.5. Again, these difficulties result from $P(\mathbf{x}, r)$ forming an increasingly steep-sided valley as the controlling parameter decreases. In particular, the Hessian matrix of the penalty transformation function (6.6.1) can be shown to be ill-conditioned as r decreases (see Lootsma, 1972).

6.7. Recent Contributions

Recent contributions in the field of transformation methods for nonlinear programming can be interpreted as attempts to overcome the computational difficulties associated with the basic transformation methods as implemented in the basic algorithm. We will examine four such approaches and show how they attempt to improve the performance of the basic algorithm.

Extrapolation Procedures

Under slightly stronger conditions on the smoothness of both the transformation function and the problem functions, Fiacco and McCormick (1966, 1968, Chap. 5) and Lootsma (1968, 1970) have shown that $\mathbf{x}(r)$ describes a "smooth" trajectory converging to $\mathbf{x}^*$ as r decreases. This result suggests that an extrapolation function as a function of r could be fitted to successive $\mathbf{x}^{(k)}$ values. The extrapolation function could then be used to predict the solution $\mathbf{x}^*$ by evaluating at $r = 0$, or alternatively could be used to predict an initial estimate of $\mathbf{x}^{(k+1)}$, the minimizing point of $T(\mathbf{x}, r^{(k+1)})$. The effect of the latter is to reduce the computational effort required to minimize $T(\mathbf{x}, r^{(k+1)})$ by beginning the minimization from a better starting point than $\mathbf{x}^{(k)}$. Fletcher and McCann (1969) have investigated the performance of extrapolated transformation methods and have concluded, on the basis of numerical results, that the fit of a quadratic extrapolation function to the previous three $\mathbf{x}^{(k)}$ values provides a reasonable initial estimate of the next minimum point.

It is clear that the extrapolation procedure does not *remove* any of the computational weaknesses discussed in Sections 6.5 and 6.6. In particular, the unconstrained minimization difficulties persist since the transformation function is unchanged. It is also possible that the $\mathbf{x}^{(k)}$ values may require more accurate determination for use in specifying the extrapolation function.

Powell's Method

As a penalty-transformation method for solving the nonlinear equality constrained problem

$$\begin{aligned} &\text{minimize} \quad F(\mathbf{x}) \\ &\text{subject to} \quad c_i(\mathbf{x}) = 0, \qquad i = 1, \ldots, t, \end{aligned}$$

Powell (1969) proposed a penalty defined by

$$\Phi(\mathbf{c}(\mathbf{x}), \mathbf{r}) = \sum_{i=1}^{t} \sigma_i(\theta_i + c_i(\mathbf{x}))^2, \qquad \mathbf{r} = (\boldsymbol{\theta}, \boldsymbol{\sigma})^T$$

$$= (\mathbf{c}(\mathbf{x}) + \boldsymbol{\theta})^T \mathbf{S}(\mathbf{c}(\mathbf{x}) + \boldsymbol{\theta}),$$

where $\boldsymbol{\theta}$ and $\boldsymbol{\sigma}$ are t-vectors of controlling parameters and $\mathbf{S} = \text{diag}(\sigma_i)$. The Powell transformation function now becomes

$$P(\mathbf{x}, \boldsymbol{\theta}, \boldsymbol{\sigma}) = F(\mathbf{x}) + (\mathbf{c}(\mathbf{x}) + \boldsymbol{\theta})^T \mathbf{S}(\mathbf{c}(\mathbf{x}) + \boldsymbol{\theta}). \tag{6.7.1}$$

Note. For $\boldsymbol{\theta} = \mathbf{0}$ and $\sigma_i = r^{-1}$, $i = 1, \ldots, t$, (6.7.1) reduces to the quadratic-loss penalty function (6.6.2).

Powell's method is based on the observation that if $\mathbf{x}^{(k)}$ minimizes $P(\mathbf{x}, \boldsymbol{\theta}^{(k)}, \boldsymbol{\sigma}^{(k)})$, then $\mathbf{x}^{(k)}$ is also a solution of the problem

$$\underset{\mathbf{x}}{\text{minimize}} \quad F(\mathbf{x})$$

$$\text{subject to} \quad \mathbf{c}(\mathbf{x}) = \mathbf{c}(\mathbf{x}^{(k)}).$$

In order to solve the equality-constrained problem, it is sufficient to find $\boldsymbol{\theta}^{(k)}$ and $\boldsymbol{\sigma}^{(k)}$ such that $\mathbf{x}^{(k)} = \mathbf{x}(\boldsymbol{\theta}^{(k)}, \boldsymbol{\sigma}^{(k)})$ solves the system of nonlinear equations

$$\mathbf{c}(\mathbf{x}(\boldsymbol{\theta}^{(k)}, \boldsymbol{\sigma}^{(k)})) = \mathbf{0}. \tag{6.7.2}$$

If at $\mathbf{x}^*$, $\mathbf{a}_i(\mathbf{x}^*)$, $i = 1, \ldots, t$, are linearly independent we have seen in Section 6.1 that the Kuhn–Tucker first-order conditions imply the existence of a unique vector of multipliers $\boldsymbol{\lambda}^*$ satisfying (6.1.1). By definition of $\mathbf{x}^{(k)}$, we have

$$\nabla P(\mathbf{x}^{(k)}, \boldsymbol{\theta}^{(k)}, \boldsymbol{\sigma}^{(k)}) = \mathbf{g}(\mathbf{x}^{(k)}) + \sum_{i=1}^{t} \sigma_i^{(k)} (\theta_i^{(k)} + c_i(\mathbf{x}^{(k)}))\, \mathbf{a}_i(\mathbf{x}^{(k)}) = \mathbf{0},$$

and using the continuity of $\mathbf{c}(\mathbf{x})$ and the consequent linear independence of $\mathbf{a}_i(\mathbf{x}^{(k)})$, $i = 1, \ldots, t$, for $\mathbf{x}^{(k)}$ sufficiently close to $\mathbf{x}^*$, we can see that the estimates

$$\boldsymbol{\lambda}^{(k)} = 2\,\mathbf{S}^{(k)} (\boldsymbol{\theta}^{(k)} + \mathbf{c}(\mathbf{x}^{(k)})) \tag{6.7.3}$$

exist and have as limit points when $\mathbf{x}^{(k)} \to \mathbf{x}^*$, the unique values $\boldsymbol{\lambda}^* = 2\mathbf{S}^*\boldsymbol{\theta}^*$ where $\boldsymbol{\theta}^*$ and $\boldsymbol{\sigma}^*$ correspond to $\mathbf{x}^*$. It is clear then that the controlling parameters θ_i and σ_i are only determined to within multiplicative constants. We can therefore fix one of the vector parameters and (6.7.2) can be regarded as a system of t equations in t variables. It has already been noted that fixing $\boldsymbol{\theta}$ reduces (6.7.1) to a basic penalty transformation in which the solution is obtained as $r = \sigma_i^{-1} = \sigma^{-1} \to 0$ and for which computational weaknesses have been identified in Section 6.6.

Powell's method, in contrast, treats $\sigma_i = \sigma$ as a "constant" and varies $\boldsymbol{\theta}$ to solve (6.7.2). In particular, it can be shown that if σ is sufficiently large, the iterative scheme

$$\boldsymbol{\theta}^{(k+1)} = \boldsymbol{\theta}^{(k)} + \mathbf{c}(\mathbf{x}(\boldsymbol{\theta}^{(k)}, \sigma^{(k)})) \tag{6.7.4}$$

will ensure arbitrarily fast linear convergence of $\mathbf{c}(\mathbf{x}^{(k)})$ to zero. Equation (6.7.4) can be interpreted as an approximation to the correction produced by Newton's method when applied to the system (6.7.2). The important feature of this result is that $r = \sigma^{-1}$ is not required to tend to zero; indeed values of σ are seldom required larger than 10^2, or exceptionally 10^3, to ensure very rapid convergence. The basic algorithm can now be modified.

Powell's Algorithm

(i) Select $\boldsymbol{\theta}^{(1)} = \mathbf{0}, \quad \sigma^{(1)} = 1, \quad k = 0.$

(ii) $k = k + 1$.

(iii) Minimize $P(\mathbf{x}, \boldsymbol{\theta}^{(k)}, \sigma^{(k)})$ to find $\mathbf{x}^{(k)}$, starting the unconstrained minimization from $\mathbf{x}^{(k-1)}$.

(iv) If $\mathbf{c}(\mathbf{x}^{(k)})$ is converging sufficiently rapidly to zero, then

$$\boldsymbol{\theta}^{(k+1)} = \boldsymbol{\theta}^{(k)} + \mathbf{c}(\mathbf{x}^{(k)}),$$
$$\sigma^{(k+1)} = \sigma^{(k)},$$

and return to (ii).

Otherwise

$$\left.\begin{aligned} \boldsymbol{\theta}^{(k+1)} &= \frac{1}{\mu}\boldsymbol{\theta}^{(k)}, \\ \sigma^{(k+1)} &= \mu\,\sigma^{(k)} \end{aligned}\right\} \mu > 1$$

and return to (ii).

Although Powell's algorithm still has the weakness of requiring repeated unconstrained minimizations, these minimizations are not beset by the computational difficulties of the basic transformations. In fact, the minimizations are well scaled and as k increases and $\mathbf{x}^{(k)} \to \mathbf{x}^*$ (i.e. $\boldsymbol{\theta}^{(k)} \to \boldsymbol{\theta}^*$), they require progressively less computational effort. The method is described in more detail by Fletcher in Chapter VIII. Despite the excellent convergence and computational properties, Powell's method is restricted to equality constrained problems.

A Hybrid Method

We now consider an extension of the basic-transformation method which solves the inequality constrained problem by using a barrier transformation while its computational properties are relatively well-behaved and, having identified the active constraints, solves the resulting equality constrained problem using Powell's method. A different extension to inequality problems has also been suggested by Rockafellar (1973) and is described and referenced by Fletcher in Chapter VIII. Osborne and Ryan (1972) and Ryan (1971) have described a hybrid transformation method based on a careful union of the barrier-function method and Powell's method. Effectively, Powell's method is used to overcome the computational weaknesses of the barrier-function method when the controlling parameter becomes small.

The hybrid method solves problem *P1* by applying a barrier-function transformation while its computational behaviour is satisfactory. Using the structural information produced by this method for reasonable values of the controlling parameter, we identify active and inactive constraints sets as described in Section 6.4. Typically only three or four $r^{(k)}$ values are required to classify all inequality constraints. Constraints classified as active are then transferred to Powell's method and are treated as equalities. The hybrid transformation function can be written as

$$T(\mathbf{x}, \boldsymbol{\theta}^{(s)}, \boldsymbol{\sigma}^{(s)}, r^{(k)}) = F(\mathbf{x}) + r^{(k)} \sum_{i \notin J^{(k)}} \phi_i(c_i(\mathbf{x})) + \sum_{i \in J^{(k)}} \sigma_i^{(s)}(\theta_i^{(s)} + c_i(\mathbf{x}))^2$$

where $J^{(k)}$ is the set of active inequality constraints identified after the minimization at $r^{(k-1)}$ and s is an iteration number for Powell's method. The basic algorithm can now be reviewed as a sequence, generated by $\{r^{(k)}\}$, of *equality constrained minimizations* of

$$\left[F(\mathbf{x}) + r^{(k)} \sum_{i \notin J^{(k)}} \phi_i(c_i(\mathbf{x}))\right].$$

These minimizations can be solved efficiently using Powell's method. Ryan (1971) has shown that the basic convergence results discussed in Section 6.4 can be extended to established convergence of the sequence of equality constrained minimizations.

In transferring the active inequality constraints from the barrier transformation to Powell's transformation we can make use of the barrier function Lagrange multiplier estimates to predict suitable values of $\boldsymbol{\theta}^{(k)}$ for Powell's method. We have from (6.4.1) and (6.7.3)

$$-r\frac{d\phi_i}{dc_i} = 2\,\sigma_i(\theta_i + c_i(\mathbf{x})),$$

and using (6.7.4) we obtain

$$\theta_i = -\frac{r}{2\sigma_i}\frac{d\phi_i}{dc_i}. \tag{6.7.5}$$

With a careful choice of σ_i, (6.7.5) can be used to provide an initial estimate for $\boldsymbol{\theta}$. Computational evidence shows first that (6.7.5) provides a very good estimate of the limiting value and Powell's method requires very few iterations to solve each equality constrained problem, and second that each unconstrained minimization of Powell's method is computationally trivial, requiring typically only two or three iterations of a quasi-Newton method. The discussion of a number of other important features of the hybrid method can be found in Osborne and Ryan (1972) and Ryan (1971).

In summary, the hybrid method overcomes the computational difficulties of the barrier-transformation method which occur for small values of controlling parameter by transferring the active inequality constraints, which cause the difficulties, to Powell's method. It can be shown that in these circumstances convergence of Powell's method is exceptionally rapid. The hybrid method does not overcome the disadvantage of requiring repeated unconstrained minimizations but it does replace a sequence of difficult barrier transformation minimizations with a sequence of very simple minimizations of Powell's transformation.

Augmented Lagrangian and Exact Transformations

A fourth and promising approach to overcoming the weaknesses of the basic algorithm can be identified in the work of Rockafellar (1973) and Fletcher (1973b). This approach is discussed in detail by Fletcher in Chapter VIII.

Chapter VII

Constrained Optimization by Direct Search

W. H. Swann

Imperial Chemical Industries, Mond Division

7.1. Introduction

Almost all of the methods for handling constraints described in the other chapters of this volume make use of the first and sometimes also the second partial derivatives of the objective function (and possibly the constraints). The motivation behind the development of such methods is easily understood. The first and second derivatives of a function define its gradient and curvature and thereby determine the existence and location of the minimum which solves the problem being studied. Hence methods using this information are likely to lead to the solution most quickly.

However in practical optimization problems it frequently occurs that evaluation of the function and constraints involves a lengthy and complicated calculation, and as a consequence it is difficult or even impossible to derive explicit expressions for the required derivatives. In these circumstances derivative values can only be obtained by means of finite-difference approximations. However, this approach can introduce truncation and/or cancellation errors which may nullify the theory underlying the chosen algorithm and lead the search astray so that it converges to the solution only very slowly, or possibly not at all. Thus it is necessary to take care when using numerical differentiation, and this has prompted research into the problem leading to, for example, Stewart's (1967) finite-difference version of the Davidon–Fletcher–Powell algorithm, and Gill and Murray's (1972a) finite-difference version of their own quasi-Newton method.

An alternative approach to using finite differences is to employ an optimization procedure which does not call for derivative values. Such methods are termed *direct-search methods*, and this chapter describes some of the techniques of this type which have been proposed for solving the constrained optimization problem.

The direct-search strategies for generating a sequence of improving approximations to the solution are based simply on comparisons of function values, and generally, though not always, the methods are heuristic in nature having little or no mathematical basis. (The most notable exceptions to this are the conjugate-direction methods exemplified by the algorithm proposed by Powell, 1964). Because of their nature they make only very limited assumptions about the function—generally no more than continuity—and as a result they have a very wide field of application. Thus not only can they be used in problems for which differentiation is difficult, but also for those cases where it may be inappropriate—when the derivatives are discontinuous, or when the function values are subject to error, as for example when they depend upon measurements on a chemical plant. These are situations in which the gradient-based methods can prove inefficient or even ineffective. Most of the better direct-search methods are little affected by such difficulties.

Of course direct-search methods may be used on the more well-behaved problems to which gradient methods may also be applied, and an important practical point to note is that they generally have the advantage of requiring less preparation. Furthermore, because of their lack of assumptions about the function they can prove more reliable and stable than gradient methods.

Therefore whilst one might be inclined to dismiss direct-search methods, or most of them, because of their lack of a theoretical basis and hence an assumed inefficiency, one should not ignore them from a practical point of view.

However, it is important to appreciate that there are deficiencies in the direct-search approach. Thus whereas gradient methods are generally supported by optimality proofs, most of the direct-search methods are not, and consequently are aimed at producing a good solution rather than an optimal one, but in the hope that in practical terms "good" will approximate "optimal". Associated with this difficulty is the problem of detecting convergence. For methods having a mathematical basis, sound convergence criteria can be derived, but this is not possible for heuristic direct-search methods. Consequently most of the latter base their termination tests on some form of law of diminishing returns and as a result they are more liable to end prematurely or to prolong the search unnecessarily. In addition, direct-search methods, using as they do only limited information about the problem, generally prove to be less efficient than methods making use of derivative values on those problems for which the latter can be used.

Therefore, while direct-search methods have an important role to play in optimization, they should be used only where their particular characteristics make them more appropriate than gradient methods.

This chapter describes some of the constrained direct-search procedures which have been most widely used in practice. Many of them are constraint-handling techniques which can be incorporated into unconstrained direct-search methods. The unconstrained methods referred to most frequently in this chapter are pattern search (Hooke and Jeeves, 1961), Powell's (1964) conjugate-direction algorithm, the DSC method (Swann, 1964), and the Simplex methods of Spendley, Hext and Himsworth (1962) and Nelder and Mead (1965). Full details of these methods are not given here; for these the reader is referred to the original papers, or to the review given in the earlier volume on unconstrained optimization (Swann, 1972).

7.2. Monte Carlo Methods

Some of the simplest direct search procedures are based on the Monte Carlo approach in which trial points are generated at random. The best feasible of these may be taken as the minimum, or some attempt may be made to use the trials to define a reduced search region within which further random trial points may be produced.

A typical implementation is the following which was proposed by Luus and Jaakola (1973). Suppose that for the kth iteration, an approximation $\mathbf{x}^{(k-1)}$ to the solution is available, together with a vector $\mathbf{l}^{(k-1)}$ the ith element of which defines the range of x_i, and a sequence of j pseudo-random numbers r_i, $i = 2, \ldots, j$ rectangularly distributed over the interval $(-0{\cdot}5, 0{\cdot}5)$. Then j new trial points are generated by

$$\mathbf{z}^{(i)} = \mathbf{x}^{(k-1)} + r_i \mathbf{l}^{(k-1)}, \qquad i = 1, 2, \ldots, j.$$

If $\mathbf{z}^{(q)}$ is the best feasible of these, then a new approximation is given by

$$\mathbf{x}^{(k)} = \mathbf{z}^{(q)},$$

the range of the variables is reduced by

$$\mathbf{l}^{(k)} = (1 - \varepsilon)\, \mathbf{l}^{(k-1)}, \qquad 0 < \varepsilon < 1,$$

and a new set of random numbers obtained so that the next iteration may proceed.

Luus and Jaakola used $j = 100$ and $\varepsilon = 0{\cdot}05$ and tested the method on a number of examples, finding it simple to program and use, reliable, and unperturbed by the presence of local minima. However to solve problems ranging from 3 variables and 10 constraints to 7 variables and 3 constraints they allowed 200 iterations, thereby generating 20,000 trial points per problem. This is an excessive amount of work for the problems considered, and although it could undoubtedly be reduced by investigating the sensitivity of the search efficiency to the number of iterations and to the parameters j and ε, it does indicate the sort of performance that can be expected using this approach.

7.3. Rejection of Non-feasible Points

Because of their basic simplicity and lack of assumptions about the function and constraints it is often thought sufficient to incorporate into the unconstrained searches very simple strategies for handling constraints. For example, at a point violating a constraint the function may just be set equal to some very large constant value, ensuring that all such points will be considered failures and consequently discarded. This procedure can be very effective as shown in Fig. 7.1 in which the basic search method is pattern search, and the pattern direction has been directed along the constraint allowing rapid progress to be made.

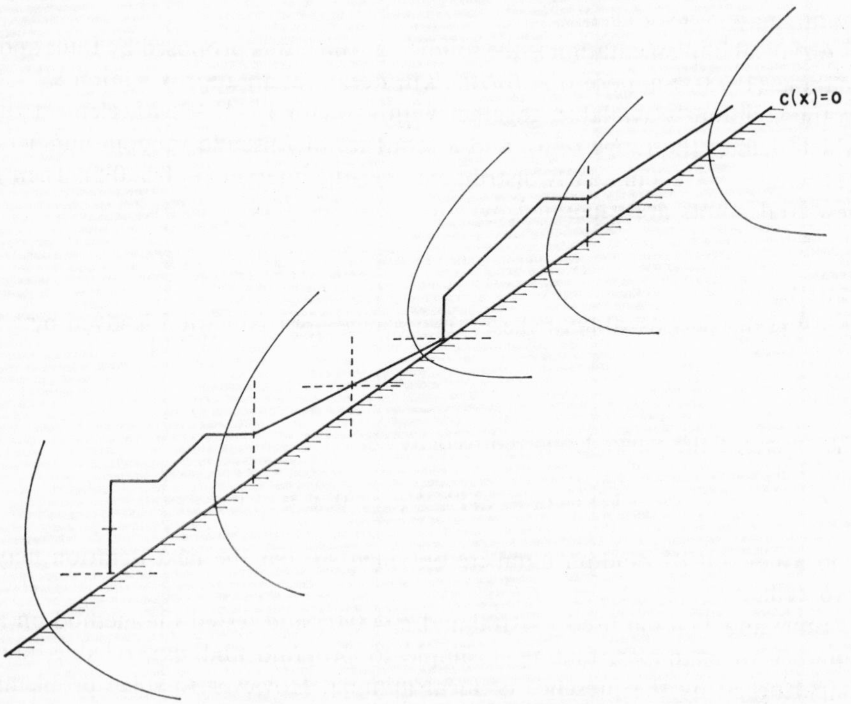

FIG. 7.1. Simple rejection with pattern search.

However a slight change in the problem, shown in Fig. 7.2, demonstrates the difficulties that can be encountered with this procedure. Thus before any progress can be made along the constraint from point A the steplengths must be considerably reduced, and it is very likely that the convergence criteria will be satisfied and the search terminated before the steps are small enough to enable further progress to be made.

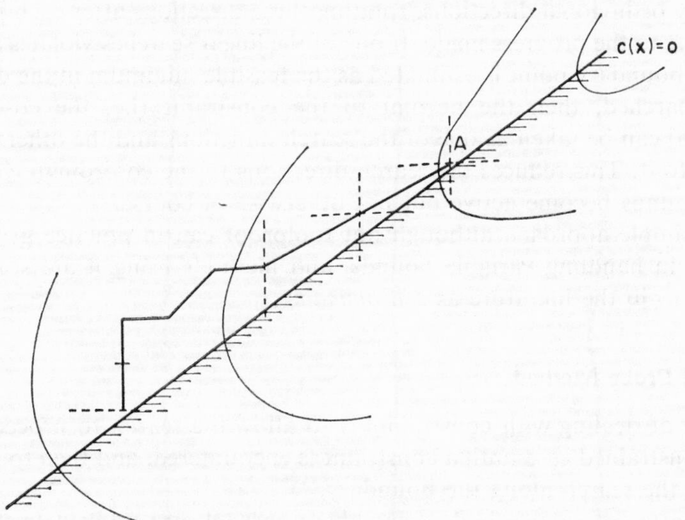

FIG. 7.2. Failure of simple rejection with pattern search.

Hence this approach generally proves to be of little use in practice, as is demonstrated by results quoted by Friedman and Pinder (1972), who combined it with pattern search, and by Lawrence and Emad (1972), who investigated three randomized procedures constrained in this manner.

7.4. Self-bounding Methods

However in the special case when the constraints are bounds on the variables, i.e.

$$c_i(\mathbf{x}) = \mathbf{a}_i^T\mathbf{x} - b_i \geqslant 0, \qquad 1 \leqslant j \leqslant n,$$

the simple rejection approach can prove effective when allied to a method whose strategy is based upon steps in the co-ordinate directions.

For example, pattern search consists of an exploration in each co-ordinate direction to establish a pattern direction, followed by a step along this pattern in the full parameter space. Bounds on the variables can be catered for by rejecting pattern steps which violate them, and resetting a variable onto its bound if the latter is violated by an exploration step. Thus progress can be made along the constraint, and since in each subsequent exploration a trial step will be made normal to the bound, the search can leave the constraint if it becomes inactive.

A similar modification can be incorporated into the DSC method which explores the parameter space by means of line searches along a set of n mutually orthogonal directions, rotating these directions after each iteration according to the progress made. If one of the linear searches violates a bound and the boundary point is estimated as the feasible minimum in the direction being searched, then the normal to the constraint (i.e. the co-ordinate direction) can be taken as one of the search directions and the others chosen normal to it. This reduces the search directions to the co-ordinate vectors if $n - 1$ bounds become active but not otherwise of course.

This simple approach although not foolproof can in practice prove very effective in handling variable bounds, and methods using it are sometimes referred to in the literature as *self-bounding*.

7.5. The Probe Method

One way of dealing with constraints is to allow the search to proceed as in the unconstrained case until a constraint is encountered, and then to attempt to guide the search along the boundary.

Early attempts at methods using this approach are typified by Singer's maze method (1962) and the probe method of Mugele (1962) which were in fact very similar in concept. In the probe search the basic procedure is a series of steps in the co-ordinate directions; successful probes are pursued until they no longer reduce the function, whereupon the search switches to a different co-ordinate. When a point is reached at which probes in all directions fail then either the solution has been approached or a ridge has been encountered. An attempt to restart is made by evaluating the function at the mid-point of the two best probes, fitting a parabola through the three points and using it to estimate the minimum in the defined direction. If this yields an improvement over the base point then the search restarts from this new estimate; otherwise the size of the steps used in the axial probes is reduced and the search restarted from the base point.

The process continues until constraint violations prevent a successful probe from being found. When this occurs trials are made at points halfway between the best feasible and best non-feasible probes, then between the worst feasible and worst non-feasible probes. When an improved feasible point is located the search restarts from it; if no such better point is found after four bisections then the search resorts to further probes from the base point using a reduced step.

Thus the search attempts to move along the active constraints. However although it is reported to have proved effective on a number of specific problems, in general the method is not very successful and is not much used.

7.6. Constraint Following in Pattern Search

The pattern search of Hooke and Jeeves is a simple direct-search method which has proved very useful in practice, and a number of proposals have been made for extending it to deal with constraints. One such procedure is the multiple gradient summation technique of Klingman and Himmelblau (1964). The basic search is the same as that used by Hooke and Jeeves except that once a pattern direction is established it is pursued for as long as the function continues to reduce, whereupon it is rejected and a new exploration made to define a new pattern. This variation is much less efficient than the original approach of continual refinement of the pattern since it limits the directions in which the pattern vector may lie.

Any move which violates a constraint is registered as a failure and is thus rejected. When an exploratory move fails to establish a pattern because of the proximity of constraints, then an adaptive move is made in which a direction pointing along the active constraints is set up and followed. The adaptive direction $\mathbf{p}$ is defined by

$$\hat{\mathbf{p}} = -\frac{\mathbf{g}}{\|\mathbf{g}\|} + \sum_{i \in J} \frac{\mathbf{a}_i}{\|\mathbf{a}_i\|},$$

$$\mathbf{p} = \frac{\hat{\mathbf{p}}}{\|\hat{\mathbf{p}}\|}$$

where $\mathbf{g}$ and $\mathbf{a}_i$ are evaluated at the base point. Thus the new direction is the vector sum of the normalized gradients of the function and the active constraints (Fig. 7.3).

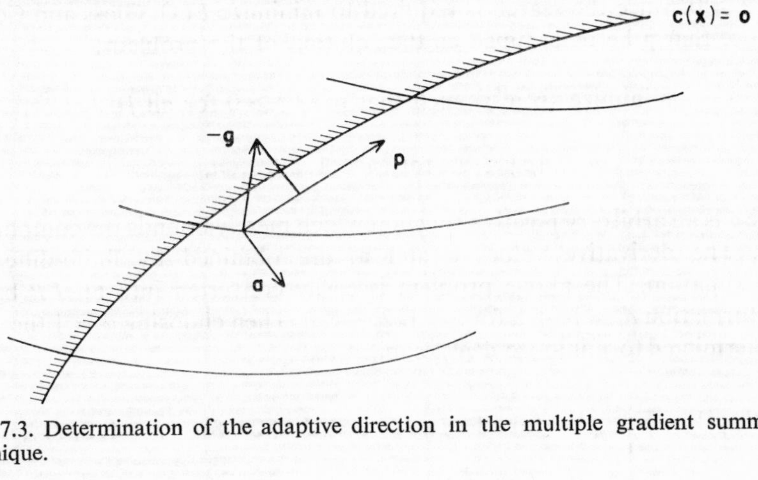

FIG. 7.3. Determination of the adaptive direction in the multiple gradient summation technique.

A single step along $\mathbf{p}$ is tried using as steplength the absolute value of the current fractional change last used in the exploratory move. If the step violates a new constraint the step is rejected and the new constraint incorporated into the adaptive direction. If the same constraint set is violated, or if the step is feasible but fails to reduce the function, the step size is reduced. However, if a successful step is made then an exploration is attempted and if this produces a pattern vector the search reverts to the normal procedure; if the exploration is thwarted by constraints then an accelerated step is taken along $\mathbf{p}$ and a new exploration performed.

Another attempt to incorporate constraints into a variation of pattern search was the sequential search procedure due to Glass and Cooper (1965). Again the unconstrained search is modified so that a pattern, once established, is followed until it not longer yields progress, but the problem of being limited to a fixed number of pattern directions is avoided by taking into account the actual values of the function when establishing the pattern. The latter is thus made to approximate to the gradient direction. Once again when constraints prevent the definition of a pattern an alternative direction $\mathbf{p}$ is defined.

Now linearizing the function about the current base point $\mathbf{x}^{(k)}$ gives

$$F^{(k+1)} = F^{(k)} + \mathbf{p}^T\mathbf{g}^{(k)},$$

where $\mathbf{x}^{(k+1)} = \mathbf{x}^{(k)} + \mathbf{p}$, and linearizing constraint c_j gives

$$c_j^{(k+1)} = c_j^{(k)} + \mathbf{p}^T\mathbf{a}_j^{(k)}.$$

If the new direction is to produce a feasible $\mathbf{x}^{(k+1)}$ then we must have $c_j^{(k+1)} \geqslant 0$, and one way of achieving this is to choose $\mathbf{p}$ such that $\mathbf{p}^T\mathbf{a}_j^{(k)} \geqslant 0$. Since the search is required to minimize $F(\mathbf{x})$, Glass and Cooper propose that $\mathbf{p}$ be determined as the solution of the problem:

$$\underset{\mathbf{p}}{\text{minimize}}\ \{\mathbf{p}^T\mathbf{g}^{(k)}\} \text{ such that } \mathbf{p}^T\mathbf{a}_j^{(k)} \geqslant 0 \text{ for all } j \in J,$$

$$|p_i| \leqslant \alpha \quad \text{for} \quad i = 1, 2, \ldots, n,$$

where α is an arbitrary positive constant which merely bounds the components of $\mathbf{p}$. The derivative values $\mathbf{g}$ and $\mathbf{a}_j$ are obtained by finite-difference approximation. The above problem is easily converted into an *LP* by the transformation $d_i = p_i + \alpha$ for $i = 1, 2, \ldots, n$. Then choosing $\alpha = 1$ the *LP* is to determine $\mathbf{d}$ to minimize $\mathbf{d}^T\mathbf{g}^{(k)}$ subject to

$$\mathbf{d}^T\mathbf{a}_j^{(k)} \geqslant \sum_{i=1}^{n} a_{ji}^{(k)} \quad \text{for all} \quad j \in J, \quad 0 \leqslant d_i \leqslant 2 \quad \text{for} \quad i = 1, 2, \ldots, n.$$

If $\mathbf{x}^{(k)}$ lies on the constraint boundary, and if the constraints are linear, then the solution to the *LP* will be a feasible direction lying in at least one of the constraints and such that the prescribed step gives the best change in the function. This direction is followed until no further progress can be made, whereupon a new exploration is performed to determine a new pattern.

In general of course the constraints will be nonlinear, so the direction $\mathbf{p}$ will lie in an approximation to at least one of the tangent hyperplanes, and if the constraint is locally convex $\mathbf{p}$ will therefore be non-feasible. Under these circumstances Glass and Cooper tighten the constraints used in the determination of $\mathbf{p}$ to be

$$\mathbf{p}^T \mathbf{a}_j^{(k)} \geqslant \beta, \qquad \beta > 0,$$

for those constraints for which the step is non-feasible. For a suitably large choice of β this will yield a feasible direction, so the *LP* is solved for an increasing sequence $\{\beta\}$ until a suitable direction is produced. The sequence $\{\beta\}$ is bounded below by 0 and above by the value which causes $\mathbf{p}$ to be normal to the constraint.

The above procedures are of course not the only solutions to the problem of determining a feasible direction when constraints impede the search. For example, since the constraint normals and the function gradient have been calculated, another possible approach would be to project the gradient into the intersection of the tangent hyperplanes in the manner of Rosen's gradient projection (1960, 1961).

The prime disadvantage of these methods however is the need to determine function and constraint derivative values, albeit at a limited number of points. As indicated in Section 7.1, when derivatives are available the gradient-based procedures are generally preferable to direct-search methods.

7.7. DSC with Linear Constraints

Earlier chapters have discussed how the special case of linear constraints can be tackled by projecting a search direction into the intersection of the active constraints. The DSC direct-search method has been extended to handle linear constraints using this concept, (Davies and Swann, 1969). The unconstrained procedure consists of searching along each of a set of n mutually orthogonal directions and rotating these directions after each iteration according to the progress being made. Whenever a constraint becomes active its normal is chosen as a search direction, and the remaining directions will thus lie in the constraint. The search then procedes in the intersection of active constraints but it retains the facility whereby it may leave any constraint which becomes inactive again. This of course is a generalization of the DSC extension outlined in Section 7.4 above, and it has proved very effective in practice.

If iteration k begins at $\mathbf{x}_0^{(k)}$ and searches successively along $\mathbf{p}_i^{(k)}$ to locate the minimum $\mathbf{x}_i^{(k)}$, $i = 1, 2, \ldots, n$, then a set of progress vectors $\mathbf{d}_1, \ldots, \mathbf{d}_n$ can be defined where $\mathbf{d}_i = \mathbf{x}_n^{(k)} - \mathbf{x}_{i-1}^{(k)}$. The search vectors for the next iteration are chosen to be

$$\mathbf{p}_1^{(k+1)} = \mathbf{d}_1,$$

$$\mathbf{p}_i^{(k+1)} = \mathbf{d}_i - \mathbf{N}_{i-1}\,\boldsymbol{\alpha}_i, \qquad i = 2, 3, \ldots, n,$$

where $\mathbf{N}_{i-1}$ is the $n \times (i-1)$ matrix whose columns are the directions vectors already chosen, i.e.

$$\mathbf{N}_{i-1} = (\mathbf{p}_1^{(k+1)}, \mathbf{p}_2^{(k+1)}, \ldots, \mathbf{p}_{i-1}^{(k+1)}),$$

and $\boldsymbol{\alpha}_i$ is chosen so that $\mathbf{p}_i^{(k+1)}$ is orthogonal to these selected directions. Any directions along which no progress was made during iteration k are simply retained for iteration $k+1$.

The choice of $\boldsymbol{\alpha}_i$ which ensures orthogonality is

$$\boldsymbol{\alpha}_i = (\mathbf{N}_{i-1}^T \mathbf{N}_{i-1})^{-1} \mathbf{N}_{i-1}^T \mathbf{d}_i$$

so that

$$\mathbf{p}_i^{(k+1)} = [\mathbf{I} - \mathbf{N}_{i-1} (\mathbf{N}_{i-1}^T \mathbf{N}_{i-1})^{-1} \mathbf{N}_{i-1}^T]\,\mathbf{d}_i = \mathbf{P}_{i-1}\,\mathbf{d}_i. \tag{7.7.1}$$

Thus $\mathbf{P}_{i-1}$ is a projection operator which projects $\mathbf{d}_i$ into the subspace orthogonal to the directions already chosen.

If m linear equality constraints given by

$$\hat{\mathbf{A}}^T\mathbf{x} - \hat{\mathbf{b}} = \mathbf{0}, \qquad m < n, \tag{7.7.2}$$

must be satisfied, then the problem is effectively only of dimension $n - m$ and only that number of search directions are required. Therefore the constraint normals $\mathbf{a}_i$, $i = 1, 2, \ldots m$, are chosen as the vectors $\mathbf{p}_1^{(k+1)}, \mathbf{p}_2^{(k+1)} \ldots,$ $\mathbf{p}_m^{(k+1)}$ so that

$$\mathbf{N}_m = (\mathbf{a}_1, \mathbf{a}_2, \ldots, \mathbf{a}_m)$$

and the remaining vectors can be found using (7.7.1). If the search is then conducted using as search directions only the vector subset $\mathbf{p}_{m+1}^{(k+1)}$, $\mathbf{p}_{m+2}^{(k+1)}, \ldots, \mathbf{p}_n^{(k+1)}$ and if $\mathbf{x}_0^{(k+1)}$ satisfies the constraints (7.7.2), then only points lying in the intersection of the space spanned by the columns of $\hat{\mathbf{A}}$ will be generated i.e., the constraints will remain satisfied throughout the iteration.

The extension to cover inequality constraints is the natural one of treating any such constraint which becomes active during an iteration as an equality in the manner described above. An important difference, however, is that the normals to active inequality constraints are included in the search direction set. Thus the search can proceed along the constraint boundary, but since line searches will also be made along the constraint normals the search can leave a constraint if it becomes inactive and return to the interior of the feasible region, and the normal will be replaced in the direction vector set at the end of the iteration. The search directions are in general no longer orthogonal of course, but if the constraints are linearly independent then so will the search directions be and they will continue to span the full parameter space.

It is important from a practical point of view to note that the matrix inversion in the calculation of $\mathbf{P}_{i-1}$ can be avoided. Thus if no constraints are active $(\mathbf{N}_{i-1}^T \mathbf{N}_{i-1}) = \mathbf{I}$ and (7.7.1) reduces to the Gram–Schmidt orthogonalization scheme. If j constraints are active then $(\mathbf{N}_{i-1}^T \mathbf{N}_{i-1})$ is of the form $\begin{bmatrix} \mathbf{P} & \mathbf{Q} \\ \mathbf{R} & \mathbf{S} \end{bmatrix}$ where $\mathbf{P}$ is the $j \times j$ matrix $(\mathbf{N}_j{}^T \mathbf{N}_j)$, $\mathbf{Q}$ and $\mathbf{R}$ are null matrices and $\mathbf{S}$ is the $(i - 1 - j) \times (i - 1 - j)$ unit matrix, assuming the directions are normalized. Thus to calculate $\mathbf{p}_i$ from (7.7.1) for $i = j + 1, j + 2, \ldots, n$, the only inverse required is $(\mathbf{N}_j{}^T \mathbf{N}_j)^{-1}$ and this can be found using recurrence relationships given by Rosen. These relationships can also be used to obtain $(\mathbf{N}_{j-1}^T \mathbf{N}_{j-1})^{-1}$ or $(\mathbf{N}_{j+1}^T \mathbf{N}_{j+1})^{-1}$ from $(\mathbf{N}_j{}^T \mathbf{N}_j)^{-1}$ which simplifies the calculation when constraints are added to or removed from the list of active constraints.

7.8. Transformation Methods: Penalty Functions

Probably the most popular way of dealing with constraints in direct-search methods is by means of the transformation methods which have been discussed by Ryan in Chapter VI. Exterior penalty functions have been widely used, from the simple type suggested by Spang (1962) for use with pattern search:

$$P(\mathbf{x}) = F(\mathbf{x}) + 10^{20} \left(\sum_j |c_j| \right),$$

to the type used by Gottfried, Bruggink and Harwood (1970), also with pattern search, which transforms the constrained problem into a sequence of unconstrained ones:

$$P^{(k)}(\mathbf{x}, r_k) = F(\mathbf{x}) + r_k \sum_j v_j c_j{}^2, \qquad v_j > 0, \tag{7.8.1}$$

for $k = 1, 2, \ldots$, and $0 < r_1 < r_2 < \ldots < r_k$. In both cases the summation is taken over violated constraints only. The penalty function, or in the latter case the sequence of functions, is minimized without any further account being taken of the constraints. Full details of the properties of penalty functions are given in Chapter VI.

7.9. Simpat

Keefer (1973) has proposed a method in which the basic search is performed using the Nelder and Mead simplex technique and general constraints are dealt with using a penalty function. Constraints which are simple variable bounds are handled using a self-bounding version of pattern search. Thus the method utilizes the efficient hill-climbing property of the simplex method with the self-bounding property of pattern search and the general constraint handling ability of penalty functions.

The basis of the procedure is to partition the problem variables into two sets:

$$\mathbf{x} = \begin{bmatrix} \mathbf{x}_1 \\ \mathbf{x}_2 \end{bmatrix}$$

where $\mathbf{x}_1$ are the variables used in the simplex search (the simplex set), and $\mathbf{x}_2$ are those used in the pattern search (the pattern set). The pattern set is comprized of those variables within a tolerance ε of their upper or lower limit, where ε is an order of magnitude larger than the smallest exploratory step used in the pattern search.

The search begins with at most $2n$ simplex iterations, an iteration being defined as a reflection of the worst vertex followed, if appropriate, by an expansion or contraction. Less than $2n$ iterations will be performed if the simplex search converges or if a new pattern variable is encountered. This latter is deemed to have occurred if a reflection violates a bound or if a successful reflection enters a feasible ε-neighbourhood of a bound, whereupon the relevant variable is transferred from the simplex set into the pattern set. Note that expansion moves which transgress bounds or enter any boundary zones are merely registered as failures. If the simplex search has converged and the pattern set is empty then the search ends; otherwise the procedure enters its pattern phase in which an initial exploration is made to determine a first pattern direction, and then at most two further pattern plus exploratory moves are attempted. The pattern phase may terminate earlier if the exploration perturbations become too small. If the pattern search has converged and either the simplex set is empty or the preceding simplex search converged then the procedure is terminated. Otherwise any variables which have left their boundary zones during the pattern search are transferred from the pattern set into the simplex set. The procedure then restarts with another simplex search. Any constraints of a general form are dealt with, in both the simplex and pattern phases, using a penalty function as given by (7.8.1).

The simplex is held in matrix form with columns corresponding to vertices of the design and rows corresponding to the appropriate variables. Whenever a variable is transferred from the simplex set into the pattern set the column representing the vertex causing the transfer is deleted, together with the row containing the transferred variable. Whenever the opposite transfer is made a new row is added in which each element is equal to the value of the transferred variable, and then a new column is added identical to the one representing the best vertex but having the newly transferred variable changed by its current exploratory step in the pattern search. This ensures that the new simplex spans the additional dimension and that the magnitude and direction of the perturbation are appropriate.

7.10. Transformation Methods: Barrier Functions

As indicated above there have been many papers published proposing the combination of direct-search methods with exterior penalty functions and their authors all claim some degree of success using them. However in many practical problems which are suitable for direct-search solution the function values in the non-feasible region, if they can be found at all, are meaningless. Hence using exterior penalty functions can seriously mislead the search which as a result may fail to converge, may converge to an incorrect solution, or may converge only very slowly to the required solution. Thus the present author has a strong preference for interior penalty or barrier functions in which the function is modified within the feasible region and all non-feasible points are rejected as failures.

Of the many barrier functions that have been proposed, two which have proved particularly useful in the context of direct-search methods are those devised by Rosenbrock and Carroll.

(a) *Rosenbrock's Barrier Function.*

One of the earliest barrier functions was that developed by Rosenbrock (1960) for use with the direct-search procedure which he also developed. The latter consists of explorations along a set of orthogonal directions which are rotated periodically according to the results of the explorations. Rosenbrock investigated a number of constraint-handling strategies based on the use of barrier functions within narrow boundary regions of the constraints. Thus the function was altered only in a neighbourhood of the constraints.

The *boundary zone* associated with the constraint $c_i(\mathbf{x}) \geqslant 0$ is defined to consist of those values of $\mathbf{x}$ for which

$$0 \leqslant c_i(\mathbf{x}) \leqslant \hat{c}_i$$

for some small positive constant $\hat{c}_i$, and a constraint is considered to be active if the current point of the search lies within its boundary zone.

Rosenbrock found a useful strategy to be to use a quadratic barrier for each active constraint as follows:

$$B(\mathbf{x}) = F_B + [F(\mathbf{x}) - F_B] \prod_{i \in J} [1 - \gamma_i^2]$$

where F_B is the best value obtained for $F(\mathbf{x})$ before the boundary zone was entered, and γ_i is the fractional penetration of the boundary zone associated with the constraint $c_i(\mathbf{x}) \geqslant 0$, given by

$$\gamma_i = \frac{\hat{c}_i - c_i(\mathbf{x})}{\hat{c}_i}, \qquad 0 \leqslant c_i(\mathbf{x}) \leqslant \hat{c}_i,$$

$$\gamma_i = 0, \qquad c_i(\mathbf{x}) > \hat{c}_i.$$

However, the effect of this particular barrier is to create a ridge parallel to the constraint, and when used in conjunction with his search routine Rosenbrock found that it often caused the current point to enter the boundary zone at an early stage and remain therein, resulting in slow progress. He argued that a preferable alternative would be a barrier which created a ridge which instead of being parallel to the constraint was at an angle to it running back towards the interior of the feasible region. Thus after a while the search will align one of its directions with the ridge and the current point, after climbing a certain distance along the ridge, will leave the boundary region. Then either progress can be made within the interior, or the search can re-enter the boundary zone but with an improved value for F_B. The particular function which Rosenbrock devised to achieve this was

$$B(\mathbf{x}) = F_B + [F(\mathbf{x}) - F_B][1 - 3\gamma_i + 4\gamma_i^2 + 2\gamma_i^3],$$

a similar barrier being applied for each active constraint.

As Dixon (1972) has pointed out this function can cause difficulties if the true minimum lies within the boundary zone though not on the constraint itself. Under these circumstances the barrier term changes sign (Fig. 7.4) and Dixon recommends that the barrier functions should be added only as long as $F(\mathbf{x}) < F_B$ to prevent the search leaving the feasible region. In fact following Rosenbrock's proposals all non-feasible points are classed as failures so the problem does not arise. However what can happen is that the search may converge on the pseudo-minimum which has been created at the constraint boundary, and Dixon's suggestion is useful in overcoming this.

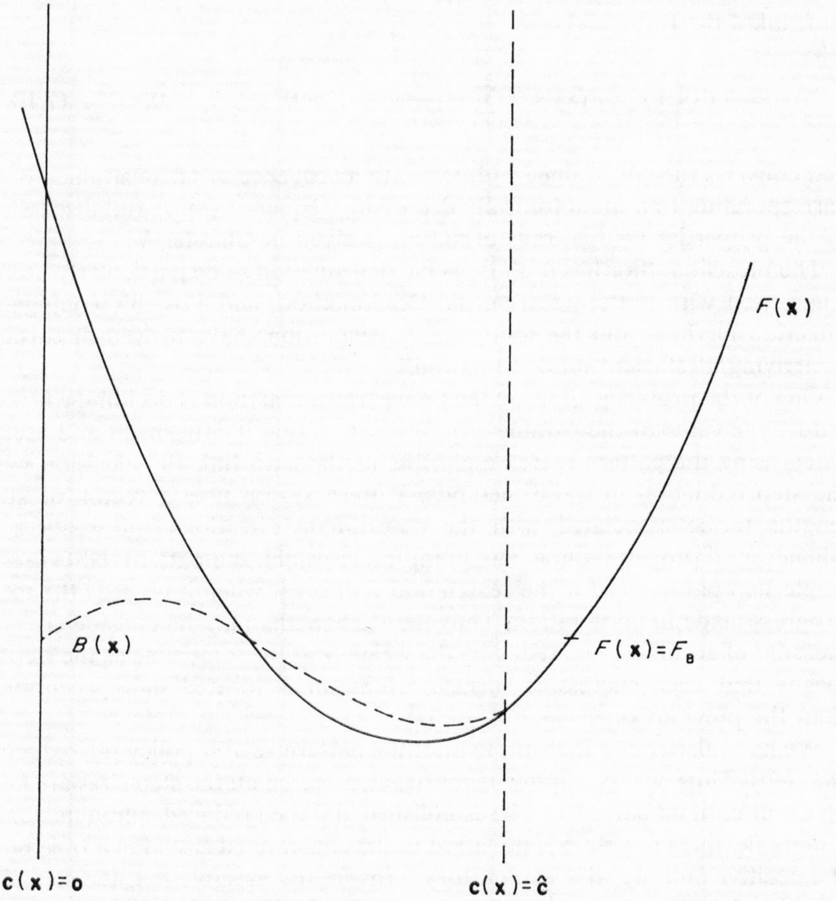

FIG. 7.4. Rosenbrock's barrier function when $F(\mathbf{x})$ has a minimum in the boundary zone.

The constrained direct-search method of Rosenbrock has been in widespread use for some years, and although sometimes rather slow it has been found to be very reliable. Note however that the barrier function was developed specifically for use with Rosenbrock's unconstrained search, and it has been found to be much less successful when used in conjunction with other direct-search procedures.

(b) *The Inverse Barrier Function*

A more generally successful barrier function is the inverse barrier, introduced by Carroll (1961) and developed principally by Fiacco and McCormick (1968). This function, which is only defined for points such that $c_i(\mathbf{x}) > 0$, for all i, takes the form

$$B(\mathbf{x}, r) = F(\mathbf{x}) + r \sum_{i=1}^{m} \frac{w_i}{c_i(\mathbf{x})}, \qquad r > 0, \qquad w_i > 0, \tag{7.10.1}$$

and converts the constrained problem into a sequence of unconstrained ones corresponding to a monotonically decreasing sequence $\{r\}$. A full discussion of the properties of this transformation is given in Chapter VI.

The present author has found this barrier function to be particularly useful when used with pattern search, the DSC method, and Powell's conjugate-direction method, and the following considerations have proved important in arriving at efficient implementations.

One of the problems of using the above transformation is deciding when to reduce the value of the parameter r. We have found it convenient and useful when using the pattern search and DSC methods to link this decision with the step reduction in those methods. Pattern search uses a vector of step lengths to be associated with the co-ordinate directions and reduces it whenever all probes about a base point fail to establish a pattern. DSC uses a single-step parameter for the search and reduces it when it exceeds the total progress made in an iteration. Thus the steplengths may be considered as a measure of accuracy, and reducing the weight r at the same time as the step(s) means that each successive surface minimum is located more accurately than the previous one.

We have also found it useful to alter the pattern search policy for reducing the steps. Thus whereas in the unconstrained search all the step sizes are held constant until no pattern can be established and then reduced simultaneously, a more flexible procedure is preferred in the constrained case. Each time both the positive and negative exploratory steps in any variable fail, the step size associated with that variable is reduced. The weight r is reduced when all step sizes have been reduced at least once, and the step sizes are reset to some proportion of the initial values on the surface just minimized.

Another problem of implementation is dealing with non-feasible points since $B(\mathbf{x}, r)$ is not defined at such points, With pattern search we prefer to count as failures any exploratory steps which violate constraints, but with violating pattern moves we follow the unconstrained philosophy of Hooke and Jeeves and perform an exploration about the pattern point in the hope that this may yield a feasible point which reduces the function. If such a point is not found, then the pattern is rejected. With the linear search methods, DSC and

Powell, whenever a constraint is violated the last step taken should be progressively reduced until a feasible point is obtained. If possible a single quadratic interpolation should then be performed and the normal rules of the method obeyed; if such action is not possible then the best feasible point is chosen as the minimum in the direction being searched.

When using Powell's method in conjunction with the barrier function (7.10.1) we have found it necessary to modify the basic procedure. The basis of the method is to explore the parameter space using a set of n independent directions. The results of the explorations are used to alter the search vectors in an attempt to produce directions such that, if the function is quadratic, they form a conjugate set and can be used to locate the optimum. The modification for constrained problems concerns the procedure for choosing the search vectors.

Powell shows that if the function being minimized is the quadratic

$$F(\mathbf{x}) = \tfrac{1}{2}\mathbf{x}^T \mathbf{G}\mathbf{x} + \mathbf{b}^T\mathbf{x} + b_0,$$

and if the search directions $\mathbf{p}_1, \mathbf{p}_2, \ldots, \mathbf{p}_n$ are scaled so that $\tfrac{1}{2}\mathbf{p}_i{}^T\mathbf{G}\mathbf{p}_i = 1$, $i = 1, 2, \ldots, n$, then the determinant Δ of the matrix whose columns are the vectors $\mathbf{p}_1, \mathbf{p}_2, \ldots, \mathbf{p}_n$ takes its maximum value when the directions are mutually conjugate, i.e., $\mathbf{p}_i{}^T\mathbf{G}\mathbf{p}_j = 0$, $i \neq j$. So in an iteration Powell searches along each of the n directions in turn, starting from $\mathbf{x}^{(i-1)}$ to find the minimum $\mathbf{x}^{(i)}$ along direction $\mathbf{p}_i$, and defines as a potential new search direction the vector $\mathbf{p}$ of total progress in the iteration. The new vector is accepted as a replacement for one of the current directions only if doing so causes Δ to increase.

Because of the scaling of the direction vectors, the displacement made by the search along $\mathbf{p}_i$, is given by

$$\mathbf{x}^{(i-1)} - \mathbf{x}^{(i)} = \alpha_i \mathbf{p}_i$$

where

$$\alpha_i = \sqrt{2[F^{(i-1)} - F^{(i)}]}.$$

So if the total progress in the iteration is given by

$$\mathbf{x}^{(n)} - \mathbf{x}^{(0)} = \mu\mathbf{p}$$

then it can be shown that α_i/μ is a measure of the change in the determinant Δ achieved by replacing $\mathbf{p}_i$ by $\mathbf{p}$. The change is an increase in Δ if $\alpha_i > \mu$, and the greatest increase is achieved by replacing $\mathbf{p}_j$ by $\mathbf{p}$ where $\alpha_j = \max_{i=1,\ldots,n} \{\alpha_i\}$. The value of α_j is easily calculated during the iteration, so it is only necessary to estimate μ to decide whether the new direction should be accepted.

To estimate μ Powell suggests evaluating the function at $\mathbf{x}^{(n+1)} = 2\mathbf{x}^{(n)} - \mathbf{x}^{(0)}$ and fitting a quadratic through $\mathbf{x}^{(0)}, \mathbf{x}^{(n)}, \mathbf{x}^{(n+1)}$ to estimate the value of the function F_m at the stationary point along $\mathbf{p}$. This stationary point is a minimum if

$$F^{(0)} - 2F^{(n)} + F^{(n+1)} > 0. \tag{7.10.2}$$

Powell recommends that if the stationary point is not a minimum then a new direction must be defined. Otherwise, μ is given by

$$\mu = \sqrt{2[F^{(0)} - F_m]} + \sqrt{2[F^{(n)} - F_m]} \quad \text{if} \quad F^{(n+1)} \geqslant F^{(0)} \tag{7.10.3}$$

and by

$$\mu = \sqrt{2[F^{(0)} - F_m]} - \sqrt{2[F^{(n)} - F_m]} \quad \text{if} \quad F^{(n+1)} \leqslant F^{(0)}. \tag{7.10.4}$$

Clearly if (7.10.3) obtains then $\mu > \alpha_j$, so Powell concludes that the old directions should be retained if

$$F^{(n+1)} \geqslant F^{(0)} \tag{7.10.5}$$

and/or

$$\sqrt{F^{(0)} - F_m} - \sqrt{F^{(n)} - F_m} > \sqrt{F^{(j-1)} - F^{(j)}}. \tag{7.10.6}$$

However on applying this method to constrained problems and using the inverse barrier function, the point $\mathbf{x}^{(n+1)}$ was found very frequently to be non-feasible, and of course $B(\mathbf{x}, r)$ is not defined for any $c_i(\mathbf{x}) \leqslant 0$. We can overcome this difficulty by defining $\mathbf{x}^{(n+1)} = \frac{1}{2}[\mathbf{x}^{(n)} + \mathbf{x}^{(0)}]$ which is feasible for convex constraints, and in this case the test given by inequality (7.10.2) must be replaced by

$$F^{(0)} - 2F^{(n+1)} + F^{(n)} > 0, \tag{7.10.7}$$

and that given by inequality (7.10.5) replaced by

$$F^{(0)} - F^{(n+1)} \geqslant 3[F^{(n+1)} - F^{(n)}].$$

Kowalik (1966) has published a method based on this variation of Powell's algorithm, and he prefers to retain the old directions when inequality (7.10.7) is not satisfied.

7.11. The Complex Method of Box

One of the more successful of the unconstrained direct-search procedures is the simplex method originally proposed by Spendley, Hext and

Himsworth. The method derives its name from its use of a regular simplex to explore the parameter space, a regular simplex in n dimensions being $n + 1$ mutually equidistant points. The basic method is just to replace the worst vertex in the simplex, i.e., the one having the highest value of $F(\mathbf{x})$, by its reflection in the centroid of the others, thereby producing a new simplex so that the procedure can be repeated. Nelder and Mead improved the performance of the method by allowing the simplex to rescale itself according to the local geometry of the function by incorporating expansion and contraction moves. Parkinson and Hutchinson (1972) have proposed further modifications including unlimited expansion followed by translation of the simplex to avoid undue distortion.

To deal with constraints both Spendley, Hext and Himsworth and Nelder and Mead suggested allocating a large positive function value to non-feasible points, leaving the simplex search to take account of the constraints automatically. In practice, Box (1965) found that this approach often led to the simplex flattening itself against a constraint and remaining thereafter in the corresponding subspace. He therefore developed a new constrained simplex method using $q \geqslant n + 1$ vertices and termed his figure a *complex*. The extra vertices were introduced to prevent the simplex losing dimensions when confronted with constraints.

To construct the initial complex, a feasible point $\mathbf{x}^{(0)}$ is required together with a range on each variable, i.e. constraints of the form

$$c_i(\mathbf{x}) = x_i - l_i \geqslant 0, \qquad i = l, 2, \ldots, n,$$

$$c_{i+n}(\mathbf{x}) = -x_i + u_i \geqslant 0, \qquad i = 1, 2, \ldots, n,$$

must be given. (The method of course is capable of handling additional more general constraints $c_i(\mathbf{x}) \geqslant 0, i = 2n + 1, 2n + 2, \ldots, m$). The remaining $q - 1$ vertices are obtained one at a time by

$$x_i^{(j)} = l_i + r_i(u_i - l_i) \qquad i = 1, 2, \ldots, n; \quad j = 1, 2, \ldots, q - 1, \qquad (7.11.1)$$

where r_i is a pseudo-random deviate rectangularly distributed over the interval (0, 1). All points generated by (7.11.1) are feasible with respect to the variable bounds, but may violate one or more of the other constraints. Any prospective vertex which is non-feasible is moved successively halfway back towards the centroid of the points already chosen, including $\mathbf{x}^{(0)}$, until feasible, which must be achieved ultimately if the constraints are convex.

As in the unconstrained simplex procedures, the worst vertex is replaced in each iteration, and again the basic move is a reflection in the centroid of the other vertices. Thus if the vertices are ordered so that

$$F^{(0)} < F^{(1)} < \ldots < F^{(q-1)} \qquad (7.11.2)$$

then $\mathbf{x}^{(q-1)}$ is replaced by $\mathbf{x}^{(r)}$ where

$$\mathbf{x}^{(r)} = (\alpha + 1)\,\bar{\mathbf{x}} - \alpha \mathbf{x}^{(q-1)},$$

$\alpha > 0$ is the reflection coefficient, and the centroid $\bar{\mathbf{x}}$ is defined to be

$$\bar{\mathbf{x}} = \frac{1}{q-1} \sum_{j=0}^{q-2} \mathbf{x}^{(j)}.$$

If $F^{(r)} > F^{(q-2)}$ then $\mathbf{x}^{(r)}$ is still worse than any other vertex, so it is moved halfway back towards the centroid. If $\mathbf{x}^{(r)}$ violates a bound on a variable, then that variable is merely reset just inside its bound; if one of the other constraints is transgressed, then successive moves halfway back towards the centroid are made until a feasible vertex is produced.

Convergence is assumed when five successive evaluations of the function yield the same result, this being taken to indicate that the complex has collapsed onto the centroid.

Box investigated the sensitivity of the method's performance to the values of the reflection coefficient α and the number of vertices q and found that the choice of neither factor was critical. However he recommended $\alpha = 1{\cdot}3$, a value exceeding unity tending to enlarge the complex and compensate for retractions towards the centroid and allowing fast progress in the early stages when remote from the solution, while for q he suggested the value $2n$, although this may be too large for $n \geqslant 5$.

The method of setting up the initial complex avoids the difficulty of constructing a figure which satisfies all the constraints and is of reasonable size. Furthermore the complex is roughly scaled to the orders of the variables, reducing the need for any scaling by the user.

The complex method therefore belies its name in that it is a simple, uncomplicated procedure, but it has been used quite extensively and successfully to solve a wide range of optimization problems.

7.12. Variations of the Complex Method

Because of its simplicity most users of the complex method modify the basic procedure to suit their particular problems, e.g. Guin (1968), Friedman and Pinder (1972), Adelman and Stevens (1972). However of the published variations the most interesting are those due to Mitchell and Kaplan (1968), Umeda and Ichikawa (1971) and Ghani (1972).

Mitchell and Kaplan were concerned that due to the random nature of the initialization process, the first complex takes no account of the given starting approximation. Thus little advantage accrues from providing a good initial estimate, and they rightly suggest this to be a deficiency of the method. They propose overcoming this by defining $q = 2n + 1$ and choosing the vertices to be the given estimate $\mathbf{x}^{(0)}$ plus, for $j = 1, 2, \ldots, n$,

$$\left.\begin{aligned} x_i^{(j)} &= x_i^{(0)} \\ x_j^{(j)} &= u_j \end{aligned}\right\}, \qquad i = 1, 2, \ldots n; i \neq j,$$

and

$$\left.\begin{aligned} x_i^{(n+j)} &= x_i^{(0)} \\ x_j^{(n+j)} &= l_j \end{aligned}\right\}, \qquad i = 1, 2, \ldots n, i \neq j.$$

Any vertex which violates a constraint is once again retracted successively halfway towards the centroid until it becomes feasible.

Umeda and Ichikawa attempted to improve the convergence rate displayed by the method by taking into account the actual function values at the vertices of the complex. If the vertex ordering defined by (7.11.2) holds, and if

$$\Delta F_j = \frac{F^{(q-1)} - F^{(j)}}{F^{(q-1)} - F^{(0)}} \quad \text{for} \quad j = 1, 2, \ldots, q-1,$$

then the centroid is now defined to be

$$\bar{\mathbf{x}} = \frac{\sum_{j=1}^{q-1} (\Delta F_j)^{\beta}\, \mathbf{x}^{(j)}}{\sum_{j=1}^{q-1} (\Delta F)^{\beta}}, \qquad \beta > 0.$$

Thus the centroid is weighted by the function values at the vertices.

The search is performed as before until

$$\left|\frac{F^{(q-1)} - F^{(0)}}{F^{(q-1)}}\right| \leqslant 0{\cdot}05.$$

This is taken to indicate that the neighbourhood of the minimum has been reached, and to refine the estimate for the solution the exponent β is set equal to 0 so that the search reverts to the Box procedure.

As a result of experimentation Umeda and Ichikawa decided that the best value for the exponent β was 1.

Ghani has incorporated a Nelder and Mead philosophy into the complex method by introducing expansion and contraction moves. Thus the basis of the procedure is to follow Box and reflect the worst vertex in the centroid of the others and to take the appropriate action if a constraint is violated. If the resulting feasible reflection is the best vertex of the new complex, i.e. $F^{(r)} < F^{(0)}$, and if no constraints were encountered in making the reflection, then an expansion step is attempted and the better of the reflection and expansion points taken as the new vertex; such an expansion is not attempted if the first reflection caused constraint violations. If the resulting feasible reflection is still the worst vertex, then the vertices are examined to determine whether or not the new point has collapsed onto the centroid; if it has then a new reflection point is generated at random, but otherwise a contraction move is attempted and accepted if the resultant point is not now the worst vertex. If the contraction move fails, then the whole complex is retracted towards the best vertex.

Although the variations outlined above seemed the most interesting and promising of those in the literature, it is the present author's experience that they introduce complications into what is basically a very simple procedure without significantly improving the efficiency of the search. The results quoted by Umeda and Ichikawa do not indicate that weighting the vertices in the manner described produces any real improvement, and this is borne out in practice, a fact which has been confirmed by Keefer (1973). The results quoted by Ghani look impressive, but the basis of his result comparison is not clear, and this author's implementation of his proposals led to no general increase in efficiency when tested on a number of practical examples. Experience with the non-random initialization procedure proposed by Mitchell and Kaplan suggests that it is very helpful when a good initial approximation to the solution is available, and should be used under these circumstances, but that otherwise progress can be seriously hampered in the early stages and the Box initialization is to be preferred.

A modification to the method which has proved very useful in practice concerns the procedure for returning to the feasible region when a reflection produces a constraint violation. The bisection step used by Box can frequently require many applications before feasibility is achieved and this can prove very expensive if each constraint calculation is lengthy, or if the function is evaluated at each step because it is inconvenient to separate the function and constraint calculations. Furthermore it is a fruitless task if the centroid itself is non-feasible as it may be if the constraints are non-convex. The following procedure overcomes the latter objection and generally proves much more effective than the bisection process.

The centroid is first tested for feasibility. If it is feasible then the new vertex is sought between it and the violating point; otherwise it is sought between the worst (i.e. reflected) vertex and the centroid. In either event the constraint values at the centroid and the reflection are used to derive a linear approximation to the constraints based on which the first bisection step (in the appropriate search interval) which would be feasible can be determined. This point is tested for feasibility and if it passes it is accepted as the new vertex. Otherwise three points are now available enabling a quadratic approximation to the constraints to be made, and again based on this the first feasible bisection step can be determined and tested. If this too proves non-feasible then the procedure reverts to the bisection process.

It is preferable to use this procedure for all constraints, although in the case of variable bounds it is not necessary to calculate the constraints at the centroid since the required bisection step can be calculated directly. Furthermore, if the constraints are known to be convex then the centroid is known to be feasible and evaluation of the constraints there can be replaced by a single bisection step and the result of this used in the linear approximation.

It may be tempting to use the linear and/or quadratic constraint approximations to try to obtain a point lying on or just within the constraint boundary. This would be a dangerous policy to adopt since it can very quickly lead to the collapse of the complex into a subspace. Basing the calculation on bisection steps tends to help prevent this from happening.

Thus the complex method and its variants are basically simple, easy to program and use, and have been widely employed over a period of years on a variety of problems with considerable success.

7.13. ACSIM

An alternative means of using simplex designs in constrained optimization has been proposed by Dixon (1973) in the form of ACSIM—accelerated constrained simplex technique. Away from the boundary the method proceeds using a simplex hill-climber interspersed with occasional full quadratic approximations to the function aimed at accelerating the search near the solution. When linear constraints are encountered the search is projected into them, with provision made for leaving them again if required; when non-linear constraints are met the search attempts to hemstitch along them.

The basic search is by means of a simplex method in which the vector through the worst vertex and the centroid of the remainder is used as a search direction, and as usual the first trial in that direction is a reflection of the worst vertex in the centroid. If a linear approximation to the function in this direction, obtained using the worst vertex and its reflection, suggests that a doubled reflection step would produce a new best vertex then such a step is taken. If this expansion trial yields an improvement over the reflection, then the three points now available are used to obtain a quadratic approximation to the function and thence to estimate the location of the minimum along the search direction; the better of this estimate and the expansion point is selected as the new vertex. If the expansion fails to produce a better point then the reflection is chosen as the replacement vertex.

However, if the reflection point is again worse than the other vertices then a contraction step is attempted and if this results in a point not now the worst then it becomes the new vertex. If the contraction step still gives the worst vertex, or if $n + 1$ successive simplex iterations fail to improve on the best vertex, then the simplex search is abandoned and a full quadratic approximation attempted on the assumption that the neighbourhood of the solution has been approached.

If the reflection point satisfies neither of these conditions then it is accepted as the new vertex.

This defines a simplex iteration.

In their description of the original simplex method, Spendley, Hext and Himsworth suggested how quadratic approximations might be incorporated into their search, and Dixon's quadratic approximation stage is based on these suggestions. Thus a simplex defines a set of oblique co-ordinate axes in terms of which the vertices may be written $(0, 0, \ldots, 0)$, $(1, 0, \ldots, 0)$, $(0, 1, \ldots, 0)$, $\ldots$, $(0, 0, \ldots, 1)$, and it is convenient to choose the best vertex as origin. Suppose the vertices are $\mathbf{v}^{(i)}$ with function values $F^{(i)}$, $i = 0, 1, \ldots, n$. Then to fit a quadratic to the function $\frac{1}{2}(n + 1)(n + 2)$ function values are required; $n + 1$ are available at the vertices and the remaining $\frac{1}{2}n(n + 1)$ can be conveniently obtained at the mid-points of the sides of the simplex. Let the mid-point of the side joining $\mathbf{v}^{(i)}$ to $\mathbf{v}^{(j)}$ be $\mathbf{v}^{(ij)}$ with function value $F^{(ij)}$, $i \neq j$. If in the newly defined co-ordinate system the function is approximated by

$$F = \tfrac{1}{2}\mathbf{z}^T\mathbf{G}\mathbf{z} + \mathbf{b}^T\mathbf{z} + b_0,$$

then

$$\begin{aligned} b_0 &= F^{(0)}, \\ b_i &= 4F^{(0i)} - F^{(ii)} - 3F^{(0)}, \qquad i = 1, 2. \ldots, n, \\ G_{ii} &= 4[F^{(0)} - 2F^{(0i)} + F^{(i)}], \qquad i = 1, 2, \ldots, n, \end{aligned}$$

and

$$G_{ij} = 4[F^{(0)} - F^{(0i)} - F^{(0j)} + F^{(ij)}], \qquad i = 1, 2, \ldots, n; \quad j = 1, 2, \ldots, n, \quad i \neq j.$$

The minimum value of the function is then

$$F_{\min} = b_0 - \mathbf{b}^T\mathbf{G}^{-1}\mathbf{b}$$

and it occurs at

$$\mathbf{z} = -\mathbf{G}^{-1}\mathbf{b}.$$

Transforming into the original co-ordinate system

$$\mathbf{z} \equiv \mathbf{x}_{\min} = \mathbf{x}^{(0)} - \mathbf{N}\mathbf{G}^{-1}\mathbf{b}$$

where the vertices are $\mathbf{x}^{(j)}, j = 0, 1, \ldots, n$ with $\mathbf{x}^{(0)}$ the best vertex, and $\mathbf{N}$ is the $n \times n$ matrix whose jth column is $\mathbf{x}^{(j)} - \mathbf{x}^{(0)}$.

While setting up the quadratic approximation Dixon takes the opportunity to search each side emanating from the best vertex for a minimum in preparation for constructing a new simplex should the quadratic approximation indicate this is required.

The quadratic estimate of the minimum value $F_{\min}$ is compared with the actual function value at the predicted solution $F(\mathbf{x}_{\min})$ and if they agree the search terminates. Otherwise the vector $-\mathbf{NG}^{-1}\mathbf{b}$ is considered as a search direction and the minimum along it located. The procedure then constructs a new simplex using information generated while preparing for the quadratic approximation and restarts with further simplex iterations.

Constraints affect the search in the following way. Considering first the simplex search, if a constraint is violated by the reflection or contraction step, then the vector through the worst vertex and the centroid is rejected as a search direction, and all of the sides emanating from the worst vertex are examined as possible alternatives. Linear approximations to the function and constraints are made along each of these sides, and the distance to the nearest constraint and the resulting change in function value estimated. The side along which greatest improvement is indicated is chosen as the new search direction.

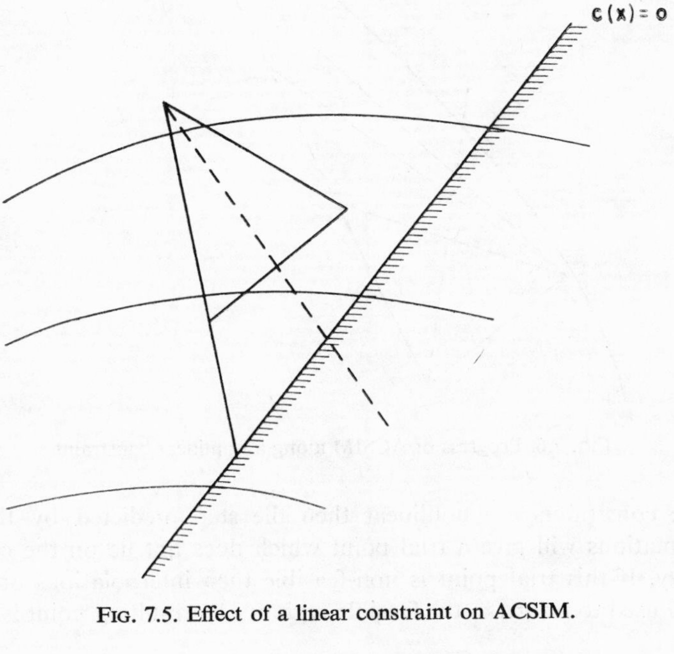

FIG. 7.5. Effect of a linear constraint on ACSIM.

The predicted step is made along the chosen direction, and when the constraints are linear this will give a trial vertex lying on the constraint as shown in Fig. 7.5. If the trial vertex is still the worst one, then a quadratic estimation of the minimum in the search direction is made and taken as the new vertex. If the trial vertex is chosen as the new vertex, however, then the search will in general proceed by rolling along the constraint for a certain distance before perhaps leaving it again. However if the linear approximations along the simplex sides indicate that no progress can be made along any side, then all but the worst vertex must lie on the constraint. In this event the worst vertex is contracted towards the centroid of the others and then deleted from the simplex. This reduces the dimension of the search which will then proceed, in the general case, in the intersection of the active constraints. If this process reduces the dimension of the search to q, then after q iterations the dimension is increased to n again and the search continued in the full parameter space, thereby preventing any undesirable restriction of the search to subspaces.

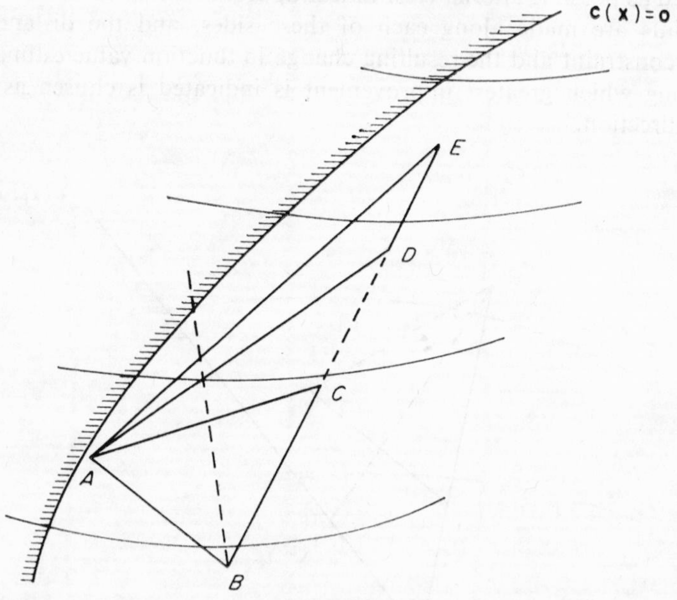

FIG. 7.6. Progress of ACSIM along a nonlinear constraint.

If the constraints are nonlinear then the step predicted by the linear approximations will give a trial point which does not lie on the constraint boundary. If this trial point is non-feasible then interpolations or reduced steps are used to return to the feasible region. The resulting point is taken as the new vertex unless it would again be the worst in the simplex whereupon a quadratic interpolation is made to locate the minimum in the search direction and the best point is chosen to be the new vertex. However if the function and constraint values at the trial vertex suggest that further progress can be made, then a quadratic approximation to the constraints is used to define a new point and if this is successful then the two new points replace the two old vertices lying on the search direction. This situation is illustrated in Fig. 7.6 in which D is the trial vertex and ultimately D and E replace B and C so the new simplex becomes ADE.

Constraint violations encountered on expansion moves and/or the subsequent parabolic estimation are dealt with simply by reducing the step length until a feasible point is found.

During the quadratic approximation stage of the search if the mid-point of any side is non-feasible, then the quadratic approximation is abandoned and the simplex reshaped about the best vertex.

At the end of each iteration the size of simplex, defined as

$$\sum_{j=0}^{n} \sum_{i=1}^{j} [F^{(j)} - F^{(i)}]^2$$

is calculated. If this falls below some preset tolerance ε for a modified simplex then a new simplex is created about the best point; if the size is less than ε for a newly created simplex convergence is assumed.

7.14. Conclusion

Direct-search methods are those which progress towards the minimum using a strategy based on the comparison of function and constraint values only. Although such methods can generally be expected to perform less efficiently than gradient-based methods, they have found widespread use in practice because of their general applicability, their robustness and reliability, and because they are easy to program and use. Of the techniques described above the transformation methods have proved most popular and most successful. However considerable interest has been shown recently in the complex method, and some of the variations produced are proving as efficient as the transformation approach. The simpat method of Keefer and Dixon's ACSIM have been developed too recently to permit any thorough investigation of their performance on practical problems, but the results quoted by the authors suggest that they may prove useful additions to the library of direct-search methods.

Chapter VIII

Methods Related to Lagrangian Functions

R. FLETCHER

Department of Mathematics,
University of Dundee

8.1. Introduction

This paper describes work which relates to the use of Lagrangian functions in devising iterative methods for the solution of nonlinear constraint problems. Some of the methods iterate with estimates $\boldsymbol{\lambda}^{(k)}$ of the (generalized) Lagrange multipliers $\boldsymbol{\lambda}^*$ and may be considered as *dual* methods, whilst others (*primal* methods) work directly with estimates $\mathbf{x}^{(k)}$ of $\mathbf{x}^*$. Some methods require independent estimates for both vectors. Most of the work is fairly recent (since 1969) but it is already possible to say that many of the methods described here will be the basis of future general-purpose numerical packages for solving nonlinear constraint problems. However at the current stage of of research it is not possible to say definitely either that one method is entirely preferable or even that the best method has yet been found.

One thing that is certain in my mind concerns the case when a penalty-function approach to the solution is required. That is to say, an easy-to-apply transformation of the problem is desired, to which an unconstrained minimization routine can be applied, off the shelf, with no numerical problems, and a guarantee of convergence in reasonable time. In this case I am sure that the Powell–Hestenes–Rockafellar penalty function described in Part I of this paper will meet the need in nearly all cases. I have no doubt for instance that a subroutine implementing such a method should appear in any numerical subroutine library. Therefore I have described the method in some detail in the hope that it will become widely understood and recognized. A particular feature of the method is that it is a dual method, controlled by parameters $\boldsymbol{\lambda}^{(k)}$ which estimate the multipliers $\boldsymbol{\lambda}^*$, and $\mathbf{x}$ is dependent on $\boldsymbol{\lambda}^{(k)}$ as $\mathbf{x}(\boldsymbol{\lambda}^{(k)})$ through the solution of the unconstrained minimization problem.

Nonetheless the method requires a sequence of unconstrained minimization problems to be solved and it is the case that more efficient methods can be obtained by avoiding this sequence. In the present state of the art these methods are neither as reliable nor as easy to program, but this situation can be expected to change. The most simple possibility, as investigated by Haarhoff and Buys (1970), is to carry out the unconstrained minimization to low accuracy, perhaps by only doing one step of the iterative process. In this case $\mathbf{x}$ is no longer determined by $\boldsymbol{\lambda}$ (as in the Powell–Hestenes–Rockafellar penalty function), so the resulting method requires estimates of both $\mathbf{x}$ and $\boldsymbol{\lambda}$. The guaranteed convergence of the Powell–Hestenes–Rockafellar penalty function has also not been demonstrated for such a modification. Once it is decided to keep an approximation $\mathbf{x}^{(k)}$ as well as $\boldsymbol{\lambda}^{(k)}$, more sophisticated possibilities open up, because it is possible to write down linearizations of the constraint functions about the current estimate $\mathbf{x}^{(k)}$. This is the subject of Part II of the paper, and in particular the developments of Section 8.5 are very promising. The methods of Part II have all given good results on test problems and the main doubts seem to be in how best to ensure global convergence of the methods.

An alternative way of avoiding the sequence of unconstrained minimizations required by a conventional penalty or barrier function, is to look for an *exact penalty function* which is a function having $\mathbf{x}^*$ as a local minimizer, so that the solution can be located in a single unconstrained minimization. It is possible to do this and recent research on the subject is described in Part III. The methods are strictly *primal* methods in that an estimate $\mathbf{x}^{(k)}$ of $\mathbf{x}^*$ is varied and estimates of Lagrange multipliers are set up which are dependent on $\mathbf{x}^{(k)}$ as $\boldsymbol{\lambda}(\mathbf{x}^{(k)})$. However the calculation of $\boldsymbol{\lambda}(\mathbf{x}^{(k)})$ is finite which is not the case for the $\mathbf{x}(\boldsymbol{\lambda}^{(k)})$ obtained when using the Powell–Hestenes–Rockafellar penalty function. Unfortunately although the line of attack is promising, the functions which have currently been constructed have some difficulties which at the moment inhibit their general use.

Although all of the methods to be described are applicable to general problems with a mixture of equality and inequality constraints, nothing is lost by restricting the discussion to the problem

$$\begin{aligned} &\underset{\mathbf{x}}{\text{minimize}} \quad F(\mathbf{x}) \\ &\text{subject to} \quad c_i(\mathbf{x}) \geqslant 0, \qquad i = 1, 2, \ldots, m, \end{aligned} \qquad P1$$

which is being referred to as *P1* in all chapters. However there are often simplifications when all the constraints are equalities, and it is therefore often convenient to refer to the equality constraint problem

$$\begin{aligned} &\underset{\mathbf{x}}{\text{minimize}} \quad F(\mathbf{x}) \\ &\text{subject to} \quad c_i(\mathbf{x}) = 0, \qquad i = 1, 2, \ldots, m. \end{aligned} \qquad (8.1.1)$$

In order for methods to be applicable, certain conditions at $\mathbf{x}^*$ must hold, and I will assume independence of the active constraint normals at $\mathbf{x}^*$, and also satisfaction of the well-known second-order sufficient conditions for a local minimum (see Chapter I). Problems which do not satisfy these conditions are rare and are usually specially constructed to show certain pathological behaviour.

Part I

The Powell–Hestenes–Rockafellar Penalty Function

8.2. The Powell–Hestenes Penalty Function

Powell (1969) has suggested that to solve the equality problem (8.1.1), a suitable penalty function is

$$\begin{aligned}\phi(\mathbf{x}, \boldsymbol{\theta}, \mathbf{S}) &= F(\mathbf{x}) + \tfrac{1}{2}(\mathbf{c}(\mathbf{x}) - \boldsymbol{\theta})^T\mathbf{S}(\mathbf{c}(\mathbf{x}) - \boldsymbol{\theta}) \\ &= F(\mathbf{x}) + \tfrac{1}{2}\sum_i \sigma_i(c_i(\mathbf{x}) - \theta_i)^2 \end{aligned} \qquad (8.2.1)$$

where $\boldsymbol{\theta} \in R^m$ and $\mathbf{S}$ is an $m \times m$ diagonal matrix with diagonal elements $\sigma_i > 0$. (In this presentation the signs of the θ_i have been changed and a factor $\frac{1}{2}$ introduced to simplify the later analysis.) In his chapter on penalty functions, Ryan has described how this penalty function is used. For any given value of the parameters $\boldsymbol{\theta}$, $\mathbf{S}$ a vector $\mathbf{x}(\boldsymbol{\theta}, \mathbf{S})$ is obtained which is a local unconstrained minimizer of $\phi(\mathbf{x}, \boldsymbol{\theta}, \mathbf{S})$. There is an outer iteration in which $\boldsymbol{\theta}$ and $\mathbf{S}$ are changed so as to cause the minimizers $\mathbf{x}(\boldsymbol{\theta}, \mathbf{S}) \to \mathbf{x}^*$. A well-known penalty function is the special case of (8.2.1) for which $\boldsymbol{\theta} = \mathbf{0}$, in which case convergence is ensured by letting $\sigma_i \to \infty$, $i = 1, 2, \ldots, m$. However Powell suggests an outer interation for use with (8.2.1) such that it is not necessary to force $\sigma_i \to \infty$ in order to achieve convergence. Rather the aim is to keep $\mathbf{S}$ constant and to let $\boldsymbol{\theta} \to \boldsymbol{\theta}^*$ where $\boldsymbol{\theta}^*$ is an optimum vector of parameters satisfying

$$\theta_i^*\sigma_i = \lambda_i^*, \qquad i = 1, 2, \ldots, m, \qquad (8.2.2)$$

where $\boldsymbol{\lambda}^*$ is the vector of Lagrange multipliers at the solution $\mathbf{x}^*$ to (8.1.1). It is only necessary to increase the σ_i when the rate of convergence of $\mathbf{c}(\mathbf{x}(\boldsymbol{\theta}, \mathbf{S}))$ to zero is not sufficiently rapid.

At about the same time Hestenes (1969) put forward his *method of multipliers*. In this he suggests using the penalty function

$$\psi(\mathbf{x}, \boldsymbol{\lambda}, \mathbf{S}) = F(\mathbf{x}) - \boldsymbol{\lambda}^T\mathbf{c}(\mathbf{x}) + \tfrac{1}{2}\mathbf{c}(\mathbf{x})^T\mathbf{S}\mathbf{c}(\mathbf{x}) \qquad (8.2.3)$$

where $\boldsymbol{\lambda} \in R^m$ and $\mathbf{S}$ is as above. (In fact Hestenes uses $\mathbf{S} = \sigma\mathbf{I}$ and therefore implicitly assumes that the constraints are well scaled.) If $\mathbf{x}(\boldsymbol{\lambda}, \mathbf{S})$ is a local unconstrained minimizer of (8.2.3) for fixed $\boldsymbol{\lambda}$, $\mathbf{S}$ and if

$$\theta_i \sigma_i = \lambda_i, \qquad i = 1, 2, \ldots, m, \tag{8.2.4}$$

then it follows on expanding (8.2.1) that

$$\phi(\mathbf{x}, \boldsymbol{\theta}, \mathbf{S}) = \psi(\mathbf{x}, \boldsymbol{\lambda}, \mathbf{S}) + \tfrac{1}{2}\boldsymbol{\theta}^T\mathbf{S}\boldsymbol{\theta}. \tag{8.2.5}$$

Because the difference between ϕ and ψ is independent of $\mathbf{x}$, it follows that $\mathbf{x}(\boldsymbol{\lambda}, \mathbf{S}) = \mathbf{x}(\boldsymbol{\theta}, \mathbf{S})$ assuming (8.2.4) holds. However the values $\phi(\mathbf{x}(\boldsymbol{\theta}, \mathbf{S}), \boldsymbol{\theta}, \mathbf{S})$ and $\psi(\mathbf{x}(\boldsymbol{\lambda}, \mathbf{S}), \boldsymbol{\lambda}, \mathbf{S})$ differ and this difference turns out to be important. If (8.2.4) holds, then the iterative methods suggested by Powell and Hestenes for changing the $\boldsymbol{\theta}$ (or $\boldsymbol{\lambda}$) parameters are the same, although Powell goes into the theory in much more detail and is able to prove strong convergence results.

Because the aim of both these penalty functions is to give rise to an algorithm in which $\mathbf{S}$ is kept constant, in much of what follows $\mathbf{S}$ will be assumed to be constant, and the explicit dependence on $\mathbf{S}$ (in $\mathbf{x}(\boldsymbol{\lambda}, \mathbf{S})$ for instance) will be dropped. In view of the equivalence between (8.2.1) and (8.2.3) it is possible to discuss these algorithms in terms of varying either the $\boldsymbol{\theta}$ parameters or the $\boldsymbol{\lambda}$ parameters, assuming they are related by (8.2.4). In fact the $\boldsymbol{\lambda}$ parameters will be chosen, both for convenience, and also because it is instructive to emphasize the interpretation of the method as being one which iterates with an approximation $\boldsymbol{\lambda}^{(k)}$ to the Lagrange multipliers in such a way as to make $\boldsymbol{\lambda}^{(k)} \to \boldsymbol{\lambda}^*$.

It is first important to show that if the optimum Lagrange multipliers $\boldsymbol{\lambda}^*$ are used as parameters in constructing $\psi(\mathbf{x}, \boldsymbol{\lambda}^*, \mathbf{S})$ then $\mathbf{x}^*$ is a local minimizer of ψ, that is to say $\mathbf{x}^* = \mathbf{x}(\boldsymbol{\lambda}^*, \mathbf{S})$. It follows from the definition of ψ in (8.2.3) that

$$\nabla\psi(\mathbf{x}^*, \boldsymbol{\lambda}^*) = \mathbf{g}^* - \mathbf{A}^*\boldsymbol{\lambda}^* + \mathbf{A}^*\mathbf{S}\mathbf{c}^* = \mathbf{0}$$

by the first-order necessary conditions described by Powell in his chapter of this book. If $\mathbf{x}^*$ satisfies the second-order sufficient conditions for a minimum, as given by Powell, it also follows that there exists some $\mathbf{S}'$ such that for all $\mathbf{S} \geqslant \mathbf{S}'$, $\nabla^2\psi(\mathbf{x}^*, \boldsymbol{\lambda}^*, \mathbf{S})$ is positive definite and hence $\mathbf{x}^*$ is not only a stationary point but is a local minimum of $\psi(\mathbf{x}, \boldsymbol{\lambda}^*, \mathbf{S})$. This result is given for example by Fletcher (1973b) where a review of the material of Part I is given in more detail.

It is useful to regard $\mathbf{x}(\boldsymbol{\lambda})$ (i.e. $\mathbf{x}(\boldsymbol{\lambda}, \mathbf{S})$ for fixed $\mathbf{S}$) as a function of $\boldsymbol{\lambda}$, implicitly determined by solving the nonlinear equations

$$\nabla\psi(\mathbf{x}, \boldsymbol{\lambda}) = \mathbf{0}. \tag{8.2.6}$$

Because $\nabla^2\psi(\mathbf{x}^*, \boldsymbol{\lambda}^*)$ is positive definite it follows from the implicit function theorem that there exists an open neighbourhood $\Omega \subset R^m$ about $\boldsymbol{\lambda}^*$, and a function $\mathbf{x}(\boldsymbol{\lambda})$ defined on Ω, such that both $\mathbf{x}(\boldsymbol{\lambda})$ is continuous and continuously differentiable, and that $\nabla^2\psi(\mathbf{x}(\boldsymbol{\lambda}), \boldsymbol{\lambda})$ is positive definite. It will be important to look at quantities derived from $\mathbf{x}(\boldsymbol{\lambda})$, in particular $\mathbf{c}(\mathbf{x}(\boldsymbol{\lambda}))$ and $\psi(\mathbf{x}(\boldsymbol{\lambda}), \boldsymbol{\lambda})$. For convenience these will be written $\mathbf{c}(\boldsymbol{\lambda})$ and $\psi(\boldsymbol{\lambda})$ respectively.

An important result which clarifies the aims involved in varying $\boldsymbol{\lambda}$ is given by Powell (1969). He points out that in finding $\mathbf{x}(\boldsymbol{\lambda}, \mathbf{S})$ to minimize $\psi(\mathbf{x}, \boldsymbol{\lambda}, \mathbf{S})$ a solution has also been found to the problem

$$\begin{aligned} &\underset{\mathbf{x}}{\text{minimize}} \quad F(\mathbf{x}) \\ &\text{subject to} \quad \mathbf{c}(\mathbf{x}) = \mathbf{c}(\mathbf{x}(\boldsymbol{\lambda}, \mathbf{S})). \end{aligned} \tag{8.2.7}$$

This result is easy to prove because the terms $-\boldsymbol{\lambda}^T\mathbf{c}(\mathbf{x}) + \frac{1}{2}\mathbf{c}(\mathbf{x})^T\mathbf{S}\mathbf{c}(\mathbf{x})$ in (8.2.3) are constant for any feasible point of (8.2.7), so the fact that $\mathbf{x}(\boldsymbol{\lambda}, \mathbf{S})$ minimizes (8.2.3) implies that (8.2.7) is also solved. The situation is illustrated in Fig. 8.1 showing that $\mathbf{x}(\boldsymbol{\lambda}, \mathbf{S})$ solves a perturbed problem to that solved by $\mathbf{x}^*$. As $\mathbf{c}(\mathbf{x}(\boldsymbol{\lambda}, \mathbf{S}))$ is being thought of as $\mathbf{c}(\boldsymbol{\lambda})$ it is clear that the aim in varying $\boldsymbol{\lambda}$ is to make $\mathbf{c}(\boldsymbol{\lambda}) = \mathbf{0}$, for it will then follow that the original problem (8.1.1) has been solved. But $\mathbf{c}(\boldsymbol{\lambda}) = \mathbf{0}$ is a system of nonlinear equations, and one way of looking at the strategies for changing $\boldsymbol{\lambda}$ is that they are an attempt to solve these nonlinear equations.

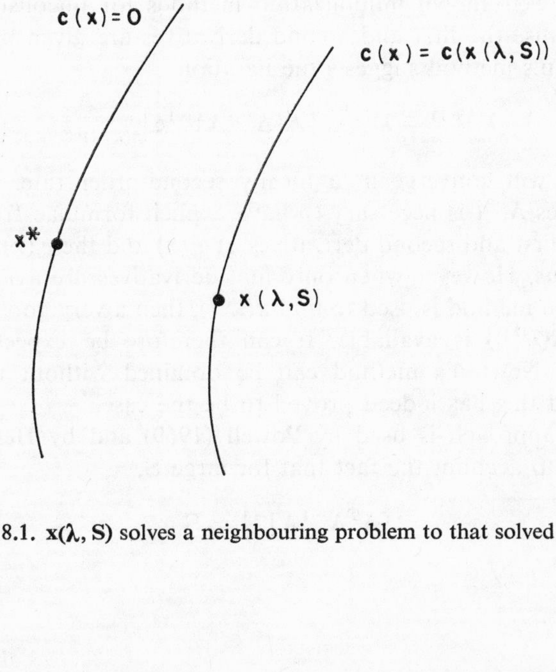

FIG. 8.1. $\mathbf{x}(\boldsymbol{\lambda}, \mathbf{S})$ solves a neighbouring problem to that solved by $\mathbf{x}^*$.

However it is possible to throw even more light on the situation by following a slightly different tack. If $\psi(\mathbf{x}(\boldsymbol{\lambda}, \mathbf{S}), \boldsymbol{\lambda}, \mathbf{S})$ with $\mathbf{S}$ fixed is written as $\psi(\boldsymbol{\lambda})$ then it is of interest to examine $\nabla_{\boldsymbol{\lambda}}\psi(\boldsymbol{\lambda})$. By the usual rule for partial derivatives

$$\mathrm{d}\psi/\mathrm{d}\lambda_i = \sum_j (\partial\psi/\partial x_j)(\partial x_j/\partial\lambda_i) + \partial\psi/\partial\lambda_i,$$

where the total derivative is used in the sense that the variation of the $\mathbf{x}$ parameter of ψ through $\mathbf{x}(\boldsymbol{\lambda}, \mathbf{S})$ is also involved. But $\partial\psi/\partial x_j = 0$ by (8.2.6) and $\partial\psi/\partial\lambda_i = -c_i$ from (8.2.3) so it follows that

$$\nabla_{\boldsymbol{\lambda}}\psi(\boldsymbol{\lambda}) = -\mathbf{c}(\boldsymbol{\lambda}). \tag{8.2.8}$$

A further application of $\mathrm{d}/\mathrm{d}\lambda_j$ in similar fashion yields the expression

$$\nabla_{\boldsymbol{\lambda}}{}^2\psi(\boldsymbol{\lambda}) = -[\mathbf{A}^T\boldsymbol{\Lambda}^{-1}\mathbf{A}]_{\mathbf{x}(\boldsymbol{\lambda})} \tag{8.2.9}$$

where $\boldsymbol{\Lambda} = \nabla_{\mathbf{x}}{}^2\psi$. Thus because $\mathbf{c}(\boldsymbol{\lambda}^*)$ is zero and $\boldsymbol{\Lambda}(\boldsymbol{\lambda}^*)$ is positive definite, (8.2.8) and (8.2.9) show that $\nabla_{\boldsymbol{\lambda}}\psi(\boldsymbol{\lambda}^*) = \mathbf{0}$, $\nabla_{\boldsymbol{\lambda}}{}^2\psi(\boldsymbol{\lambda}^*)$ is negative definite, and hence that $\boldsymbol{\lambda}^*$ is the local maximizer of $\psi(\boldsymbol{\lambda})$. In fact if the original problem (8.1.1) has special features which imply that $\mathbf{x}(\boldsymbol{\lambda})$ is the global minimizer of $\psi(\mathbf{x}, \boldsymbol{\lambda})$, then $\boldsymbol{\lambda}^*$ is the global maximizer of $\psi(\boldsymbol{\lambda})$. This follows from the inequality

$$\psi(\mathbf{x}(\boldsymbol{\lambda}), \boldsymbol{\lambda}) \leqslant \psi(\mathbf{x}^*, \boldsymbol{\lambda}) = \psi(\mathbf{x}^*, \boldsymbol{\lambda}^*)$$

by virtue of $\mathbf{c}(\mathbf{x}^*) = \mathbf{0}$.

It is convenient therefore to derive methods for varying the parameters $\boldsymbol{\lambda}$ by employing well-known minimization methods for unconstrained minimization. Because the first and second derivatives are given by (8.2.8) and (8.2.9), Newton's method suggests the iteration

$$\boldsymbol{\lambda}^{(k+1)} = \boldsymbol{\lambda}^{(k)} - [\mathbf{A}^T\boldsymbol{\Lambda}^{-1}\mathbf{A}]^{-1}\mathbf{c}\,|_{\mathbf{x}(\boldsymbol{\lambda}^{(k)})}. \tag{8.2.10}$$

This iteration will converge at a locally second-order rate. Because this method requires $\boldsymbol{\Lambda}$, it is necessary to have explicit formulae from which to evaluate both first and second derivatives of $F(\mathbf{x})$ and the $c_i(\mathbf{x})$. This can be disadvantageous. However when only first derivatives are available, and if a quasi-Newton method is used to find $\mathbf{x}(\boldsymbol{\lambda}^{(k)})$, then a very good approximation of $\boldsymbol{\Lambda}^{-1}(\mathbf{x}(\boldsymbol{\lambda}^{(k)}))$ is available. It can therefore be expected that the advantages of Newton's method can be obtained without using second derivatives and this has indeed proved to be the case.

A different approach is used by Powell (1969) and by Hestenes (1969) which takes into account the fact that for large $\mathbf{S}$,

$$[\mathbf{A}^T\boldsymbol{\Lambda}^{-1}\mathbf{A}]^{-1} \approx \mathbf{S} \tag{8.2.11}$$

(see Fletcher, 1973b). When this is used in (8.2.10) the iteration

$$\boldsymbol{\lambda}^{(k+1)} = \boldsymbol{\lambda}^{(k)} - \mathbf{S}\mathbf{c}^{(k)} \tag{8.2.12}$$

is obtained, which is the formula suggested by Hestenes (1969). In terms of the $\boldsymbol{\theta}$ parameters, by virtue of (8.2.4), this iteration can be written

$$\boldsymbol{\theta}^{(k+1)} = \boldsymbol{\theta}^{(k)} - \mathbf{c}^{(k)}, \tag{8.2.13}$$

which is the equivalent formula given by Powell (1969). One special merit of these formulae is in their simplicity. Because they do not require derivatives, they are especially convenient when the minimization routine as applied in $\mathbf{x}$-space does not require derivatives. Furthermore by making $\mathbf{S}$ sufficiently large, (8.2.11) can be satisfied to any desired relative accuracy, and hence an arbitrarily fast-rate of linear convergence of $\boldsymbol{\lambda}^{(k)}$ to $\boldsymbol{\lambda}^*$ can be obtained.

These results concern only local convergence, and to ensure global convergence the σ_i parameters must be changed. A strategy to do this is also suggested by Powell (1969), and is motivated by the result for fixed $\boldsymbol{\lambda}$ that

$$\text{if} \quad \sigma_i \to \infty \quad \text{then} \quad c_i \to 0 \quad \text{and} \quad c_i \sim \text{const}/\sigma_i, \tag{8.2.14}$$

where $\mathbf{c} = \mathbf{c}(\mathbf{x}(\boldsymbol{\lambda}, \mathbf{S}))$. Powell therefore suggests that if $\|\mathbf{c}^{(k+1)}\|_\infty/\|\mathbf{c}^{(k)}\|_\infty$ is not sufficiently small (0·25 is suggested) then certain of the σ_i should be increased by a fixed ratio (10 is suggested). This sort of strategy has been found to work well and ensures convergence of the algorithm. Once $\mathbf{S}$ becomes sufficiently large and $\mathbf{c}$ sufficiently small, the local convergence results show that the test $\|\mathbf{c}^{(k+1)}\|_\infty/\|\mathbf{c}^{(k)}\|_\infty < 0{\cdot}25$ will always be satisfied. Hence ultimately $\mathbf{S}$ will remain constant and the iterative formula for varying $\boldsymbol{\lambda}^{(k)}$ alone will be used.

8.3. The Rockafellar Generalization

Rockafellar (1973) has suggested that a suitable modification of the Hestenes function (8.2.3) to solve the inequality problem *P1* is to use the penalty function

$$\Psi(\mathbf{x}, \boldsymbol{\lambda}, \mathbf{S}) = F(\mathbf{x}) + \sum_i \begin{cases} -\lambda_i c_i + \frac{1}{2}\sigma_i {c_i}^2, & \text{if} \quad c_i \leqslant \lambda_i/\sigma_i, \\ -\frac{1}{2}{\lambda_i}^2/\sigma_i, & \text{if} \quad c_i \geqslant \lambda_i/\sigma_i, \end{cases} \tag{8.3.1}$$

where $c_i = c_i(\mathbf{x})$. Actually Rockafellar considers the simple case for which $\sigma_i = \sigma, i = 1, 2, \ldots, m$. The effect of this generalization is more clearly seen however if it is written as a modification of Powell's function,

$$\Phi(\mathbf{x}, \boldsymbol{\theta}, \mathbf{S}) = F(\mathbf{x}) + \tfrac{1}{2}\sum_i \sigma_i (c_i - \theta_i)_-^2 \tag{8.3.2}$$

as given by Fletcher (1973b), where a_- is defined as

$$a_- = \min(a, 0) = \begin{cases} a & \text{if} \quad a < 0 \\ 0 & \text{if} \quad a \geqslant 0, \end{cases}$$

and where θ_i and λ_i are related by (8.2.4). In these circumstances, (8.3.1) and (8.3.2) are equivalent and (8.2.5) is again true.

The theoretical and practical details associated with these functions closely parallels those for the equality penalty functions and a review of them is given by Fletcher (1973b). As before $\mathbf{x}(\boldsymbol{\theta}, \mathbf{S})$ is the local unconstrained minimizer of $\Phi(\mathbf{x}, \boldsymbol{\theta}, \mathbf{S})$ for fixed $\boldsymbol{\theta}$, $\mathbf{S}$ and there is an outer iteration in which $\boldsymbol{\theta}$, $\mathbf{S}$ are varied so as to cause $\mathbf{x}(\boldsymbol{\theta}, \mathbf{S}) \to \mathbf{x}^*$. Again the case $\boldsymbol{\theta} = \mathbf{0}$ is well known and convergence can be forced by letting $\sigma_i \to \infty$, $i = 1, 2, \ldots, m$. However difficulties then arise because the second-derivative discontinuities tend to infinity and occur at points which tend to x^*. In the form (8.3.2) given here the discontinuities are bounded and are usually remote from the solution, and practical experience shows no ill-effects on the performance of the unconstrained minimization routine applied to $\Phi(\mathbf{x}, \boldsymbol{\theta}, \mathbf{S})$.

Most of the theoretical results for the equality case can be extended to the inequality problem. For instance second-order sufficiency conditions for the latter show that $\mathbf{x}^* = \mathbf{x}(\boldsymbol{\lambda}^*, \mathbf{S})$ for any $\mathbf{S} \geqslant \mathbf{S}'$. Furthermore $\mathbf{x}(\boldsymbol{\lambda}, \mathbf{S})$ obtained by minimizing $\Psi(\mathbf{x}, \boldsymbol{\lambda}, \mathbf{S})$ also solves a related problem to *P1*, namely

$$\begin{aligned} &\underset{\mathbf{x}}{\text{minimize}} \quad F(\mathbf{x}) \\ &\text{subject to} \quad c_i(\mathbf{x}) \geqslant \min\left(c_i(\mathbf{x}(\boldsymbol{\lambda}, \mathbf{S})), \theta_i\right), \qquad i = 1, 2, \ldots, m \end{aligned} \tag{8.3.3}$$

where $\theta_i = \lambda_i/\sigma_i$. Moreover, writing $\Psi(\mathbf{x}(\boldsymbol{\lambda}, \mathbf{S}), \boldsymbol{\lambda}, \mathbf{S})$ as $\Psi(\boldsymbol{\lambda})$ as before, then

$$\mathrm{d}\Psi/\mathrm{d}\lambda_i = -\min(c_i, \theta_i) \tag{8.3.4}$$

and

$$\nabla_{\lambda}{}^2\Psi(\boldsymbol{\lambda}) = \begin{bmatrix} -\mathbf{A}^T\boldsymbol{\Lambda}^{-1}\mathbf{A} & \mathbf{0} \\ \mathbf{0} & -\mathbf{S}^{-1} \end{bmatrix} \tag{8.3.5}$$

where the columns of $\mathbf{A}$ are taken from the constraints i: $c_i < \theta_i$ and those of $\mathbf{S}^{-1}$ from the constraints i: $c_i \geqslant \theta_i$. It follows from (8.2.4) and the Kuhn–Tucker conditions that $\nabla_{\lambda}\Psi(\boldsymbol{\lambda}^*) = \mathbf{0}$ and because $\nabla_{\lambda}{}^2\Psi(\boldsymbol{\lambda}^*)$ is negative definite, so $\Psi(\boldsymbol{\lambda})$ has a local minimum at $\boldsymbol{\lambda}^*$. It is particularly interesting to note that $\boldsymbol{\lambda}^*$ is the *unconstrained* minimizer of $\Psi(\boldsymbol{\lambda})$ and in particular that the constraints $\boldsymbol{\lambda} \geqslant \mathbf{0}$ will hold automatically and do not have to be imposed explicitly. A stronger result can again be stated when $\mathbf{x}(\boldsymbol{\lambda})$ is known to be the global minimizer of $\Psi(\mathbf{x}, \boldsymbol{\lambda})$, namely that $\boldsymbol{\lambda}^*$ is the global maximizer of $\Psi(\boldsymbol{\lambda})$, by virtue of the inequalities

$$\Psi(\mathbf{x}(\boldsymbol{\lambda}), \boldsymbol{\lambda}) \leqslant \Psi(\mathbf{x}^*, \boldsymbol{\lambda}) \leqslant \Psi(\mathbf{x}^*, \boldsymbol{\lambda}) + \tfrac{1}{2} \sum_{i:\lambda_i<0} \lambda_i^2/\sigma_i = \Psi(\mathbf{x}^*, \boldsymbol{\lambda}^*).$$

Strategies for an iterative method to vary $\boldsymbol{\lambda}^{(k)}$ can again be deduced, by using the derivative expressions (8.3.4) and (8.3.5) with Newton's method for minimizing $\Psi(\boldsymbol{\lambda})$. However in view of the implicit inequalities $\boldsymbol{\lambda} \geqslant \mathbf{0}$ and the discontinuities in (8.3.5) as $\boldsymbol{\lambda}$ is changed, it is probably preferable to choose $\boldsymbol{\lambda}^{(k+1)}$ to solve a subproblem

$$\underset{\boldsymbol{\lambda}}{\text{maximize}}\ \{Q^{(k)}(\boldsymbol{\lambda})\}\ \text{subject to}\ \boldsymbol{\lambda} \geqslant \mathbf{0}, \tag{8.3.6}$$

where $Q^{(k)}(\boldsymbol{\lambda})$ is a quadratic function derived by truncating a Taylor expansion for $\Psi(\boldsymbol{\lambda})$ about $\boldsymbol{\lambda}^{(k)}$ after the quadratic term. This formulation can also be used to determine a more simple correction formula analogous to (8.2.12) and (8.2.13). This is the formula

$$\theta_i^{(k+1)} = \theta_i^{(k)} - \min(c_i^{(k)}, \theta_i^{(k)}), \qquad i = 1, 2, \ldots, m, \tag{8.3.7}$$

with an equivalent expression holding for $\boldsymbol{\lambda}^{(k+1)}$ in terms of $\boldsymbol{\lambda}^{(k)}$.

A wide range of numerical evidence is reported by Fletcher (1973b). He compares the Newton-like methods based on (8.2.10) and (8.3.6) with the Powell/Hestenes correction (8.2.12) and (8.3.7), and concludes that whilst both are effective, the Newton-like method is somewhat more efficient in reducing both the numbers of minimizations and the number of function evaluations required to achieve a certain accuracy. When compared against other penalty or barrier functions, this approach has a number of good features which are not found together in any other method. These include good conditioning of Φ with no singularities, and global convergence of the method without the need to make $\mathbf{S} \to \infty$. Local convergence is rapid and high accuracy can be obtained in very few minimizations (4–6 in practice). Furthermore the Hessian matrix can be carried forward from one iteration to the next, and updated when necessary, so the computational effort for the successive minimizations goes down rapidly. Most important of all for a penalty or barrier function is that it is very easy to program the method by incorporating an existing quasi-Newton routine for unconstrained minimization. There are no difficult decisions about how to define Φ in the feasible region, or how to adapt the linear search to cope with singularities. There is also no need to supply an initial feasible point to start off the whole process. Finally compared with other penalty or barrier functions, the new method also seems to be more efficient in terms of the number of function evaluations required.

Part II

Methods which Solve Linearly Constrained Subproblems

8.4. Murray's Method

One of the virtues of the Powell–Hestenes–Rockafellar penalty function is that it avoids the ill-conditioning which would occur in (8.2.1) or (8.3.2) as $\mathbf{S} \to \infty$. An interesting idea which also has this property is due to Murray (1969a), and relates the idea of a penalty function to that of attempting to solve linearly constrained subproblems which approximate the original problem in some way. Discussing the equality problem (8.1.1) for the moment; if the special case $\boldsymbol{\theta} = \mathbf{0}$, $\mathbf{S} = \sigma\mathbf{I}$ of (8.2.1) is considered,

$$\phi(\mathbf{x}, \sigma) = F(\mathbf{x}) + \tfrac{1}{2}\sigma\mathbf{c}^T\mathbf{c} \tag{8.4.1}$$

then it is possible to derive Murray's algorithm from ideas which have already been given in Part I. It has been pointed out that the minimizer $\mathbf{x}(\sigma)$ of (8.4.1) equivalently solves a constrained problem (see 8.2.7) related to (8.1.1), and Murray's algorithm can be viewed as an attempt to solve an approximate form of this problem. As with conventional methods of solving (8.4.1), a sequence of increasing values $\sigma^{(k)} \to \infty$ is chosen, although the decision on what value of $\sigma^{(k+1)}$ to use is only taken when the subproblem relating to $\sigma^{(k)}$ has been solved. For any $\sigma^{(k)}$, an estimate $\mathbf{x}^{(k)}$ is held of the minimizer $\mathbf{x}(\sigma^{(k)})$, and a value of $\sigma^{(k+1)}$ is chosen. Then an approximate problem to (8.2.7) with $\sigma = \sigma^{(k+1)}$ is defined by using Taylor series expansions about $\mathbf{x}^{(k)}$ to derive a quadratic approximation $Q^{(k)}(\mathbf{x})$ to $F(\mathbf{x})$ and a linear approximation to the constraint functions, namely

$$\mathbf{c}^{(k)} + \mathbf{A}^{(k)T}(\mathbf{x} - \mathbf{x}^{(k)}) = \mathbf{c}(\mathbf{x}(\sigma^{(k+1)})). \tag{8.4.2}$$

The right-hand side of this equation can be simplified using the result (8.2.14) which holds asymptotically as $\sigma \to \infty$ and shows that $\sigma^{(k+1)}\mathbf{c}^{(k+1)} \approx \sigma^{(k)}\mathbf{c}^{(k)}$. Thus the subproblem which is used in Murray's method to determine $\mathbf{x}^{(k+1)}$ is

$$\begin{aligned} &\underset{\mathbf{x}}{\text{minimize}}\ \{Q^{(k)}(\mathbf{x})\} \\ &\text{subject to } \mathbf{A}^{(k)T}(\mathbf{x} - \mathbf{x}^{(k)}) = -(1 - \sigma^{(k)}/\sigma^{(k+1)})\,\mathbf{c}^{(k)} \end{aligned} \tag{8.4.3}$$

and this is a quadratic programming problem.

In replacing the minimization of $\phi(\mathbf{x}, \sigma)$ in (8.4.1) by the solution of (8.4.3), the ill-conditioning associated with $\sigma^{(k)} \to \infty$ is avoided. Another advantage associated with this formulation is that the problem is less likely to become unbounded—it is possible that this may be true of (8.4.1) by moving in a direction which is along the constraint normals and which is therefore away from the feasible region of (8.1.1). Biggs (1972) has looked at a development of the method in which a more accurate relationship than (8.2.14) is used to estimate $\mathbf{c}(\mathbf{x}(\sigma^{(k+1)}))$ on the right-hand side of the linearized constraints (8.4.2). He claims that this gives better numerical results than those obtained by the Murray method, but the results of both of these methods are better than those obtained by using a conventional penalty function (including that described in Part I of this paper). However what is not known is to what extent this is due to solving a linearly constrained subproblem, and to what extent to the fact that the minimization of $F(\mathbf{x})$ is replaced by the one step minimization of the quadratic approximation. This latter strategy can be carried out merely by making a quadratic approximation to a conventional penalty function (without the linearized constraints) and might enable comparable result to be obtained.

There is some freedom in choosing $Q^{(k)}(\mathbf{x})$, for instance if the exact Hessian $\nabla^2 F^{(k)}$ is not available, then an approximation updated at each iteration might be used. In fact it is more appropriate, when making linearizations of this nature, to define $Q^{(k)}(\mathbf{x})$ using the Hessian of a Lagrangian function, so as to take into account the curvature of the constraints. This point is taken up in detail in the next section, so comment will be deferred until then. It is also simple to generalize the method to deal with inequalities, by solving a quadratic programming problem with inequality constraints. Although this is done differently by Murray (1969a) and by Biggs (1972), the development given here suggests that the point $\mathbf{x}^{(k+1)}$ should solve a linearization of (3.3), namely

$$\min_{\mathbf{x}} \{Q^{(k)}(\mathbf{x})\}$$

$$\text{subject to} \quad \begin{aligned} &\mathbf{a}_i^T(\mathbf{x}-\mathbf{x}^{(k)}) \geqslant -(1-\sigma^{(k)}/\sigma^{(k+1)})c_i^{(k)} && \text{if} \quad c_i^{(k)} < 0 \\ &\mathbf{a}_i^T(\mathbf{x}-\mathbf{x}^{(k)}) \geqslant -c_i^{(k)} && \text{if} \quad c_i^{(k)} \geqslant 0. \end{aligned}$$

The algorithm stated here is not strictly one in which estimates of Lagrange multipliers are varied, but this idea can be incorporated into the algorithm. Indeed Murray (1969a) does use this idea indirectly because after an iteration he multiplies the constraint functions by the multipliers from the subproblem (4.3). The effect of changing $\sigma^{(k)}$ here is much more akin to that of changing $\boldsymbol{\lambda}$ (rather than σ) in the Powell–Hestenes–Rockafellar algorithm. For instance the value $\sigma^{(k+1)} = \infty$ can be chosen, in which case the subproblem (8.4.3) becomes a linearization of the original problem (1.1). This illustrates a disadvantage of the Murray–Biggs formulation in that the role of σ in forcing global convergence is no longer applicable. Thus some additional rules have to be introduced which relate convergence to the particular heuristic chosen for increasing σ. Another apparent disadvantage of the Murray method is that this best available choice of $\sigma^{(k+1)} = \infty$ is not usually made. However Murray (1969a) gets round this to a large extent by using the solution to (8.4.3) not directly, but to determine a search direction along which $F(\mathbf{x})$ is minimized. Nonetheless the multipliers obtained from (4.3) do depend on $\sigma^{(k+1)}$ and thus are not the best available (although this disadvantage could also be circumvented, as indeed Murray (private communication) points out).

8.5. Methods with Second-order Convergence

In this section methods will be examined which linearize the original problem directly in an attempt to generate an algorithm in which a sequence of linearly constrained subproblems are solved. The only difference here between an equality constrained problem and an inequality constrained problem is that they give rise to equality and inequality constrained subproblems respectively. Therefore the discussion will be restricted to equality constraints. First of all the mechanism of carrying out a linearization is examined. The reason for carrying out a linearization is to produce a linearly constrained subproblem (in the limit of an iterative process) which has $\mathbf{x}^*$ as a local minimizer. Now if the Lagrangian function is defined by

$$L(\mathbf{x}, \boldsymbol{\lambda}) = F(\mathbf{x}) - \boldsymbol{\lambda}^T \mathbf{c}(\mathbf{x})$$

then the first-order conditions $\nabla L(\mathbf{x}^*, \boldsymbol{\lambda}^*) = \mathbf{0}$ imply that

$$L(\mathbf{x}, \boldsymbol{\lambda}^*) = F^* + \tfrac{1}{2}\boldsymbol{\delta}^T \mathbf{W}^* \boldsymbol{\delta} + o(\|\boldsymbol{\delta}\|^2)$$

where $\mathbf{W}^* = \nabla^2 F^* - \sum_i \lambda_i^* \nabla^2 c_i^*$, and where $\boldsymbol{\delta} = \mathbf{x} - \mathbf{x}^*$. But sufficient conditions for a local minimum are that the first-order conditions hold and that

$$\exists\, a > 0: \ \boldsymbol{\delta}^T \mathbf{W}^* \boldsymbol{\delta} > a \boldsymbol{\delta}^T \boldsymbol{\delta} \ \ \forall\, \boldsymbol{\delta}: \ \mathbf{A}^{*T} \boldsymbol{\delta} = \mathbf{0} \quad (\boldsymbol{\delta} \neq \mathbf{0}).$$

Hence $\mathbf{x}^*$ solves

$$\underset{\mathbf{x}}{\text{minimize}}\ L(\mathbf{x}, \boldsymbol{\lambda}^*) \quad \text{subject to} \quad \mathbf{A}^{*T} \boldsymbol{\delta} = \mathbf{0}. \tag{8.5.1}$$

Now the constraints of (8.5.1) are linearizations of $\mathbf{c}(\mathbf{x}) = \mathbf{0}$ about $\mathbf{x}^*$ so the aim has been achieved of setting up a linearly constrained problem with the same local minimizer as the original problem (8.1.1).

To enable a practical algorithm to be determined, the problem (8.5.1) must be the limit of a sequence of problems set up in terms of estimates $\mathbf{x}^{(k)}, \boldsymbol{\lambda}^{(k)}$ of the solution and the multipliers. A suitable generalization of (8.5.1) gives the subproblem

$$\begin{aligned}&\underset{\mathbf{x}}{\text{minimize}}\ L(\mathbf{x}, \boldsymbol{\lambda}^{(k)})\\ &\text{subject to } \mathbf{c}^{(k)} + \mathbf{A}^{(k)T}(\mathbf{x} - \mathbf{x}^{(k)}) = \mathbf{0}.\end{aligned} \tag{8.5.2}$$

The minimizer of (8.5.2) is not affected by adding a multiple $\boldsymbol{\lambda}^{(k)}$ of the constraint equation into the objective function and this gives the problem

$$\begin{aligned}&\underset{\mathbf{x}}{\text{minimize}}\ \{F(\mathbf{x}) - \boldsymbol{\lambda}^{(k)T}(\mathbf{c}(\mathbf{x}) - \mathbf{c}^{(k)} - \mathbf{A}^{(k)T}(\mathbf{x} - \mathbf{x}^{(k)}))\}\\ &\text{subject to } \mathbf{c}^{(k)} + \mathbf{A}^{(k)T}(\mathbf{x} - \mathbf{x}^{(k)}) = \mathbf{0},\end{aligned} \tag{8.5.3}$$

which is this basis of a method proposed by Robinson (1972). The reason for using (8.5.3) and not (8.5.2) is that if $(\mathbf{x}^{(k)}, \boldsymbol{\lambda}^{(k)}) = (\mathbf{x}^*, \boldsymbol{\lambda}^*)$ is substituted, then not only is $\mathbf{x}^*$ the solution of (8.5.3) but $\boldsymbol{\lambda}^*$ is also the multiplier vector of the linear constraint equations. Thus $(\mathbf{x}^*, \boldsymbol{\lambda}^*)$ is a fixed point of (8.5.3), and this suggests an iterative method in which $\mathbf{x}^{(k+1)}$ is chosen as the minimizer of (8.5.3) and $\boldsymbol{\lambda}^{(k+1)}$ as the corresponding multiplier vector of the linear constraint equations. This (Robinson's) method requires a sequence of linearly constrained minimization problems with a general nonlinear objective function to be solved. An objection therefore is that the subproblem is not very tractable, requiring a sequence of nonlinear problems which are at least as difficult to solve as unconstrained problems. Furthermore the convergence of the iterative method for $(\mathbf{x}^{(k)}, \boldsymbol{\lambda}^{(k)})$ is not guaranteed, and therefore there would seem to be no advantages over the Powell–Hestenes–Rockafellar approach.

Since however the result (8.5.1) is based on the behaviour of the leading quadratic term of L, it is valid to make a quadratic approximation to the objective function in (8.5.3). This gives rise to a method in which $\mathbf{x}^{(k+1)}, \boldsymbol{\lambda}^{(k+1)}$ are chosen as the solution and multipliers of the subproblem

$$\begin{aligned}&\underset{\mathbf{x}}{\text{minimize}}\ \{\tfrac{1}{2}(\mathbf{x} - \mathbf{x}^{(k)})^T\mathbf{W}^{(k)}(\mathbf{x} - \mathbf{x}^{(k)}) + \mathbf{g}^{(k)T}(\mathbf{x} - \mathbf{x}^{(k)})\}\\ &\text{subject to } \mathbf{c}^{(k)} + \mathbf{A}^{(k)T}(\mathbf{x} - \mathbf{x}^{(k)}) = \mathbf{0}\end{aligned} \tag{8.5.4}$$

where

$$\mathbf{W}^{(k)} = \boldsymbol{\nabla}^2 F^{(k)} - \sum_i \lambda_i^{(k)} \boldsymbol{\nabla}^2 c_i^{(k)}.$$

This method is the basis of SOLVER (Wilson, 1963), as interpreted by Beale (1967). The method requires the solution of a sequence of quadratic programming problems in general, although as (8.5.4) applies to equality constraints, its solution satisfies the linear (Lagrangian) equations

$$\begin{bmatrix} \mathbf{W}^{(k)} & -\mathbf{A}^{(k)} \\ -\mathbf{A}^{(k)T} & \mathbf{0} \end{bmatrix} \begin{bmatrix} \mathbf{x}^{(k+1)} - \mathbf{x}^{(k)} \\ \boldsymbol{\lambda}^{(k+1)} \end{bmatrix} = \begin{bmatrix} -\mathbf{g}^{(k)} \\ \mathbf{c}^{(k)} \end{bmatrix}. \tag{8.5.5}$$

In the form (8.5.4) the method requires second derivatives of the problem functions to be explicitly available. However by approximating $\mathbf{W}^{(k)}$ by any matrix $\mathbf{\Gamma}^{(k)}$ such that $\mathbf{\Gamma}^{(k)} \to \mathbf{W}^*$ like $O(\mathbf{x}^{(k)} - \mathbf{x}^*)$, then the properties of the method are unaffected. Thus it is likely that updating methods could be used to advantage to estimate $\mathbf{W}^*$ when only first derivatives are available.

Before investigating the properties of such methods it is noted that the approximation to F always involves $\mathbf{W} = \nabla^2 F - \sum_i \lambda_i \nabla^2 c_i$ rather than just $\nabla^2 F$ and it is instructive to enquire what would happen if $\nabla^2 F$ were used instead of $\mathbf{W}$ (this might happen for reasons of convenience, say). It is possible that $\boldsymbol{\delta}^T \nabla^2 F^* \boldsymbol{\delta}$ may be negative for some $\boldsymbol{\delta}$ such that $\mathbf{A}^{*T}\boldsymbol{\delta} = \mathbf{0}$, in which case the sequence of problems thus constructed would not have $\mathbf{x}^*$ as a minimizer in the limit. The sufficient conditions ensure that this cannot happen when $\mathbf{W}$ is used. Nonetheless if this does not happen (for instance it cannot when $F(\mathbf{x})$ is strictly convex) then there seems to be no objection to making a quadratic approximation to $F(\mathbf{x})$ without modifying the Hessian. Murray (1969a) comments on the fact that he was able to approximate $F(\mathbf{x})$ without ill-effect and this would seem to be the reason. In particular it suggests that methods which approximate $\nabla^2 F$ or $\mathbf{W}$ by a matrix which is kept strictly positive definite might work well. An interesting observation in this respect is that $\mathbf{W}^{(k)}$ can be replaced by $\mathbf{W}^{(k)} + \mathbf{A}^{(k)}\mathbf{D}^{(k)}\mathbf{A}^{(k)T}$, $(\mathbf{D}^{(k)} > 0)$, in (8.5.5) without affecting $\mathbf{x}^{(k+1)}$. This observation follows because by definition of the inverse

$$\begin{bmatrix} \mathbf{W}^{(k)} & -\mathbf{A}^{(k)} \\ -\mathbf{A}^{(k)T} & \mathbf{0} \end{bmatrix}^{-1} \begin{bmatrix} -\mathbf{A}^{(k)} \\ \mathbf{0} \end{bmatrix} = \begin{bmatrix} \mathbf{0} \\ \mathbf{I} \end{bmatrix},$$

so use of the well known Householder modification formula shows that

$$\begin{bmatrix} \mathbf{W}^{(k)} + \mathbf{A}^{(k)}\mathbf{D}^{(k)}\mathbf{A}^{(k)T} & -\mathbf{A}^{(k)} \\ -\mathbf{A}^{(k)T} & \mathbf{0} \end{bmatrix}^{-1} = \begin{bmatrix} \mathbf{W}^{(k)} & -\mathbf{A}^{(k)} \\ -\mathbf{A}^{(k)T} & \mathbf{0} \end{bmatrix}^{-1} - \begin{bmatrix} \mathbf{0} & \mathbf{0} \\ \mathbf{0} & \mathbf{D}^{(k)} \end{bmatrix}, \tag{8.5.6}$$

and this equation can be substituted to compare the solutions of (8.5.5) with or without the $\mathbf{A}^{(k)}\mathbf{D}^{(k)}\mathbf{A}^{(k)T}$ term. Choice of $\mathbf{D}^{(k)}$ sufficiently large ensures that as $\mathbf{x}^{(k)} \to \mathbf{x}^*$, the matrices $\mathbf{W}^{(k)} + \mathbf{A}^{(k)}\mathbf{D}^{(k)}\mathbf{A}^{(k)T}$ are positive definite for all k sufficiently large, assuming that sufficient conditions hold at $\mathbf{x}^*$. Thus it is possible to use or to approximate these matrices if positive definiteness is required. Furthermore by setting $\mathbf{D}^{(k)} = \mathbf{S}^{(k)}$ the matrix $\mathbf{W}^{(k)} + \mathbf{A}^{(k)}\mathbf{D}^{(k)}\mathbf{A}^{(k)T}$

is closely related to the Hessian matrix $\nabla^2\psi(\mathbf{x}^{(k)}, \boldsymbol{\lambda}^{(k)})$ derived from the Powell–Hestenes penalty function (they differ only in the term $\sum_i \sigma_i c_i \nabla^2 c$ which is negligible in the limit). This enables a close connexion to be established (below) between another Lagrangian method and the penalty function.

An interesting feature of algorithms like those based on (8.5.3) and (8.5.4) is that if they converge they do so at a second-order rate. However the analysis is of interest, and explains some other characteristics of the methods. If errors $\mathbf{e}^{(k)} = \mathbf{x}^{(k)} - \mathbf{x}^*$ and $\boldsymbol{\Delta}^{(k)} = \boldsymbol{\lambda}^{(k)} - \boldsymbol{\lambda}^*$ are defined, then the equations (8.5.5) together with the Taylor series

$$\mathbf{c}^* = \mathbf{c}^{(k)} - \mathbf{A}^{(k)T}\mathbf{e}^{(k)} + O(\|\mathbf{e}^{(k)}\|^2)$$
$$\mathbf{g}^* = \mathbf{g}^{(k)} - \nabla^2 F^{(k)}\mathbf{e}^{(k)} + O(\|\mathbf{e}^{(k)}\|^2)$$
$$\nabla c_i^* = \nabla c_i^{(k)} - \nabla^2 c_i^{(k)}\mathbf{e}^{(k)} + O(\|\mathbf{e}^{(k)}\|^2)$$

show that $\mathbf{e}^{(k+1)}$, $\boldsymbol{\Delta}^{(k+1)}$ satisfy the equations

$$\begin{bmatrix} \mathbf{W}^{(k)} & -\mathbf{A}^{(k)} \\ -\mathbf{A}^{(k)T} & \mathbf{0} \end{bmatrix} \begin{bmatrix} \mathbf{e}^{(k+1)} \\ \boldsymbol{\Delta}^{(k+1)} \end{bmatrix} = \begin{bmatrix} \sum_i \Delta_i^{(k)} \nabla^2 c_i^{(k)} \mathbf{e}^{(k)} + O(\|\mathbf{e}^{(k)}\|^2) \\ O(\|\mathbf{e}^{(k)}\|^2) \end{bmatrix}$$
$$= \begin{bmatrix} O(\|\mathbf{e}^{(k)}\|^2) + O(\|\mathbf{e}^{(k)}\|\,\|\boldsymbol{\Delta}^{(k)}\|) \\ O(\|\mathbf{e}^{(k)}\|^2) \end{bmatrix} \qquad (8.5.7)$$

If $\mathbf{A}^*$ is assumed to be of full rank, then it follows from the second order sufficient conditions for a solution that

$$\begin{bmatrix} \mathbf{W}^* & -\mathbf{A}^* \\ -\mathbf{A}^{*T} & \mathbf{0} \end{bmatrix}$$

is non-singular.

Therefore (8.5.7) shows that if the iteration converges (and if $\mathbf{x}^{(1)}$, $\boldsymbol{\lambda}^{(1)}$ is sufficiently close to $\mathbf{x}^*$, $\boldsymbol{\lambda}^*$ it must converge) then it does so at a second-order rate. The particular form of the R.H.S. of (8.5.7) however gives rise to some interesting observations. For instance, if $\mathbf{x}^{(k)} = \mathbf{x}^*$, so that $\mathbf{e}^{(k)} = \mathbf{0}$, then $(\mathbf{x}^{(k+1)}, \boldsymbol{\lambda}^{(k+1)}) = (\mathbf{x}^*, \boldsymbol{\lambda}^*)$; that is to say if $\mathbf{x}$ is correct, then any errors in $\boldsymbol{\lambda}$ are annihilated. This suggests that when using (8.5.4), to have $\mathbf{x}^{(1)}$ accurate is more important than $\boldsymbol{\lambda}^{(1)}$, which need not be too accurate. This situation is in contrast to the Powell–Hestenes–Rockafellar penalty function where an inaccurate value of $\boldsymbol{\lambda}^{(k)}$ definitely limits the extent to which $\mathbf{x}(\boldsymbol{\lambda}^{(k)})$ agrees with $\mathbf{x}^*$ (assuming $\mathbf{S}$ fixed).

To force global convergence of SOLVER-like algorithms some addition must be made to the basic algorithm of (8.5.4). A Marquardt–Levenberg damping term has been suggested, and also bounds on the size of step permitted on an iteration, for instance $\|\mathbf{x} - \mathbf{x}^{(k)}\|_\infty \leqslant h^{(k)}$. However it is not obvious how to manipulate the parameters which occur when using these ideas. For instance it is not possible to look for a sufficiently large reduction in $F(\mathbf{x})$ as a criterion for reducing the damping term (or increasing $h^{(k)}$), because the amount by which the constraints are violated must be taken into account. Once this problem is solved satisfactorily then I believe that algorithms like (8.5.4) will be of great value in solving nonlinear problems.

Further light on this problem is shed by an idea of Bard and Greenstadt (1969). They show that the correction given by SOLVER can be divided into two parts by using the expression

$$\begin{bmatrix} \mathbf{W}^{(k)} & -\mathbf{A}^{(k)} \\ -\mathbf{A}^{(k)T} & \mathbf{0} \end{bmatrix}^{-1} = \begin{bmatrix} \mathbf{W}^{(k)-1} & \mathbf{0} \\ \mathbf{0} & \mathbf{0} \end{bmatrix} - \begin{bmatrix} \mathbf{W}^{(k)-1}\mathbf{A}^{(k)} \\ \mathbf{I} \end{bmatrix} (\mathbf{A}^{(k)T}\mathbf{W}^{(k)-1}\mathbf{A}^{(k)})^{-1} [\mathbf{A}^{(k)T}\mathbf{W}^{(k)-1} \quad \mathbf{I}]$$

which can readily be verified. On substitution into (8.5.5), this shows that the solution can be divided into two steps, in the first of which $\boldsymbol{\lambda}$ is kept constant at the value $\boldsymbol{\lambda}^{(k)}$, and just $\mathbf{x}^{(k)}$ is varied. Bard and Greenstadt also show that the Lagrangian function for (5.8.4) is *minimized* in this step. The second step then varies both $\mathbf{x}$ and $\boldsymbol{\lambda}^{(k)}$ giving a second-order estimate of $\mathbf{x}^*$, $\boldsymbol{\lambda}^*$, and along this step the Lagrangian function is *maximized.* They therefore consider a two-step algorithm in which these steps are taken alternately. This type of algorithm may merit further consideration because in making each step the aim of either minimizing or maximizing the Lagrangian is well defined. However the idea is closely related to the Powell–Hestenes penalty function when $\mathbf{S} = \mathbf{0}$. The step in which $\boldsymbol{\lambda}^{(k)}$ is kept fixed is then equivalent to minimizing approximately the penalty function (8.2.3) for fixed $\boldsymbol{\lambda}^{(k)}$. The second step is also equivalent to one step of the Newton method (8.2.10) for obtaining $\boldsymbol{\lambda}^{(k+1)}$ and the corresponding change in $\mathbf{x}$ is the predicted value of the change $\mathbf{x}(\boldsymbol{\lambda}^{(k+1)}) - \mathbf{x}(\boldsymbol{\lambda}^{(k)})$. Furthermore by modifying $\mathbf{W}^{(k)}$ by the addition of $\mathbf{A}^{(k)}\mathbf{D}^{(k)}\mathbf{A}^{(k)T}$, and using (8.5.6) as described earlier, with $\mathbf{D}^{(k)} = \mathbf{S}^{(k)}$, then a close connexion between the Bard and Greenstadt method and the penalty-function method is established for any $\mathbf{S}^{(k)}$. The aims of the different methods are illustrated in Fig. 8.2. In this figure $\mathbf{x}(\boldsymbol{\lambda}^{(k)})$ is the solution of the problem (8.2.7), which is implied by the definition of $\mathbf{x}(\boldsymbol{\lambda}^{(k)})$ as the minimizer of the penalty function (8.2.3) for fixed $\boldsymbol{\lambda}^{(k)}$.

It is instructive that the Murtagh and Sargent method (see Sargent's chaper in this book) is based on carrying out the operations for the penalty-function method (or the Bard and Greenstadt method) in the opposite order.

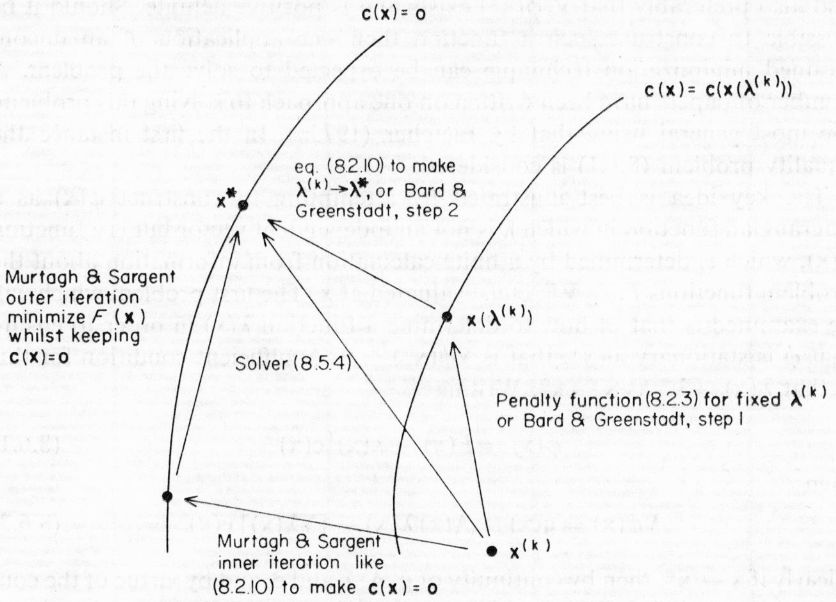

FIG. 8.2. The aims of different Lagrangian methods.

That is to say, (8.2.10) is used as an inner iteration to vary $\boldsymbol{\lambda}$ whilst also making the appropriate correction to $\mathbf{x}$ (see equation (5.3.17) of Sargent's paper) so as to ensure $\mathbf{c}(\mathbf{x}) = \mathbf{0}$. The outer iteration is based on $\mathbf{S}$ in equation (5.3.12) of Sargent's paper, giving the correction to $\mathbf{x}$ which minimizes $F(\mathbf{x})$ subject to staying on the constraints. This is equivalent to the minimization phase of Powell–Hestenes penalty function, or to step 1 of the Bard and Greenstadt method.

Part III
Exact Penalty Functions

8.6. Fletcher's Method

One disadvantage of the conventional penalty function (that in Part I for instance) is that the solution is obtained only in the limit of a sequence of unconstrained minimization problems. It is attractive therefore to try to construct a function $\phi(\mathbf{x})$ of which $\mathbf{x}^*$ is a local minimizer, a so-called *exact penalty function*. To enable conventional techniques to be used to advantage, it is necessary that ϕ is smooth, particularly in that $\nabla\phi(\mathbf{x}^*)$ exists and is zero, and also preferably that $\nabla^2\phi(\mathbf{x}^*)$ exists and is positive definite. Should it be possible to construct such a function then one application of an unconstrained minimization technique can be expected to solve the problem. A number of papers have been written on one approach to solving this problem, the most general being that by Fletcher (1973a). In the first instance the equality problem (8.1.1) is considered.

The key idea is best illustrated by attempting to construct $\phi(\mathbf{x})$ as a Lagrangian function in which $\boldsymbol{\lambda}$ is not an independent vector but is a function $\boldsymbol{\lambda}(\mathbf{x})$, which is determined by a finite calculation from information about the problem functions F, c_i, ∇F, etc., evaluated at $\mathbf{x}$. The first problem which will be examined is that of how to determine a function $\boldsymbol{\lambda}(\mathbf{x})$ in order to ensure that ϕ is stationary at $\mathbf{x}^*$, that is $\nabla\phi(\mathbf{x}^*) = \mathbf{0}$. A sufficient condition for this is that $\boldsymbol{\lambda}(\mathbf{x}) \to \boldsymbol{\lambda}^*$ as $\mathbf{x} \to \mathbf{x}^*$. Writing

$$\phi(\mathbf{x}) = F(\mathbf{x}) - \boldsymbol{\lambda}(\mathbf{x})^T\mathbf{c}(\mathbf{x}) \tag{8.6.1}$$

then

$$\nabla\phi(\mathbf{x}) = \mathbf{g}(\mathbf{x}) - \mathbf{A}(\mathbf{x})\,\boldsymbol{\lambda}(\mathbf{x}) - [\nabla\boldsymbol{\lambda}(\mathbf{x})]\,\mathbf{c}(\mathbf{x}). \tag{8.6.2}$$

Clearly if $\mathbf{x} \to \mathbf{x}^*$, then by continuity of $\mathbf{g}$, $\mathbf{A}$, $\boldsymbol{\lambda}$ and $\mathbf{c}$, and by virtue of the conditions $\mathbf{g}^* = \mathbf{A}^*\boldsymbol{\lambda}^*$ and $\mathbf{c}^* = \mathbf{0}$, the result $\nabla\phi(\mathbf{x}^*) = \mathbf{0}$ follows.

One way in which a convergent $\boldsymbol{\lambda}(\mathbf{x})$ can be constructed is to set

$$\boldsymbol{\lambda}(\mathbf{x}) = \mathbf{A}^{+T}\mathbf{g}|_x \tag{8.6.3}$$

which is the least-squares solution of the over-determined linear equations $\mathbf{A}\boldsymbol{\lambda} = \mathbf{g}$. This gives

$$\phi(\mathbf{x}) = F(\mathbf{x}) - \mathbf{c}(\mathbf{x})^T\mathbf{A}^+(\mathbf{x})\,\mathbf{g}(\mathbf{x}), \tag{8.6.4}$$

and it is easy to see that $\nabla\phi(\mathbf{x}^*) = \mathbf{0}$. It is important therefore to investigate whether $\mathbf{x}^*$ is in fact a local minimum of (8.6.4). Some further matrix algebra establishes the equation

$$\nabla^2\phi(\mathbf{x}^*) = \hat{\mathbf{P}}\mathbf{W}^*\hat{\mathbf{P}} - \mathbf{P}\mathbf{W}^*\mathbf{P}, \tag{8.6.5}$$

where $\mathbf{P}$ is the projection matrix $\mathbf{A}^*\mathbf{A}^{*+}$ for which $\mathbf{P}\mathbf{A}^* = \mathbf{A}^*$, where $\hat{\mathbf{P}} = \mathbf{I} - \mathbf{P}$, and where $\mathbf{W}^* = \nabla^2F^* - \sum_i \lambda_i{}^*\nabla c_i{}^{2*}$. Because of the second-order sufficiency conditions $\mathbf{v}^T\mathbf{W}^*\mathbf{v} > \mathbf{0}$ for all $\mathbf{v}$: $\mathbf{A}^{*T}\mathbf{v} = \mathbf{0}$, it follows that $\hat{\mathbf{P}}\mathbf{W}^*\hat{\mathbf{P}}$ is positive semi-definite, but unfortunately nothing much can be said about the term $-\mathbf{P}\mathbf{W}^*\mathbf{P}$. Indeed it is not difficult to construct examples for which this term has negative eigenvalues. Thus (8.6.4) is not suitable for an exact penalty function as it stands.

Further progress can be made however by noting that the curvature of $\phi(\mathbf{x})$ may be wrong only in directions which have components along the normals, i.e. the columns of $\mathbf{A}^*$. This follows by virtue of (8.6.5) and the definition of $\mathbf{P}$. It is therefore possible to add a squared term of the form $\mathbf{c}(\mathbf{x})^T\mathbf{Q}\mathbf{c}(\mathbf{x})$ into ϕ, with $\mathbf{Q}$ positive definite, so that the condition $\nabla\phi(\mathbf{x}^*) = \mathbf{0}$ is not affected, but so that positive curvature is obtained. One particular choice is $\mathbf{Q} = q\mathbf{A}^+\mathbf{A}^{+T}$ for some scalar $q > 0$ giving the function

$$\phi(\mathbf{x}) = F(\mathbf{x}) - [\mathbf{c}^T\mathbf{A}^+\mathbf{g}]_{\mathbf{x}} + q[\mathbf{c}^T\mathbf{A}^+\mathbf{A}^{+T}\mathbf{c}]_{\mathbf{x}}. \tag{8.6.6}$$

Again $\nabla\phi(\mathbf{x}^*) = \mathbf{0}$ for (8.6.6) and it is possible to show that

$$\nabla^2\phi(\mathbf{x}^*) = \hat{\mathbf{P}}\mathbf{W}^*\hat{\mathbf{P}} + \mathbf{P}(2q\mathbf{I} - \mathbf{W}^*)\mathbf{P}. \tag{8.6.7}$$

Now by choosing q sufficiently large, the last term of (8.6.7) can be made positive definite, a practical choice being $q > \frac{1}{2}\|\mathbf{W}^*\|_2$. Hence the augmented Lagrangian function of (8.6.6) is an exact penalty function of the type required.

Numerical experiments have been carried out using (8.6.6) which indicate that the theory of the method is well founded. However there is one feature that puts the function $\phi(\mathbf{x})$ at a substantial disadvantage as compared to the Powell–Hestenes function for example. To calculate $\phi(\mathbf{x})$ in (8.6.6) requires not only $F(\mathbf{x})$ and $\mathbf{c}(\mathbf{x})$ but also $\nabla F(\mathbf{x})$ and $[\nabla c_i(\mathbf{x})] \equiv \mathbf{A}(\mathbf{x})$. To calculate $\nabla\phi$ therefore requires second derivatives of F and $\mathbf{c}$ in addition to the above information. Thus if only first derivatives of F and $\mathbf{c}$ are available, a minimization method without derivatives must be applied to ϕ. When using the Powell–Hestenes function however, first derivatives of the penalty function can be calculated in the same circumstances, and therefore the minimization can be carried out much more efficiently. Experiments have been carried out with (8.6.6) in which $\nabla\phi$ is estimated by neglecting curvature terms, and although encouraging numerical results have been obtained, the approach is rather messy and it is difficult to guarantee convergence.

If second derivatives of F and $\mathbf{c}$ are available then there are no difficulties. Although $\nabla^2\phi(\mathbf{x})$ is not available, it happens that $\nabla^2\phi(\mathbf{x}^*)$ depends only on second derivatives. Therefore it is possible to calculate a matrix $\mathbf{\Gamma}(\mathbf{x})$ using only second-derivative information, such that $\mathbf{\Gamma}(\mathbf{x}) \to \nabla^2\phi(\mathbf{x}^*)$ as $\mathbf{x} \to \mathbf{x}^*$. This enables second-order convergence of a Newton-like iteration to be ensured. In these circumstances therefore the apparent advantage of the exact penalty function over the conventional penalty function is a real one.

The extension of these ideas to solve inequality problems is by no means obvious because to resort to an active set strategy for instance would mean that the definition of $\phi(\mathbf{x})$ would change every time the active set changed. However Fletcher (1973a) showed that it is possible to construct an exact penalty function in the sense defined above, even for the inequality problem *P1*. The idea is best seen if $\phi(\mathbf{x})$ in (8.6.6) is not regarded as an augmented

Lagrangian function, but as an ordinary Lagrangian function like (8.6.1) in which $\boldsymbol{\lambda}(\mathbf{x})$ is defined by

$$\boldsymbol{\lambda}(\mathbf{x}) = [\mathbf{A}^{+}(\mathbf{g} - q\mathbf{A}^{+T}\mathbf{c})]_{\mathbf{x}}. \qquad (8.6.8)$$

Now it turns out that $\boldsymbol{\lambda}(\mathbf{x})$ defined in this way is the vector of Lagrange multipliers of the problem

$$\begin{aligned} &\underset{\boldsymbol{\delta}}{\text{minimize}} \; \{Q(\boldsymbol{\delta}) \equiv \tfrac{1}{2}q\boldsymbol{\delta}^T\boldsymbol{\delta} + \mathbf{g}^T\boldsymbol{\delta}\} \\ &\text{subject to } \mathbf{l}(\boldsymbol{\delta}) \equiv \mathbf{A}^T\boldsymbol{\delta} + \mathbf{c} = \mathbf{0}. \end{aligned} \qquad (8.6.9)$$

The coefficients $\mathbf{g}$, $\mathbf{A}$ and $\mathbf{c}$ are $\mathbf{g}(\mathbf{x})$, $\mathbf{A}(\mathbf{x})$ and $\mathbf{c}(\mathbf{x})$ and so the multiplier vector of the linear constraints in (8.6.9) will be a function $\boldsymbol{\lambda}(\mathbf{x})$, and in fact (8.6.8) is an expression for these multipliers. This problem is a quadratic programming problem with equality constraints.

This relationship suggests how an exact penalty function can be constructed for an inequality constraint problem. The general form (8.6.1) is again used, but $\boldsymbol{\lambda}(\mathbf{x})$ is defined in the following way. The quantities $\mathbf{g}(\mathbf{x})$, $\mathbf{A}(\mathbf{x})$ and $\mathbf{c}(\mathbf{x})$ are calculated and the subproblem (8.6.9) is solved, excepting that the linear constraints are

$$\mathbf{l}(\boldsymbol{\delta}) \equiv \mathbf{A}^T\boldsymbol{\delta} + \mathbf{c} \geqslant \mathbf{0}.$$

The multiplier vector of these constraints then becomes $\boldsymbol{\lambda}(\mathbf{x})$. Because the solution of a quadratic programming problem is a finite calculation, the same is therefore true for the determination of $\phi(\mathbf{x})$. In fact (8.6.9) is a *least-distance problem* which is a particularly simple form of a quadratic programming problem, and advantage can be taken of this to give simple methods for its solution.

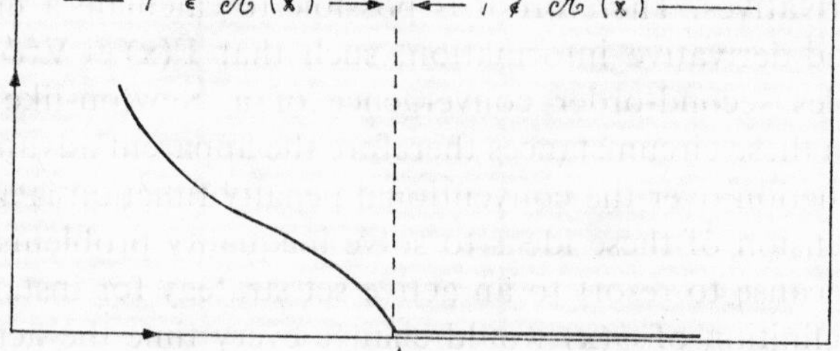

FIG. 8.3. Derivative discontinuity in $\boldsymbol{\lambda}(\mathbf{x})$ for inequalities.

A useful way of looking at what is happening is that the solution of the quadratic programming subproblem for inequalities is being used to give an indication of which constraints should be treated as equalities. Thus an active set of inequality constraint indices $\mathscr{A}(\mathbf{x})$ is determined such that $\lambda_i > 0$, $i \in \mathscr{A}(\mathbf{x})$, and $\lambda_i = 0$, $i \notin \mathscr{A}(\mathbf{x})$. The penalty function which is constructed for inequalities is equivalent to using (8.6.6) with the constraints $i \in \mathscr{A}(\mathbf{x})$. The way in which $\mathscr{A}(\mathbf{x})$ is chosen ensures the continuity of $\phi(\mathbf{x})$. In fact x-space can be thought of as being divided up into regions in each of which $\mathscr{A}(\mathbf{x})$ is constant, and such that $\mathscr{A}(\mathbf{x})$ differs in only one constraint index between neighbouring regions. Then if $\mathbf{x}$ is varied smoothly so as to pass from one region to the next, some $\lambda_i(\mathbf{x})$ which is greater than zero in one region will vary smoothly until it becomes zero on the boundary of the region. Then it will stay fixed at zero in the other region. This in general causes a discontinuity in derivative of $\lambda_i(\mathbf{x})$ as illustrated in Fig. 8.3.
The fact that derivative discontinuities can occur in $\boldsymbol{\lambda}(\mathbf{x})$ means that the same is true of $\phi(\mathbf{x})$, with the important exception that a derivative discontinuity in $\phi(\mathbf{x})$ cannot occur at $\mathbf{x}^*$ because $\lambda_i(\mathbf{x}^*)$ will be multiplied by $c_i(\mathbf{x}^*)$ which is zero. Usually however there is a region about $\mathbf{x}^*$ in which $\mathscr{A}(\mathbf{x})$ is constant and $\phi(\mathbf{x})$ is smooth.

It is not clear what effect these discontinuities have on the rate of convergence of the minimization method. Limited numerical experiments have been carried out and on small problems the correct active set is soon determined and the solution is found in a very few function evaluations. However on one larger problem the active set took much longer to determine and the relative performance of the method *vis-a-vis* other methods, was not outstanding. It may be that the presence of these first-derivative discontinuities in $\phi(\mathbf{x})$ for $\mathbf{x}$ remote from the solution, slows down the rate of convergence of the unconstrained minimization routine. Until these difficulties have been resolved satisfactorily, use of exact penalty functions for inequality constraints is limited.

Chapter IX

Algorithms and Future Developments

PHILIP E. GILL AND WALTER MURRAY

Division of Numerical Analysis and Computing, National Physical Laboratory

9.1. Introduction

The purpose of this discussion of algorithms is to give a general guide to the state of current research in each particular area. We shall not attempt to catalogue the algorithms that are available, since the same or similar algorithms from different sources may have different names, and since the names of algorithms often change over time. We shall give possible sources of program listings and documentation, but it should be noted that inevitably the development of high-quality and reasonably portable software lags behind the development of theoretical algorithms. Since the methods discussed in this book are relatively new, few of them have yet been implemented for general use; however, they should be available in the next year or so.

In recent years there has been a radical change in the manner in which algorithms are disseminated, especially in the United Kingdom. Previously a new optimization method was published in some research journal; either the method was accompanied by a short program implementing its ideas or such a program was obtainable from the author on application. Usually, these programs were written simply to test out the new ideas in the methods and were required to work only on a limited number of selected examples. They would, for instance, rarely cater for saddle points or zero Lagrange multipliers. Little attention was given to documentation or even the standard of the coding. Progressively, optimization methods have grown more complex so that it is now very difficult and time-consuming for an isolated individual to write his own computer implementation of a new method. Fortunately, due to a greater awareness on the part of authors and software specialists, the need to provide reliable, efficient, portable and fully documented software is now recognized. In the UK this new spirit has resulted in the creation of the Numerical Algorithms Group (NAG—originally called the Nottingham Algorithms Group) which is an organization concerned with the creation of a high-quality numerical library in ALGOL and FORTRAN. The numerical analysis community in the UK has lent considerable support to the group and now channels much of its new material through NAG.

The discussion of "future developments" in this chapter will include a wide range of desirable, likely and unlikely developments. The results of future research are notoriously difficult to predict with any accuracy, and consequently we shall be concerned primarily with broad trends. Often there is little activity in a research area because it is thought that all possible progress has taken place. One or two key papers may awaken new interest, and a searching and critical re-examination may then lead to more significant results. Conversely, progress may be considered unlikely because the problems involved are considered insuperable. However, a result that does not even solve the problem in a practical way can give new hope of an ultimate solution and thereby lead to rapid and fruitful developments.

9.2. Sources of Computer Listings

The following are sources of program listings in the area of mathematical programming.

Numerical Algorithms Group, Oxford University Computing Laboratory, 13 Banbury Road, Oxford OX2 6NN.

Division of Numerical Analysis and Computing, National Physical Laboratory, Teddington, Middlesex TW11 0LW.

Division of Computer Science, Atomic Energy Research Establishment, Harwell, Didcot, Oxfordshire OX11 0RA.

Numerical Optimization Centre, Hatfield Polytechnic, Hertfordshire.

George Washington University, Washington DC.

Madison Academic Computing Center, Madison, Wisconsin.

Applied Mathematics Division, Argonne National Laboratory, Illinois 60439.

In addition, programs are published in a number of journals such as the Computer Journal, B.I.T. and the Communications of the ACM (though the last is shortly to be superseded by the ACM's new journal—Transactions on Mathematical Software).

The development of optimization procedures is unlikely to reach the level of those in linear algebra, say, where very specific guarantees can be made concerning the computed results. It will always be necessary for the user of an optimization procedure to be able to intelligently interpret the computed results. Advice on how to do this is usually given in the documentation and some general comments are given in Murray (1972b). The options open to a user wishing to solve a particular problem can be numerous and the inexperienced user would be well advised to seek professional help. The options arise because there are a number of algorithms to solve each category of problem. In addition it may be desirable to transform a problem to one of a different type; even when the optimum form of the problem is known, the user may be unable to judge whether the effort of providing a routine to compute first derivatives, say, is worthwhile.

The contents of the routines available from the individual organizations listed are not necessarily different, since a degree of co-operation exists between a number of them. The research organizations are usually the root source of the algorithms in the NAG and Argonne libraries and so they will have available additional routines which are judged unsuitable for inclusion in these libraries or which have still to be processed. (An algorithm may be judged unsuitable because it is very machine-dependent or simply because the pressure to limit the total number of routines in the library has forced some to be excluded on the grounds that they are too specialized.)

NAG are currently developing their library for a range of different machines and, although they were originally set up as a project within the UK university system, they are now planning to market their library to any interested party. Part of this library service would include a supporting consulting service which for the optimization area would come from the NPL. They are not planning to market individual routines but currently these can be obtained by writing to the NPL.

9.3. Test Problems and Comparative Evaluation of Algorithms

To measure the efficiency and reliability of an algorithm by well-defined and objective criteria is a substantial problem, which becomes more difficult as the complexity of algorithms grows. The problem is particularly acute in optimization, where different authors use completely different measures to compare algorithms, and may fail to mention the details of an implementation required for an adequate comparison. There are two principal prerequisites for meaningful comparisons to be made: a comprehensive set of test problems, and a detailed analysis of comparable algorithms.

Test Problems

It is not obvious how to specify what constitutes an adequate set of test problems for a particular area, but certain necessary principles appear self-evident.

(a) There should be a sufficient number of diverse problems to prevent peculiarities of the test functions being unfairly exploited in algorithm design. It is not uncommon for an author to adjust the free parameters or to choose a strategy in an algorithm so that it will give the best results on a few special examples. (Naturally, we distinguish between the success of an algorithm at coping with a particular problem only, and its ability to cope with a general difficulty illustrated by the problem.) If performance is always assessed on a large number of dissimilar test problems, the algorithm designer will be less able to appear successful by "tuning" his algorithm to cater for specialized problems only.

(b) Some of the test problems should contain features known to cause difficulty and the testing process must ensure that the difficulties actually are encountered. For example, a method for unconstrained optimization must be tested on a function with a saddle point, and, in addition, it must be guaranteed that the method has dealt with the saddle point rather than simply avoided it through random deviations in the search directions. Similarly, test problems for unconstrained minimization must force the algorithm to face an ill-conditioned or singular Hessian at the solution, a region where the Hessian is indefinite, wide variation of scaling, and so on.

The essential point is that the test problems should fulfill several requirements:

(i) they should test everything that can possibly go wrong with the algorithm;

(ii) they should include enough ordinary problems so that a realistic comparison can be made of algorithms for general use;

(iii) they should contain general features that are typical of a large set of problems, and for which one might design an algorithm.

There is a fairly extensive set of test problems for the dense unconstrained case, but even this area suffers from some of the deficiencies mentioned. For example, there is a concentration of small problems; and a lack of clarity about which features are represented by the test functions chosen.

The task of cataloguing test problems is too vast for a single individual and the Mathematical Programming Society have recently set up a working party. Anyone who wishes to contribute problems or give assistance should write to J. A. Tomlin, Systems Optimization Laboratory, Stanford University, Stanford, California 94305.

Comparative Evaluation of Algorithms

If one wishes to know whether a new method is superior to others, one needs to study a thorough comparison of its performance on a set of test problems. For example, one needs to know how the superiority of the new algorithm is defined—that is, does it take fewer iterations? fewer function evaluations? fewer arithmetic operations per iteration? will it succeed on functions where other methods fail? etc. For this purpose there must be given a clear definition of what constitutes an "iteration" of the algorithm (for example, it includes solving a set of linear equations, updating a factorization, performing an exact line search, etc). The information provided should make clear the characteristics of problems for which the algorithm (a) takes fewer function evaluations than other procedures; (b) takes less computing time than other procedures; (c) requires less storage than other procedures; (d) fails to converge but does not recognize failure; (e) fails to converge but recognizes failure; (f) produces an accurate solution.

The free parameters that are available must also be thoroughly checked, and the effect of adjusting each should be examined to determine the result in various kinds of situations. For example, in the dense unconstrained case a parameter controlling the accuracy of the linear search may have a large effect on the results, depending on the kind of function.

The computer implementation of an algorithm should be examined as well. It is possible to take advantage of language, machine and compiler features to yield a faster solution time, but this may correspond to a complete lack of coherence, program structure and modularity. Furthermore, the behaviour of an algorithm on a particular example may alter completely on a computer with a different wordlength. It is therefore important to consider which parts of the algorithm may be machine dependent. It can be extremely difficult to determine behaviour on different machines, particularly with algorithms for large structured problems, where special features of each machine must be utilized to execute the program.

In summary, it is essential that a standardized analysis be carried out for each algorithm, so that the person with a problem to be solved can make a correct choice of algorithm for his problem, and the developer of a new algorithm can compare every aspect of his algorithm with those already available. Unfortunately not all programs that are generally available have been subjected to the sort of comparison discussed here, but a program distributed by a good numerical software library will usually be thoroughly validated. As a matter of good practice the user should always seek to perform his own rudimentary check.

(i) Are there enough test problems and are they representative?

(ii) Has the wordlength of the computer been given with the test results?

(iii) Bearing in mind the effect of (i) and (ii) are the test results competitive with those of comparable methods?

(iv) Are good values of the free parameters easy to determine?

9.4. Unconstrained Optimization

Although this book is not concerned directly with unconstrained optimization, successful development in that field has been the springboard for the more recent successes on constrained problems. Accordingly, some review of the subject is appropriate here.

Satisfactory algorithms for all categories of unconstrained problems are now available as high-quality software. Future development is likely to concern refinement of existing methods primarily, although there always exists a possibility of radical change—such as by altering the nature of the underlying approximation. All algorithms other than some direct search methods are in some way based on a quadratic approximation to $F(\mathbf{x})$; for example, many of the algorithms converge in a finite number of iterations when $F(\mathbf{x})$ is a quadratic function. Jacobson and Oksman (1972) have proposed a new method which is able to minimize a wider class of functions than quadratics in a finite number of iterations. The class of functions they considered satisfies the relationship

$$F(\mathbf{x}) = \frac{1}{\gamma}(\mathbf{x} - \overset{*}{\mathbf{x}})^T \mathbf{g}(\mathbf{x}) + F(\overset{*}{\mathbf{x}}), \tag{9.4.1}$$

where the scalar γ is termed the *degree of homogeneity*. It is clear that if $F(\mathbf{x})$ is a quadratic then it satisfies (9.4.1) with $\gamma = 2$. Methods based on this approach have yet to prove as efficient as the best alternative algorithms, and this may be because the procedure determines a poor value of γ when the optimal γ should be 2, as it is for most problems. However this alternative model does attempt to deal with the outstanding difficulty of the Hessian matrix being positive semi-definite either at the solution or elsewhere. If the notion of quadratic approximation were superseded, a substantial re-appraisal would certainly occur.

In any algorithm where the search direction is based on the gradient or some approximation to the gradient, it is usually necessary to have some alternative means of generating a search direction if the gradient is zero or close to zero. In Newton-type methods this is often easy since a direction of negative curvature (see Chapter II, Section 2.3) will usually suffice. For quasi-Newton methods the "alternative search procedure" is based on a direct search strategy. In practice it is desirable to use the "alternative search procedure" not only at saddle points but whenever the regular search direction is making unsatisfactory progress. Unfortunately, in the latter case the alternative search procedure is rarely successful. A possible refinement would be the discovery of an "alternative search procedure" which could generate an adequate search direction whenever the quasi-Newton method was making slow progress. This type of development would be very similar to that which has already been successful in linear search procedures, where an interval-reducing step is taken if the step based on interpolation methods is deemed unsatisfactory.

It is possible that superior quasi-Newton updating formulae will be discovered, although in our view the probability of radical improvement is small. A subject of some interest in this area is the question of whether or not the Hessian approximation converges, both theoretically and numerically, to the Hessian at the solution.

We do not expect a significant overall improvement in the efficiency of existing algorithms, but we believe that refinements will occur which will reduce the number of problems on which current algorithms fail. Most of the expected refinements will have little or no effect on the user since they will involve only minor alterations to existing routines.

9.5. Linearly Constrained Optimization

The successes in unconstrained optimization have to a large extent been incorporated in algorithms for the linearly constrained case, although the associated high-quality software is not yet generally available. Obviously, any further improvement of unconstrained algorithms will have an immediate impact on linearly constrained algorithms. Experience with the latest algorithms is still very limited and the optimum choice of free parameters etc., and the effect these have on an algorithm's efficiency is still not fully known. For example, it may be that the best quasi-Newton updating formula for the linearly constrained case is different from that for the unconstrained case. these details can be settled only after extensive testing, and this is difficult to undertake since currently there is an inadequate set of test problems.

The area developing most rapidly is the adaptation of algorithms for linear constraints to sparse and structured problems. This extension is, except in some simple cases, far from straightforward; many fundamental problems and difficulties still exist, although the results given in Chapter IV indicate the significant progress that has been made. Since every advantage must be taken of machine design and the large input/output and data-handling procedures available, the software for the large sparse case will undoubtedly be less portable. Unfortunately this also means that the implementations will be quite sensitive to changes in machine architecture and the best algorithm as well as the optimal implementation might change with a fundamental alteration in machine design. In particular, the size of core on new machines has grown to such an extent that a large percentage of problems can now be solved in-core. Such a trend may well be only temporary since awareness of the improved potential of a machine eventually leads to an increase in the dimension and complexity of the problems to be solved. The advent of virtual memory and virtual machines with sophisticated operating systems has had a counterproductive effect on large-scale mathematical programming since there is less scope for optimizing the transfer of data in and out of core.

9.6. Nonlinearly Constrained Optimization

The construction of a reliable and efficient computer program usually involves the following stages of development: (a) the theoretical formulation of the method; (b) a practical validation of the method using a pilot program; (c) the refinement of the pilot program. It is our view that, in contrast to the linearly constrained and unconstrained cases, there is no efficient method for problems with nonlinear constraints which has passed through all these development stages and that existing generally-available software is either unreliable, or inefficient, or both. Although it will be only a matter of time before some pilot programs are refined into good software, significant theoretical work appears to be necessary before the situation will bear any resemblance to that prevailing in unconstrained or linearly constrained optimization.

The detailed implementation of an algorithm can involve considerable computational difficulties in the nonlinear case, as the following example illustrates. Suppose that along a direction of search we require the maximum possible step which does not violate any of the inactive nonlinear constraints. In the linear case the distance to an inactive constraint can be computed using two inner products, but in the nonlinear case the zero of a nonlinear function must be found. The construction of an algorithm to find the zero of a nonlinear function can be a non-trivial exercise and it may be preferable not to require such a computation, in much the same way as exact univariate minimizations are sometimes avoided in unconstrained minimization.

Of the methods for which numerical software is generally available, those based on "classical" penalty and barrier functions are the most common (see Chapter VI). However, they have not yet benefitted from recent improvements in unconstrained and linearly constrained techniques described in Chapters II and III. Such improved software should become available shortly since it exists in one or two private libraries; moreover it is likely to be of value for some time due to the lengthy process of producing alternative methods as high-quality software.

It is generally believed that strategies which are based in some way upon the properties of the Lagrangian give the best rate of convergence and have superior numerical properties (see Chapter VIII for a discussion of these methods). However, current Lagrangian methods still experience the following difficulties on certain types of problem.

(i) Nearly all Lagrangian methods generate a sequence of points which lie partially or totally within the non-feasible region. Since it may be impossible to evaluate the function in the non-feasible region or such values may be meaningless, there is a need for more algorithms which generate a sequence of feasible approximations to the solution. An advantage of such algorithms is that a usable "sub-optimal" solution will be found whenever the algorithm is terminated.

(ii) In general, Lagrangian techniques assume that the Kuhn–Tucker conditions are satisfied at the solution, and if this is not the case the methods will perform poorly.

(iii) Most of the Lagrangian methods discussed in Chapter VIII depend critically on having good estimates of the Lagrange multipliers and we have already mentioned in Chapter III that this is a difficult problem even in the linearly constrained case. It may not be necessary to improve the *accuracy* of these estimates, but merely to ensure that the type of error is acceptable—by analogy, consider the error in a quasi-Newton approximate Hessian matrix; given an acceptable magnitude of error it is desirable for the approximate Hessian to be positive definite. When the projected Hessian of the Lagrangian function is positive definite but nearly singular, Lagrangian methods will be more sensitive than usual to errors in the Lagrange multipliers. This is because these errors could cause the projected Hessian of the approximate Lagrangian to become indefinite.

Some benefits can be obtained by taking a fresh look at well-established methods. Recently there has been new interest in the penalty function

$$F(\mathbf{x}) + r \sum_{i \in I} |c_i(\mathbf{x})|, \tag{9.6.1}$$

where r is a scalar and I is the index set of violated constraints. This differs from the "classical" penalty functions in that only a single value of the penalty parameter is required. The algorithm is similar to the ideal penalty function discussed by Fletcher in Chapter VIII. Although the properties of this penalty function have been known for some time it has not been given serious consideration due to discontinuities in the first derivatives. Conn (1973) has suggested how this difficulty can be overcome and has presented an algorithm which is feasible computationally although it lacks the simplicity of the original approach, which involves merely the application of an algorithm for unconstrained minimization to the function (9.6.1).

As yet, the satisfactory extension of algorithms to sparse and structured problems has occurred only for trivial cases. Developments in the linearly constrained area will accelerate this process, since the software can be adapted for many problems with nonlinear constraints. For many algorithms, however, sparsity and structure must exist in the Hessian of each constraint as well as in the Hessian of the objective function and the matrix of constraint gradients. Absence of this additional sparsity will necessitate use of methods which do not depend on the Hessian of the Lagrangian function.

All the methods discussed in this volume have been designed to solve the continuous variable problem. In many practical situations, however, variables may be required as integers or members of some other discrete set. For example, x_i might be (i) the *number* of components of a particular type in a piece of equipment or (ii) a *dimension* of a component which can be obtained only in particular sizes. Optimization problems which involve discrete variables constitute the field of *Integer Programming*. Integer *linear* programming has been well studied and, although rapid developments continue, many satisfactory algorithms are generally available.

In the above examples of discrete variables the continuous solution may have a valid interpretation (e.g. equipment built of components with non-standard sizes) and/or the number of possible values of x_i may be large. In other situations, however, x_i may represent a choice between alternatives which differ qualitatively (e.g. alternative materials for a manufacturing process). In the latter cases, values of x_i which differ from the assigned possibilities may have no meaning. Mathematically these two categories of problems do not differ, but the success of a given algorithm may vary widely depending on which type of problem is being solved. Very little general work has been done on integer/discrete nonlinear programming, principally because of the limited success achieved so far in integer linear programming and continuous nonlinear programming. Particular problems of this type have been solved on an *ad hoc* basis and we expect that general purpose algorithms will become available in the next few years.

9.7. Global Optimization

The problem considered in this book is to find a "solution" of the problem

$$\underset{\mathbf{x}}{\text{minimize}}\,\{F(\mathbf{x})\} \quad \text{for} \quad \mathbf{x} \in R \subset E^n.$$

We interpret a solution as being a point $\overset{*}{\mathbf{x}} \in R$ such that for all small feasible perturbations, say $\overset{*}{\mathbf{x}} + \mathbf{y}$ we have

$$F(\overset{*}{\mathbf{x}}) \leqslant F(\overset{*}{\mathbf{x}} + \mathbf{y}). \tag{9.7.1}$$

Clearly it would be useful to find a "global minimum", $\overline{\mathbf{x}}$, such that

$$F(\overline{\mathbf{x}}) \leqslant F(\mathbf{x}), \qquad \text{for } all\, \mathbf{x} \in R.$$

All the algorithms discussed so far in this book seek only to determine an $\overset{*}{\mathbf{x}}$ satisfying (9.7.1); although $\overline{\mathbf{x}}$ may inadvertently be found, it would not be possible to confirm this fact.

What are the prospects of extending or generalizing the available algorithms to determine a global minimum? McCormick (1972) reviews methods that have been specifically designed for global optimization. In this section we shall review some work subsequent to McCormick's paper which suggests that it is extremely unlikely that an efficient general purpose global optimization algorithm will ever be devised for any but a very narrow class of functions. The primary difficulty is finding a balance between techniques to achieve efficient convergence on well-behaved functions and safeguards to guarantee success on difficult functions. In this context the "efficiency" of an algorithm is loosely measured by the number of function evaluations required to find the desired minimum to within a given tolerance. When searching for a global minimum the decision mentioned above must be weighted heavily in favour of safeguards, and efficiency becomes almost impossible to achieve.

Functions of a Single Variable

There might seem to be some hope of finding an efficient algorithm for global minimization in the one-variable case, since a bound on the second derivative of $F(\mathbf{x})$ implies a limit to the number of local minima that can occur in a finite interval $[a, b]$. Moreover the bound on the second derivative implies the existence of a minimum separation between different local minima. The lower the bound, the fewer the possible local minima and the larger the interval about each point which cannot contain a minimum. Thus the bound on the second derivative enables us to construct an algorithm to find the global minimum of the function within a specified interval. (Such an algorithm would obviously be iterative, but only a finite number of function evaluations are required to find the global minimum to any prescribed tolerance, no matter how small. This last remark may seem superfluous, but we wish to avoid algorithms that find global minima by the construction of several infinite sequences.) An algorithm based on the observations described above has been given by Brent (1973), together with some numerical experience.

The Figs 9.1 and 9.2 illustrate the conflicting requirements of efficiency and the need to find a global minimum. Any efficient algorithm designed to find a local minimum in the interval $[a, b]$ will almost certainly miss the global minimum in Fig. 9.1. Conversely any algorithm that can guarantee finding the global minimum of the function given in Fig. 9.1 is likely to be very inefficient at finding the minimum of the function given in Fig. 9.2. There is no way to avoid this inefficiency without placing more restrictions on $F(\mathbf{x})$ or requiring more information about the function and its derivatives.

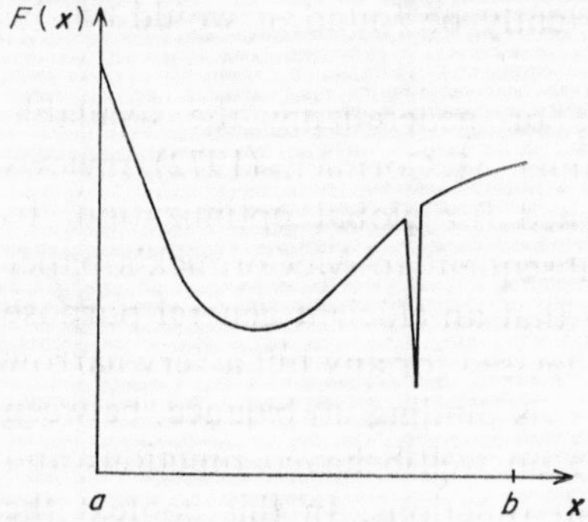

FIG. 9.1.

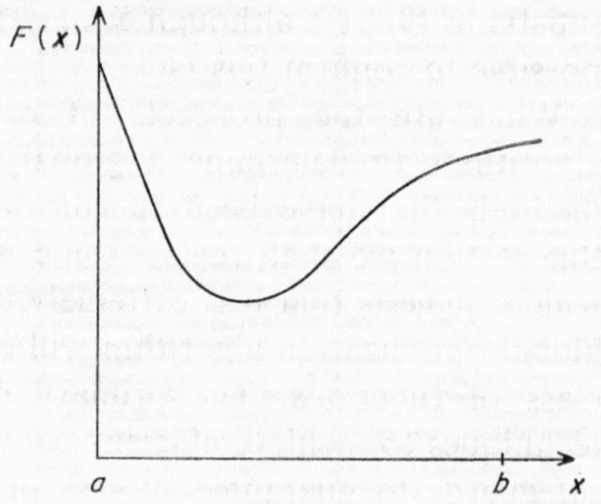

FIG. 9.2.

Brent has also shown how to use a method for one-variable global minimization recursively to yield the global minimum of an n-dimensional function in a given n-dimensional interval. The bounds required for this algorithm concern the diagonal elements of the Hessian matrix of $F(\mathbf{x})$. As in the earlier examples of one-dimensional functions, the algorithm is grossly inefficient when applied to even very simple problems of low dimension.

Finding the Global Minimum of an Indefinite Quadratic Programming Problem

In our standard notation the indefinite quadratic programming (IQP) problem is of the form

$$\underset{\mathbf{x}}{\text{minimize}} \ \{\tfrac{1}{2}\mathbf{x}^T\mathbf{G}\mathbf{x} + \mathbf{c}^T\mathbf{x}\} \ \text{ subject to } \mathbf{A}^T\mathbf{x} \geqslant \mathbf{b}, \tag{9.7.2}$$

where $\mathbf{G}$ is a symmetric matrix, but not necessarily positive definite. From the brief discussion of IQP given in Chapter II, Section 2.8, the global optimum of (9.7.2) is also the unique solution of the QP problem.

$$\underset{\mathbf{x}}{\text{minimize}} \ \{\tfrac{1}{2}\mathbf{x}^T\mathbf{G}\mathbf{x} + \mathbf{c}^T\mathbf{x}\} \ \text{ subject to } \hat{\mathbf{A}}^T\mathbf{x} = \hat{\mathbf{b}},$$

where the equality constraints are a subset of the inequality constraints given in (9.7.2). Since there are only a finite number of constraint subsets, the number of local minima is also finite. In theory all the local minima could be evaluated and the global solution chosen from these. Such an algorithm would be extremely inefficient since the number of constraint subsets is large even for a modest number of constraints. However, this technique would be feasible for problems with a very small number of constraints—no matter how many variables.

If additional information were known, such as the number of zero or negative eigenvalues of **G**, then some assertions could be made concerning the minimum number of constraints active at a local minimum. Such information may drastically reduce the number of constraint subsets required to be examined, since many subsets could be eliminated without the need to find their corresponding stationary point.

A more sophisticated approach has been proposed by Ritter (1966), the basis of which is to exclude any known local minima by adding additional linear constraints—sometimes known as "cutting planes". (This general principle has been used by a number of workers in trying to determine the global solution to more general mathematical programming problems.) The difficulty is to make a significant "cut", or division, of the feasible region without excluding (as yet) undetermined local minima and, if possible. without introducing new spurious local minima.

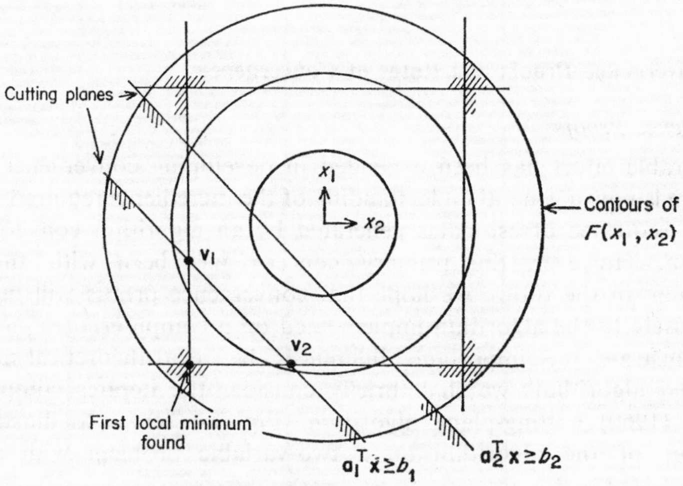

FIG. 9.3.

Recently Zwart (1973) has shown that Ritter's reasoning contains a flaw and that the algorithm cannot be guaranteed to find a global minimum; however, even if the algorithm could be guaranteed convergent, it would still be extremely inefficient. In Fig. 9.3 the technique of introducing cutting planes is applied to the problem

$$\underset{x_1, x_2}{\text{minimize}} \{-x_1{}^2 - x_2{}^2\} \text{ subject to } |x_i| \leqslant 1, \qquad i = 1, 2.$$

If the cut $\mathbf{a}^T\mathbf{x} = b_1$ is introduced we have the undesirable effect of introducing two new local minima at the points $\mathbf{v}_1$ and $\mathbf{v}_2$. However, if a "deeper", or more significant, cut is made the number of local minima is one less than that of the original problem. Clearly, the fundamental difficulty is that a significant amount of computation could be undertaken finding superfluous local minima.

Global Optimization for General Problems

Given the difficulties experienced with two of the simplest problems, it is unlikely that a guaranteed, yet reasonably efficient, algorithm for the general problem will be developed. Any progress will probably be in heuristic algorithms, a number of which (c.f. Hartman 1973) have already been developed. Unfortunately, to date they are not only inefficient but also require vast amounts of storage. We would, however, expect some reasonably efficient algorithms to be developed which guarantee to find the global minimum for special categories of problems provided the number of local minima is small.

9.8. Convergence Proofs and Rates of Convergence

Convergence Proofs

Considerable effort has been expended in developing convergence proofs, and there is now a general understanding of the ingredients required to prove that the sequence of estimates generated by an algorithm converges to a minimum. However, the primary concern has been with theoretical algorithms. In the future we hope that convergence proofs will be related more closely to the algorithm implemented on a computer.

To illustrate the important differences between theoretical and implemented algorithms we shall briefly consider the iterates computed by Kelley's (1960) cutting-plane algorithm. Fig. 9.4 serves to illustrate the behaviour of the algorithm on a two-variable problem with a single constraint $\mathbf{c}(\mathbf{x}) \geqslant \mathbf{0}$.

There is no loss of generality in assuming that $F(\mathbf{x})$ is linear. The feasible region is first embedded in a set of linear constraints which are usually taken to be simple bounds on the variables. The solution over this set, say $\mathbf{x}^{(1)}$, is then determined by the solution of the appropriate linear program. A new linear constraint $\mathbf{a}_1^T\mathbf{x} \geqslant b_1$ is added (the linear approximation to $\mathbf{c}(\mathbf{x})$ expanded about $\mathbf{x}^{(1)}$), and a second *LP* problem is solved, yielding $\mathbf{x}^{(2)}$. This process continues until a sufficiently close approximation to the solution is obtained.

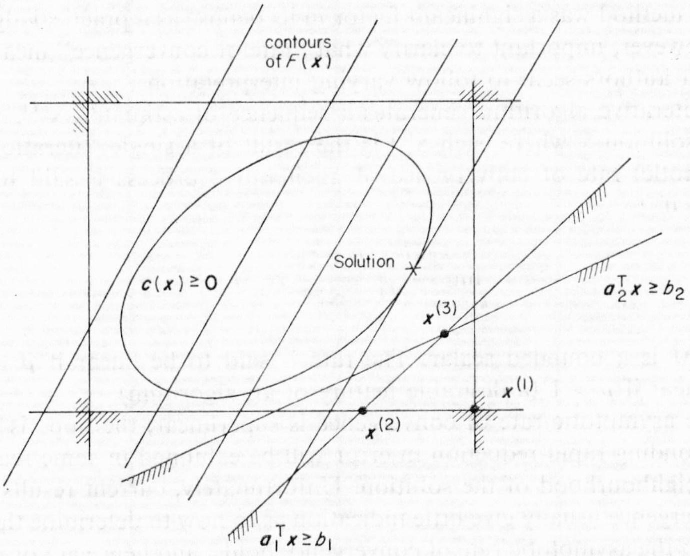

FIG. 9.4.

A critical requirement of the convergence proof for this algorithm is linear independence of successive hyperplanes. It can easily be seen from the figure that although the constraints added remain theoretically independent, some become almost parallel as the solution is approached. Moreover the solution of each subproblem becomes increasingly ill-determined as the contours of the objective function become almost parallel to the constraint hyperplanes. On a computer, numerical linear dependence would eventually occur and the algorithm would fail.

Another point to be considered in evaluating the usefulness of a convergence proof is that nearly all proofs are based upon assumptions that cannot be readily verified. The trend is progressively to weaken the initial assumptions and so generalize a proof; for a generalized proof to have increased usefulness it is important to weaken the right assumptions. For example, we believe that a valuable generalization occurs in not assuming convexity but that little practical value results from proving that a Newton-type method will converge on functions whose first derivatives are continuous and satisfy a Lipschitz condition. (In the latter case the algorithms are nearly always applied to problems for which continuity of the second derivatives may be assumed.)

Rates of Convergence

The importance of the rate of convergence of an algorithm has recently been recognized; indeed, the known poor linear-convergence rate of the steepest-descent method was a significant factor in its demise as a practical algorithm. It is, however, important to clarify what "rate of convergence" means, since different authors seem to follow varying interpretations.

Any iterative algorithm generates a sequence of estimates, $\mathbf{x}^{(1)}$, $\mathbf{x}^{(2)}$, etc, to the solution $\overset{*}{\mathbf{x}}$ where each $\mathbf{x}^{(k)}$ is the result of a single "iteration". The (asymptotic) rate of convergence of an iterative process is said to be the scalar ρ if

$$\lim_{k\to\infty} \frac{\|\mathbf{x}^{(k+1)} - \overset{*}{\mathbf{x}}\|}{\|\mathbf{x}^{(k)} - \overset{*}{\mathbf{x}}\|^{\rho}} = M,$$

where M is a bounded scalar. The rate is said to be linear if $\rho = 1$, and superlinear if $\rho > 1$ (a desirable feature of an algorithm).

If the asymptotic rate of convergence is superlinear, the hope is that the corresponding rapid reduction in error will be exhibited in some reasonably large neighbourhood of the solution. Unfortunately, current results on rate of convergence usually give little indication as to how to determine the region in which the asymptotic rate of convergence holds, and hence are of no value in guiding the numerical computation. Obviously there is a great need for future work in this area.

Sometimes reference is made to a "K-step" convergence rate, usually in connexion with conjugate-direction algorithms. A K-step asymptotic convergence rate ρ is defined as the scalar such that

$$\lim_{k\to\infty} \frac{\|\mathbf{x}^{(k+K)} - \overset{*}{\mathbf{x}}\|}{\|\mathbf{x}^{(k)} - \overset{*}{\mathbf{x}}\|^{\rho}} = M.$$

It is incorrect to assume that a K-step rate of ρ simply implies a one-step rate of $\rho^{1/K}$. On the contrary, such algorithms may have $K-1$ steps whose convergence rates are linear followed by one step which is quadratic ($\rho = 2$).

If the statements made about convergence rates are examined in detail, many are found to be misleading. In fact the rate of convergence depends upon the definition of an "iteration" or "step", so that widely varying rates of convergence can be deduced by using different definitions of an iteration. A method said to have a quadratic rate of convergence may turn out to have K-step quadratic convergence, where K is large and possibly not even finite, if a reasonable definition of "step" is used.

A case in point is a recent algorithm for the nonlinearly constrained problem, for which a quadratic rate of convergence was claimed. Each iteration involved the solution of a linearly constrained problem, so that between $\mathbf{x}^{(k)}$ and $\mathbf{x}^{(k+1)}$ a further sequence of intermediate points was generated. In addition, the method recommended for the linearly constrained subproblem involved yet another sequence of iterates, generated during an exact linear search at each step. Therefore, between $\mathbf{x}^{(k)}$ and $\mathbf{x}^{(k+1)}$ lies a sequence of sequences of iterates, so that the one-step quadratic convergence rate is not as impressive as it would appear initially.

This is not the only example of lack of clarity about rate of convergence, and in fact few, if any, reliable algorithms have a true one-step quadratic rate of convergence. Much work remains to be done, to measure the amount of work required to determine $\mathbf{x}^{(k+1)}$ from $\mathbf{x}^{(k)}$ for each algorithm, and to show that each "step" is finite. Certainly a reasonable comparison of rates of convergence can be made only if similar definitions are used in all the analysis.

9.9. Scaling

We define scaling to be a procedure which modifies the statement of a problem so that the performance of a given method will be improved.

The most common application of scaling in numerical analysis occurs in the solution of the linear algebraic equations $\mathbf{Ax} = \mathbf{b}$ where a transformation of the variables is made. Let $\mathbf{V}_1$ and $\mathbf{V}_2$ be two non-singular matrices such that

$$\mathbf{x} = \mathbf{V}_1\mathbf{y},$$

and

$$\mathbf{V}_2\mathbf{A}\mathbf{V}_1\mathbf{y} = \mathbf{V}_2\mathbf{b}.$$

We are free to choose the matrices $\mathbf{V}_1$ and $\mathbf{V}_2$, the most common objective being to minimize the condition number $\kappa(\overline{\mathbf{A}}) = \|\overline{\mathbf{A}}\|\,\|\overline{\mathbf{A}}^{-1}\|$, where $\overline{\mathbf{A}} = \mathbf{V}_2\mathbf{A}\mathbf{V}_1$. Unfortunately, even if the transformations $\mathbf{V}_1$ and $\mathbf{V}_2$ are restricted to be diagonal matrices $\mathbf{D}_1$ and $\mathbf{D}_2$, minimizing $\kappa(\overline{\mathbf{A}})$ is a more lengthy process than the computation of $\mathbf{x}$.

The general view is that a matrix will have poor numerical properties if the elements of different rows and/or columns are of widely differing magnitude. Thus the most common scaling technique is to multiply the rows and columns by constants so that they attain more or less equal norms for some vector norm; this form of scaling is termed "equilibration". Van Der Sluis (1969, 1970) has shown that if row scaling alone is used and the diagonal matrix $\mathbf{D}_2$ is chosen so that the rows have equal infinity norm then $\mathbf{D}_2\mathbf{A}$ has minimal condition number if the condition number is defined as

$$\kappa'(\mathbf{A}) = \|\mathbf{A}^{-1}\|_\infty \max \quad |a_{i,j}|.$$

Unfortunately this particular norm may not be meaningful in a practical context, and Curtis and Reid (1972) have noted that infinity-norm equilibration is not always effective—especially for large sparse matrices. Another possible technique is to construct an easily-computable function of the size of the elements of the matrix $\mathbf{D}_2\mathbf{A}\mathbf{D}_1$ and choose $\mathbf{D}_1$ and $\mathbf{D}_2$ to minimize this function. Two suggestions for such a function have been the following:

(i) $$\phi = \sum (\log_\beta |a_{ij}| - \rho_i - c_j)^2, \quad \text{(Hamming, 1971)} \qquad (9.9.1)$$

where the sum is taken over all ij such that $a_{ij} \neq 0$ and β is the machine radix. Once the minimization has been performed the matrices $\mathbf{D}_1$ and $\mathbf{D}_2$ can be chosen as $(\mathbf{D}_2)_i = \beta^{-R_i}$ and $(\mathbf{D}_1)_j = \beta^{-C_j}$ where R_i and C_j are the nearest integers to ρ_i and c_j respectively.

(ii) $$\phi = \max \left| \log_\beta |a_{ij}| - R_i - C_j \right|, \quad \text{(Fulkerson \& Wolfe, 1962)} \qquad (9.9.2)$$

where R_i and C_j are integers.

Curtis and Reid (1972) report that $\mathbf{D}_1$ and $\mathbf{D}_2$ obtained by minimizing (9.9.1) or (9.9.2) give better results than straightforward row equilibration. However, the minimization of (9.9.1) or (9.9.2) is a non-trivial task.

The basic difficulty with scaling linear equations is that it is not known at present what constitutes a well-scaled matrix and until this is known, a consistently effective scaling procedure cannot be devised.

When applied to optimization problems both the scope for the improvement of existing methods and the difficulties increase. The nonlinearity of the function implies that it is more difficult to scale the problem initially since the function and its derivatives may vary significantly over the region of interest. This difficulty is illustrated in the unconstrained case where each iteration requires the solution of a set of linear equations with the Hessian as coefficient matrix, the elements of which may vary considerably with $\mathbf{x}$. (One objective in scaling the Hessian matrix so that its condition number is small is to cause unit changes in the variables to generate a change of comparable magnitude in the objective function.) Many algorithms can be shown theoretically to be invariant (that is, generate the same sequence of points) under a linear transformation of the variables, implying that their behaviour would be identical, regardless of scaling. However, this theoretical result does not hold for any implementation on a computer, and scaling can be quite beneficial in reducing numerical error.

In the case of linear programming, the matrix of constraint coefficients is generally known *a priori* and can be processed before the computation begins. Experience with such schemes has been varied. Tomlin (1973) reports that scaling the constraint matrix using (9.9.1) and (9.9.2) has little effect in solving the problem.

In addition to improving the numerical characteristics of an optimization problem at each iteration, scaling can be used to reduce the number of iterations required. For example, at each iteration of the simplex method for linear programming a decision is made, based on the magnitude of the Lagrange multipliers, to alter the current set of active constraints, $\mathbf{A}^T$. Pre-multiplying $\hat{\mathbf{A}}^T$ by a diagonal matrix with positive and unequal elements "scales" each constraint and thereby alters the relative sizes of the multipliers, so that a different path may be taken by the simplex algorithm. A natural question is whether we can choose a diagonal matrix to obtain a consistent reduction in the number of iterations.

In summary, use of an inadequate scaling technique may cause a vast class of solutions to be unobtainable even though they are well determined by the given system. Even in the simpler areas, success in automatic scaling has been modest and as yet there are no consistently successful automatic scaling procedures—so that it is necessary to rely to a large extent on the intuition and understanding of the person posing the problem. At the very least, however, the user should ensure that the engineering or physical units which have been used for different parts of the solution are comparable.

References

Abadie, J. and Carpentier, J. (1969). Generalization of the Wolfe reduced gradient method to the case of nonlinear constraints. *In* "Optimization" (R. Fletcher, ed.), 37–49. Academic Press, London and New York.

Abadie, J. and Guigou, J. (1970). Numerical experiments with the GRG method. *In* "Integer and Nonlinear Programming" (J. Abadie, ed.). North-Holland Publishing Co. Amsterdam.

Adelman, A. and Stevens, W. F. (1972). Process optimization by the complex method. *A.I.Ch.E. Journal* **18**.

Alway, G. G. and Martin, D. W. (1965). An algorithm for reducing the bandwidth of a matrix of symmetrical configuration. *Comput. J.* **8,** 264–272.

Armijo, L. (1966). Minimization of functions having Lipschitz-continuous first partial derivatives. *Pacific J. Math.* **16,** 1–3.

Arrow, K. J., Hurwicz, L. and Uzawa, H. (1958). "Studies in Linear and Nonlinear Programming." Stanford University Press, Stanford.

Bard, Y. and Greenstadt, J. L. (1969). A modified Newton method for optimization with equality constraints. *In* "Optimization" (R. Fletcher, ed.). Academic Press, London and New York.

Bartels, R. H. and Golub, G. H. (1969). The Simplex method of linear programming using LU decomposition. *Comm. ACM* **12,** 266–268.

Beale, E. M. L. (1967). Numerical methods. *In* "Nonlinear Programming" (J. Abadie, ed.). North-Holland Publishing Co. Amsterdam.

Biggs, M. C. (1972). Constrained minimization using recursive equality quadratic programming. *In* "Numerical Methods for Nonlinear Optimization" (F. A. Lootsma, ed.). Academic Press, London and New York.

Box, M. J. (1965). A new method of constrained optimization and a comparison with other methods. *Comput. J.* **8,** 42–52.

Branin, F. H. and Hoo, S. K. (1972). A method for finding multiple extrema of a function of *n* variables. *In* "Numerical Methods for Nonlinear Optimization" (F. A. Lootsma, ed.), 231–237. Academic Press, London and New York.

Brent, R .P. (1973). "Algorithms for Minimization without Derivatives." Prentice-Hall, Englewood Cliffs, New Jersey.

Brown, K. M. and Dennis, J. E. Jr (1972). Derivative-free analogue of the Levenberg–Marquardt and Gauss algorithms for nonlinear least squares approximation. *Numer. Math.* **18,** 289–297.

Broyden, C. G. (1972). Quasi-Newton methods. *In* "Numerical Methods for Unconstrained Optimization" (W. Murray, ed.), 87–106. Academic Press, London and New York.

Carrol, C. W. (1961). The created response surface technique for optimizing nonlinear restrained systems. *Op. Res.* **9,** 169–184.

Conn, A. R. (1973). Constrained optimization using a non-differentiable penalty function. *SIAM J. Num. Anal.* **10,** 760–784.

Curtis, A. R. and Reid, J. K. (1972). On the automatic scaling of matrices for Gaussian elimination. *J. Inst. Maths Applics* **10**, 118–124.

Curtis, A. R., Powell, M. J. D. and Reid, J. K. (1974). On the estimation of sparse Jacobian matrices. *J. Inst. Maths Applics* **13**, 117–119.

Dantzig, G. S. (1963). "Linear Programming and Extensions". Princeton University Press, Princeton, N. J.

Davidon, W. (1959). Variable metric methods for minimization. AEC Res. and Devel. Rept. ANL—5990. Argonne Nat'l. Lab. Argonne Illinois.

Davies, D. and Swann, W. H. (1969). Review of constrained optimization. *In* "Optimization" (R. Fletcher, ed.). Academic Press, London and New York.

Dixon, L. C. W. (1972). "Nonlinear Optimization." English University Press, London.

Dixon, L. C. W. (1973). ACSIM—An accelerated constrained Simplex technique. *Computer Aided Design* **5** 23–32.

Elkin, R. (1968). Convergence theorems for Gauss-Seidel and other minimization algorithms. Ph.D. Diss. University of Maryland, College Park, Maryland.

Fiacco, A. V. and McCormick, G. P. (1966). Extensions of SUMT for nonlinear programming: equality constraints and extrapolation. *Mgnt Sci.* **12,** 816–829.

Fiacco, A. V. and McCormick, G. P. (1968). "Nonlinear Programming: Sequential Unconstrained Minimization Techniques." Wiley, New York.

Fletcher, R. (1971). A general quadratic programming algorithm. *J. Inst. Maths Applics* **7** 76–91.

Fletcher, R. (1972a). An algorithm for solving linearly constrained optimization problems. *Math. Prog.* **2,** 133–165.

Fletcher, R. (1972b.) Minimizing general functions subject to linear constraints. *In* "Numerical Methods for Nonlinear Optimization" (F. A. Lootsma, ed.), 279–296. Academic Press, London and New York.

Fletcher, R. (1972c). Fortran subroutines for minimization by quasi-Newton methods. AERE Rept. R. 7125.

Fletcher, R. (1973a). An exact penalty function for nonlinear programming with inequalities. *Math. Prog.* **5,** 129–150.

Fletcher, R. (1973b). An ideal penalty function for constrained optimization, AERE Rept. CSS2.

Fletcher, R. and McCann, A. P. (1969). Acceleration techniques for nonlinear programming. *In* "Optimization" (R. Fletcher, ed.). Academic Press, London and New York.

Fletcher, R. and Powell, M. J. D. (1963). A rapidly convergent descent method for minimization. *Comput. J.* **6,** 163–168.

Fletcher, R. and Reeves, C. M. (1964). Function minimization by conjugate gradients. *Comput. J.* **7,** 149–154.

Forrest, J. J. H. and Tomlin, J. A. (1972). Updating triangular factors of the basis to maintain sparsity in the product-form Simplex method. *Math. Prog.* **2,** 263–278.

Fox, L. (1964). "An Introduction to Numerical Linear-algebra." Oxford University Press, London.

Friedman, P. and Pinder, K. L. (1972). Optimization of a simulation model of a chemical plant. *Ind. Eng. Chem. Process Des Develop.* **11,** 512–520.

Frisch, K. R. (1955). The logarithmic potential method of convex programming. Memorandum May 13, 1955, University Institute of Economics, Oslo.

Fulkerson, D. R. and Wolfe, P. (1962). An algorithm for scaling matrices. *SIAM Rev.* **4,** 142–146.

Geoffrion, A. (1970a). Elements of large-scale mathematical programming. Part 1: Concepts. *Mgnt Sci.* **16,** 652–675.

Geoffrion, A. (1970b). Elements of large-scale mathematical programming. Part 2: Synthesis of algorithms and bibliography. *Mgnt Sci.* **16,** 676–691.

George, J. A. (1971). Computer implementation of the finite element method. Report STAN-CS-71-208, Computer Science Department, Stanford University, Stanford, California.

Ghani, S. N. (1972). An improved complex method of function minimization. *Computer Aided Design.* **4,** 71–78.

Gill, P. E. and Murray, W. (1972a). Quasi-Newton methods for unconstrained optimization. *J. Inst. Maths Applics* **9,** 91–108.

Gill, P. E. and Murray, W. (1972b). Two methods for the solution of linearly constrained and unconstrained optimization problems. *Nat. Phys. Lab. Rept NAC* **25.**

Gill, P. E. and Murray, W. (1973a). A numerically stable form of the Simplex algorithm. *J. Linear Algebra Applics.* **7,** 99–138.

Gill, P. E. and Murray, W. (1973b). The numerical solution of a problem in the calculus of variations. *In* "Recent Mathematical Developments in Control" (D. J. Bell, ed.), 97–122. Academic Press, London and New York.

Gill, P. E. and Murray, W. (1973c) Quasi-Newton methods for linearly constrained optimization. *Nat. Phys. Lab. Rept. NAC* **32.**

Gill, P. E. and Murray, W. (1974). Safeguarded steplength algorithms for optimization using descent methods. *Nat. Phys. Lab. Rept NAC* **37.**

Gill, P. E., Murray, W. and Picken, S. M. (1972). The implementation of two modified Newton algorithms for unconstrained optimization. *Nat. Phys. Lab. Rept NAC* **24.**

Gill, P. E., Murray, W. and Pitfield, R. A. (1972). The implementation of two revised quasi-Newton algorithms for unconstrained optimization. *Nat. Phys. Lab. Rept NAC* **11.**

Gill, P. E., Murray, W. and Saunders, M. A. (1973). The simplex method using the LQ factorization in product form. Paper presented at VIII International Symposium on Mathematical Programming, Stanford University, Stanford, California.

Gill, P. E., Golub, G. H., Murray, W. and Saunders, M. A. (1974). Methods for modifying matrix factorizations. *Math. Comput.* **28,** 505–535.

Gill, P. E., Murray, W. and Saunders, M. A. (1974). Methods for computing and modifying the LDV factors of a matrix. *Nat. Phys. Lab. Rept NAC* **56.**

Glass, H. and Cooper, L. (1965). Sequential search: a method for solving constrained optimization problems. *JACM* **12,** 71–82.

Goldfarb, D. (1969). Extension of Davidon's variable metric method to maximization under linear inequality and equality constraints. *SIAM J. appl. Math.* **17,** 739–764.

Goldfeld, S. M., Quandt, R. E. and Trotter, H. F. (1966). Maximization by quadratic hill climbing. *Econometrica* **34,** 541–551.

Goldstein, A. and Price, J. (1967). An effective algorithm for minimization. *Numer. Math.* **10,** 184–189.

Gottfried, B. S., Bruggink, P. R. and Harwood, E. R. (1970). Chemical process optimization using penalty functions. *Ind. Eng. Chem. Process Des Develop.* **9,** 581–587.

Greenstadt, J. L. (1967). On the relative efficiencies of gradient methods. *Math. Comput.* **21,** 360–367.

Griffith, R. E. and Stewart, R. A. (1961). A nonlinear programming technique for the optimization of continuous processing systems. *Mgnt Sci.* **7,** 379–392.

Grigoriadis, M. D. (1971). A projective method for structured nonlinear programs *Math. Prog.* **1,** 321–358.

Grigoriadis, M. D. and Ritter, K. (1969). A decomposition method for structured linear and nonlinear programs. *J. Comput. and System Sciences* **3,** 335–360.

Guin, J. A. (1968). Modification of the complex method of constrained optima. *Comput. J.* **10,** 416–417.

Haarhoff, P. C. and Buys, J. D. (1970). A new method for the optimization of a nonlinear function subject to nonlinear constraints. *Comput. J.* **13,** 178–184.

Hamming, R .W. (1971). "Introduction to Applied Numerical Analysis.'' McGraw-Hill, New York.

Hartman, J. K. (1973). A new method for global optimization. Naval Postgraduate School, Technical report NPS55HH73041A.

Hebden, M. D. (1973). An algorithm for minimization using exact second derivatives. AERE Rept TP.515.

Hellerman, E. and Rarick, D. (1971). Reinversion with the preassigned pivot procedure. *Math. Prog.* **1,** 195–216.

Hellerman, E. and Rarick, D. (1972) The partitioned preassigned pivot procedure (P^4). *In* "Sparse Matrices and their Applications" (D. J. Rose and R. A. Willoughby, eds), 67–76. Plenum Press, New York.

Hestenes, M. R. (1966). "Calculus of Variations and Optional Control Problems." Wiley, New York.

Hestenes, M. R. (1969). Multiplier and gradient methods. *J. Opt. Theory Appl.* **4,** 303–320.

Hestenes, M. R. and Stiefel, E. (1952). Methods of conjugate gradients for solving linear systems. *J. Res. Nat. Bur. Standards* **49,** 409–436.

Hooke, R. and Jeeves, T. A. (1961). Direct search solution of numerical and statistical problems. *JACM* **8,** 212–229.

Jacobson, D. H. and Oksman, W. (1972). An algorithm that minimizes homogeneous functions of N variables in $N + 2$ iterations and rapidlym inimizes general functions *J. Math. Anal. Applics* **38,** 535–552.

Keefer, D. L. (1973). Simpat: self-bounding direct search method for optimization. *Ind. Eng. Chem. Process Des Develop.* **12,** No. 1.

Kelley, J. E. Jr (1960). The cutting plane method for solving convex programs. *J. Soc. ind. appl. Math.* **8,** 703–712.

Klingman, W. R. and Himmelblau, D. M. (1964). Nonlinear programming with the aid of a multiple gradient summation technique. *JACM* **11,** 400–415.

Kowalik, J. (1966). Nonlinear programming procedures aid design optimization. *Acta Polytechnica Scandinavica.* Mathematics and Computing Machinery Series **13,** Trondheim.

Kuhn, H. W. and Tucker, A. W. (1951). Nonlinear programming. *In* "Proceedings of the Second Berkeley Symposium on Mathematical Statistics and Probability" (J. Neyman, ed.), 481–493. University of California Press.

Lanczos, C. (1950). An iteration method for the solution of the eigenvalue problem of linear differential and integral operators. *J. Res. Nat. Bur. Standards* **45,** 255–282.

Lawrence, J. P. III and Emad, F. P. (1972). An adaptive randomized pattern search. *In* Proceedings of 1972 IEEE Conference on Decision Control and 11th Symposium on Adaptive Processes. New Orleans, 13–15 December 1972, 421–425.

Lemke, C. E. (1968). On complementary pivot theory. *In* "Mathematics of the Decision Sciences, Part I" (G. B. Dantzig and A. F. Veinott, eds), 95–114. American Mathematical Society.

Levenberg, K. (1944). A method for the solution of certain problems in least squares. *Quart. Appl. Math.* **2,** 164–168.

Lootsma, F. A. (1968). Extrapolation on logarithmic programming. *Philips Res. Rept* **23,** 108–116.

Lootsma, F. A. (1969). Hessian matrices of penalty functions for solving constrained optimization problems. *Philips Res. Rept* **24,** 322–331.

Lootsma, F. A. (1970). Boundary properties of penalty functions for constrained minimization. *Philips Res. Rept Supp.* **3.**

Lootsma, F. A. (1972). A survey of methods for solving constrained minimization problems via unconstrained minimization. *In* "Numerical Methods for Nonlinear Optimization" (F. A. Lootsma, ed.). Academic Press, London and New York.

Luus, R. and Jaakola, T. H. I. (1973). Optimization by direct search and systematic reduction of the size of search region. *A.I.Ch.E. Journal* **19,** 760–766.

Mangasarian, O. L. (1969). "Nonlinear Programming." McGraw-Hill, New York.

Marquardt, D. (1963). An algorithm for least squares estimation of nonlinear parameters. *SIAM J. appl. Math.* **11,** 431–441.

McCormick, G. P. (1969). Anti-zigzagging by bending. *Mgnt Sci.* **15,** 315–320.

McCormick, G. P. (1970). A second order method for the linearly constrained nonlinear programming problem. *In* "Nonlinear Programming" (J. B. Rosen, O. L. Mangasarian and K. Ritter, eds), 207–243. Academic Press, London and New York.

McCormick, G. P. (1972). Attempts to calculate global solutions of problems that may have local minima. *In* "Numerical Methods for Nonlinear Optimization" (F. A. Lootsma, ed.), 209–221. Academic Press, London and New York.

Mifflin, R. (1972). On the convergence of the logarithmic barrier function, *In* "Numerical Methods for Nonlinear Optimization" (F. A. Lootsma, ed.). Academic Press, London and New York.

Mitchell, R. A. and Kaplan, J. L. (1968). Nonlinear constrained optimization by a non-random complex method. *J. Res. Nat. Bur. Standards* (Engr. and Instr.) **72C,** 249.

Mugele, R. A. (1962). A program for optimal control of nonlinear processes. *IBM Systems Journal* **1,** 2–17.

Murray, W. (1969a). An algorithm for constrained minimization. *In* "Optimization" (R. Fletcher, ed.). Academic Press, London and New York.

Murray, W. (1969b). Constrained optimization. *Nat. Phys. Lab. Rept* Ma **79.**

Murray, W. (1971a). Analytical expressions for the eigenvalues and eigenvectors of the Hessian matrices of barrier and penalty functions. *J. Opt. Theory Applics.* **7,** 189–196.

Murray, W. (1971b). An algorithm for finding a local minimum of an indefinite quadratic program. *Nat. Phys. Lab. Rept NAC* **1.**

Murray, W. (1972a). Second derivative methods. *In* "Numerical Methods for Unconstrained Optimization" (W. Murray, ed.), 57–71. Academic Press, London and New York.

Murray, W. (1972b). Failure, the causes and cures. *In* "Numerical Methods for Unconstrained Optimization" (W. Murray, ed.), 107–122. Academic Press, London and New York.

Murray, W. (1972c). The relationship between the approximate Hessian matrices generated by a class of quasi-Newton methods. *Nat. Phys. Lab. Rept NAC* **12.**

Murtagh, B. A. and Sargent, R. W. H. (1969). A constrained minimization method with quadratic convergence. *In* "Optimization" (R. Fletcher, ed.), 215–246. Academic Press, London and New York.

Murtagh, B. A. and Saunders, M. A. (1973). Variable metric projection on large sparse systems. Paper presented at the VIII International Symposium on Mathematical Programming, Stanford University, Stanford, California.

Nelder, J. A. and Mead, R. (1965). A Simplex method for function minimization. *Comput. J.* **7,** 308–313.

Ortega, J. M. and Rheinboldt, W. C. (1970). "Iterative Solution of Nonlinear Equations in Several Variables." Academic Press, New York and London.

Osborne, M. R., and Ryan, D. M. (1970). On penalty function methods for nonlinear programming problems. *J. Math. Anal. Applics.* **31,** 559–578.

Osborne, M. R. and Ryan, D. M. (1972). A hybrid algorithm for nonlinear programming. *In* "Numerical Methods for Nonlinear Optimization" (F. A. Lootsma, ed.), Chapter 28. Academic Press, London and New York.

Paige, C. C. (1973). An error analysis of a method for solving matrix equations. *Maths. Comput.* **27,** 355–359.

Paige, C. C. and Saunders, M. A. (1973). Solution of sparse indefinite systems of equations and least squares problems. Report STAN-CS-73-399, Computer Science Department, Stanford University, Stanford, California.

Parkinson, J. M. and Hutchinson, D. (1972). An investigation into the efficiency of variants of the Simplex method. *In* "Numerical Methods for Nonlinear Optimization" (F. A. Lootsma, ed.). Academic Press, London and New York.

Peters, G. and Wilkinson, J. H. (1970). The least squares problem and pseudo-inverses. *Comput. J.* **13,** 309–316.

Pooch, U. W. and Nieder, A. (1973). A survey of indexing techniques for sparse matrices. *Comp. Surveys* **5,** 109–133.

Powell, M. J. D. (1964). An efficient method of finding the minimum of a function of several variables without calculating derivatives. *Comput. J.* **7,** 155.

Powell, M. J. D. (1969). A method for nonlinear constraints in minimization problems. *In* "Optimization" (R. Fletcher, ed.), Chapter 19. Academic Press, London and New York.

Reid, J. K. (1971a). A note on the stability of Gaussian elimination. *J. Inst. Maths Applics* **8,** 374–375.

Reid, J. K. (1971b). On the method of conjugate gradients for the solution of large sparse sets of linear equations. *In* "Large Sparse Sets of Linear Equations" (J. K. Reid, ed.), 231–254. Academic Press, London and New York.

Reid, J. K. (1973). Sparse linear programming using the Bartels–Golub decomposition. Presented at the VIII International Symposium on Mathematical Programming, Stanford University, Stanford, California.

Ritter, K. (1966). A method for solving maximum problems with a non-concave quadratic objective function. *Z. Wahrscheinlichk Verew Geb.* **4,** 340–351.

Robinson, S. M. (1972). A quadratically convergent algorithm for general programming problems. *Math. Prog.* **3,** 145–156.

Rockafellar, R. T. (1973). Augmented Lagrange multiplier functions and duality in non-convex programming. To appear in *SIAM J. Control.*

Rosen, J. B. (1960). The gradient projection method for non-linear programming. Part I: linear constraints. *SIAM J. Appl. Math.* **8**, 181–217.

Rosen, J. B. (1961). The gradient projection method for nonlinear programming. Part II: nonlinear constraints. *J. Soc. ind. appl.* **9**, 514–532.

Rosen, J. B. (1963). Convex partition programming. In "Recent Advances in Mathematical Programming" (R. L. Graves and P. Wolfe, eds), 159–176. McGraw Hill, New York.

Rosenbrock, H. H. (1960). An automatic method for finding the greatest or least value of a function. *Comput. J.* **3**, 175–184.

Ryan, D. M. (1971). Transformation methods in nonlinear programming. Ph.D.Diss., Australian National University.

Sargent, R. W. H. (1973). Convergence properties of projection methods for nonlinear programming, Presented at VIIIth International Symposium on Mathematical Programming, Stanford University, Stanford, California.

Sargent, R. W. and Murtagh, B. A. H. (1973). Projection methods for nonlinear programming. *Math. Prog.* **4**, 245–268.

Saunders, M. A. (1972a). Large-scale linear programming using the Cholesky factorization. Report STAN-CS-72-252, Computer Science Department, Stanford University, Stanford, California.

Saunders, M. A. (1972b.) Product form of the Cholesky factorization for large-scale linear programming. Report STAN-CS-72-301, Computer Science Department, Stanford University, Stanford, California.

Schechter, S. (1962). Iteration methods for nonlinear problems. *Trans. Amer. Math. Soc.* **104**, 179–189.

Schechter, S. (1968). Relaxation methods for convex problems. *SIAM J. Num. Anal.* **5**, 601–612.

Schechter, S. (1970). Minimization of a convex function by relaxation. *In* "Integer and Nonlinear programming" (J. Abadie, ed.), 177–189. North-Holland Publishing Co. Amsterdam.

Schubert, L. K. (1970). Modification of quasi-Newton method for nonlinear equations with a sparse Jacobian. *Math. Comput.* **24**, 27–30.

Singer, E. (1962). Simulation and optimization of oil refinery design. *Chem. Eng. Progr. Symp. Ser.* **37, 58.**

Spang, H. A. (1962). A review of minimization techniques for nonlinear functions. *SIAM Rev.* **4**, 343–365.

Spendley, W., Hext, G. R. and Himsworth, F. R. (1962). Sequential application of simplex designs in optimization and evolutionary design. *Technometrics* **4**, 441–461.

Stewart, G. W. III (1967). A modification of Davidon's minimization method to accept difference approximations to derivatives. *JACM* **14**.

Swann, W. H. (1964). Report on the development of a new direct search method of optimization. ICI Limited, CIL Research Note 64/3.

Swann, W. H. (1972). Direct search methods. *In* "Numerical Methods for Unconstrained Optimization" (W. Murray, ed.). Academic Press, London and New York.

Tomlin, J. A. (1973). On scaling linear programming problems. Presented at the VIIIth International Symposium on Mathematical Programming, Stanford University, Stanford, California.

Umeda, T. and Ichikawa, A. (1971). A modified complex method for optimization. *Ind. Eng. Chem. Process Des Develop.* **10**, 236–243.

Van Der Sluis, A. (1969). Condition numbers and equilibration of matrices. *Numer. Math.* **14**, 14–23.

Van Der Sluis, A. (1970). Condition, equilibration and pivoting in linear algebraic systems. *Numer. Math.* **15**, 74–86.

Weil, R. L. and Kettler, P. C. (1971). Rearranging matrices into block-angular form for decomposition (and other) algorithms. *Mgnt Sci.* **18**, 98–108.

Wilkinson, J. H. (1965). "The Algebraic Eigenvalue Problem." Oxford University Press, London.

Wilson, R. B. (1963). A simplicial algorithm for concave programming. Ph. D. Diss. Graduate School of Business Administration, Harvard University, Boston.

Wolfe, R. (1966). On the convergence of gradient methods under constraints. Research Rept. IBM Zurich Laboratory.

Wolfe, P. (1967). Methods for nonlinear constraints. *In* "Nonlinear Programming" (J. Abadie, ed.), 120–131, North-Holland Publishing Co. Amsterdam.

Zangwill, W. J. (1967). Nonlinear programming via penalty functions. *Mgnt Sci.* **13**, 344–358.

Zoutendijk, G. (1960). "Methods of Feasible Directions." Elsevier, Amsterdam.

Zoutendijk, G. (1970). Nonlinear programming, computational methods. *In* "Integer and Nonlinear Programming" (J. Abadie, ed.). North-Holland Publishing Co. Amsterdam.

Zwart, P. B. (1973). Nonlinear programming: counter examples to global optimization algorithms by Ritter and Tui. *Op. Res.* **21**, 1260–1266.

Author Index

Numbers in italics indicate the Reference pages where the references are given in full.

Subject Index

C

M

N

T

U

V

W

Z